Ferry ? OK page 84

Stein if with Tobolsky

Wolf Schmieder et al
(one reference p 173

Nielsen et al — one reference
page 83

Julian Gibbs - no reference
Dutch school - Heijboer - one reference
p 174
Appendices — why

what is Vyram
p 65

appendix K what meaning

of Ti ? why not

chapter or page

chapt VI — Equilibrium
WHY? what to do with phys
properties - a subject
interest - author?

Properties
and Structure
of Polymers

WILEY SERIES ON THE SCIENCE AND TECHNOLOGY OF MATERIALS

Advisory Editors: J. H. Hollomon, J. E. Burke, B. Chalmers, R. L. Sproull, A. V. Tobolsky

New York
London

Properties

and Structure

of Polymers

by

Arthur V. Tobolsky

PROFESSOR
DEPARTMENT OF CHEMISTRY
PRINCETON UNIVERSITY

John Wiley & Sons, Inc.

Preface

This book attempts to outline the basic principles of the mechanical behavior of polymers in terms of molecular architecture and dynamics.

The intentions were to develop the subject by proceeding from familiar concepts to those of greater novelty and also to avoid tedious mathematical complexity without sacrificing rigor or depth. A few sections are necessarily of greater mathematical difficulty.

Only selected topics could be treated in a book of modest size, and the choices were naturally guided by my own research experiences. Many of the original experimental results are presented to show how the theoretical formulations were developed from, or compelled by, the experimental facts.

This book is dedicated to my students and coworkers in this field through whose mutual efforts a new body of knowledge was created.

For the last ten years my researches in viscoelasticity were partially supported by the Office of Naval Research.

ARTHUR V. TOBOLSKY

Princeton, N. J.
May, 1960

v

Contents

CHAPTER I

Elasticity and Viscosity

1. COMPRESSION OF ISOTROPIC SUBSTANCES, EQUATIONS OF STATE, BULK MODULUS

The elastic behavior of matter under compression is one of the most familiar of all phenomena to the student of physical science, whether chemist, physicist or engineer. Indeed the modern conception of the atomic-molecular theory of matter arose equally from Dalton's interpretation of the law of multiple proportions, and from Avogadro's interpretation of the gas laws of Boyle and Charles. In modern terminology the Avogadro principle is expressed as follows,

1.1 $$p = NkT/V$$

1

where p is the pressure that N molecules existing in the ideal gaseous state at a temperature T exert on the walls of the confining container whose volume is V. The constant $\mathbf{k}$ in equation 1.1 is Boltzmann's constant, which is equal to 1.38×10^{-16} erg/deg. For one mole of gas the quantity N in equation 1.1 is Avagadro's number, $\mathbf{N} = 6.023 \times 10^{23}$. Alternatively, the equation of state for an ideal gas is written as

1.2 $$p = n\mathbf{R}T/V$$

where n is the number of moles of gas and $\mathbf{R} = \mathbf{Nk}$ is the gas constant, which is numerically equal to 8.3156×10^7 ergs/deg mole.

In general, for any substance, whether solid, liquid or gaseous, one can write a relation among pressure, volume and temperature which describes the elastic behavior in compression. Such a relation is known as an equation of state. For any stable substance the volume at constant temperature decreases with increasing pressure. Throughout this chapter we shall discuss the equation of state for various assemblies of N molecules (or n moles) in the gaseous, liquid or solid state. In many cases the equation of state is particularized to one mole of substance, in which circumstance N is replaced by $\mathbf{N}$.

It is well known that metals or ionic crystals will yield or rupture when extended or sheared only a minute fraction of their original length, whereas liquids or gases can *not* be extended or sheared at all in any elastically recoverable manner. On the contrary, it is possible to compress solids *and* liquids *and* gases up to enormous pressures in a thermodynamically reversible manner. Time effects in compression can be neglected under many experimental conditions.

The familiarity and simplicity of the concept of compression, together with the general absence of time effects during static compression, make it a useful starting point for a discussion of the elastic properties of matter.

At this point it is necessary to define our first elastic constant, namely, the isothermal bulk modulus B.

1.3 $$B = -V(\partial p/\partial V)_T$$

The bulk modulus is the reciprocal of the thermodynamic compressibility; in cgs units its dimensions are dynes per square centimeter, which are the dimensional units of pressure or of energy per unit volume. It measures the elastic resistance of a substance to compression so that a substance that is difficult to compress will have a high bulk modulus. The bulk modulus for any value of (p, V, T) can be obtained from the equation of state. For example, the bulk modulus of an ideal gas can be obtained directly from equations 1.1 and 1.3.

1.4 $B = p$ for ideal gas

For an ideal gas at 1 atm pressure

$$B = 1 \text{ atm} = 1.013 \times 10^6 \text{ dynes/cm}^2$$

An ideal gas at 1 atm pressure is an easily compressed substance and therefore has a low value of B. Most liquids at atmospheric pressure have a bulk modulus that is approximately 10^4 times as large, namely, 10^{10} dynes/cm^2. The least compressible solids such as diamond, rhodium, tungsten, and iridium have values of B at atmospheric pressure considerably larger than 10^{12} dynes/cm^2. On the other hand, the bulk modulus at atmospheric pressure of the most compressible solids such as neon, nitrogen, argon and cesium are only slightly larger than 10^{10} dynes/cm^2.

Although the bulk modulus of an ideal gas varies proportionally to the pressure, the bulk moduli of liquids and solids are much more slowly varying functions of the pressure. Indeed there is not much change in B between zero pressure and 100 atm pressure for most liquids and solids. Also the temperature dependence of B for liquids and especially solids is generally quite small. For example, the bulk modulus of NaCl is 3.0×10^{11} dynes/cm^2 at 0°K and 2.4×10^{11} dynes/cm^2 at room temperature. The corresponding values for KCl are 2.1×10^{11} dynes/ cm^2 at 0°K and 1.8×10^{11} dynes/cm^2 at room temperature.

For purposes of comparison, Table I.1 shows the values of B at atmospheric pressure and at room temperature (or other convenient temperature) of several liquids and solids. The solids, for purposes of convenience, are classified as molecular crystals, metallic crystals, ionic crystals and valence crystals.

Although our concern is mainly with B values at atmospheric pressure, it is interesting to consider the effects of quite high pressures.

A fairly surprising feature of the compression of liquids at high pressures is their rather uniform behavior. Most organic liquids and liquid water contract by 20 to 30% of their initial volume when the pressure is raised from 1 to 20,000 atm and by 36 to 39% when brought to 50,000 atm.[1] Whereas there is nearly a thousandfold range in the bulk moduli of solids at atmospheric pressure, at 100,000 atm the range of the B values of all solids is much narrower, with an approximate average value [1] of 10^{12} dynes/cm^2.

Table I.1

BULK MODULI OF SOME REPRESENTATIVE SUBSTANCES

Substance	$B \times 10^{-12}$, dynes/cm^2	Substance	$B \times 10^{-12}$, dynes/cm^2
Liquids		*Metals (Continued)*	
Acetone (0°C)	0.0124	Mg	0.33
Benzene (35°)	0.0101	Al	0.66
Chloroform (20°)	0.0086	Fe	1.6
Ether (34.8°)	0.0049	Cu	1.5
Ethyl alcohol (20°)	0.0081	Ag	0.97
Glycerin (14.9°)	0.0461	Pb	0.42
Mercury (0°)	0.259	Ni	2.3
Water (0°)	0.0193	Ti	1.2
Water (20°)	0.0204	W	3.6
Molecular Crystals		*Ionic Salts*	
Neon	0.010	LiF	0.65
Argon	0.016	LiCl	0.29
Nitrogen	0.019	LiBr	0.23
Valence and Valence-		LiI	0.17
Type Crystals		NaF	0.46
C (diamond)	5.5	NaCl	0.24
Be	1.2	NaBr	0.20
Ge	0.70	NaI	0.14
Bi	0.33	KCl	0.18
Metals		KBr	0.15
Li	0.11	KI	0.12
Na	0.062	NaCl (0°K)	0.30
K	0.027		

Reference I.1

1. S. D. Hamann, *Physico-chemical Effects of Pressure*, Chapter 3, pp. 36–60, Academic Press, New York, 1957.

2. STATISTICAL THERMODYNAMICS OF COMPRESSION

The first and second laws of thermodynamics as applied to isotropic substances subjected to pure compression are embodied in the following two equations:

2.1
$$dU = dQ - dW$$

2.2
$$dU = T\,dS - p\,dV$$

where U is the internal energy of the substance, dQ the heat absorbed through the boundaries, dW the work done by the substance on the environment, S the entropy of the substance and p the pressure.

Equation 2.2 can be rearranged as follows:

2.3
$$p = T\left(\frac{\partial S}{\partial V}\right)_T - \left(\frac{\partial U}{\partial V}\right)_T = -\left(\frac{\partial A}{\partial V}\right)_T$$

In equation 2.3 $A = U - TS$ is the Helmholtz free energy. The most powerful theoretical method for deriving the equation of state of any substance comes from a knowledge of the energy levels of the substance. This enables one to calculate A as a function of volume and temperature through the partition function Q (see Appendix A). The equation of state is then obtained by

2.4
$$p = -\left(\frac{\partial A}{\partial V}\right)_T = \mathbf{k}T\left(\frac{\partial \ln Q}{\partial V}\right)_T$$

A detailed scrutiny of equation 2.3 gives added insight. It is clear that the pressure p of a substance is comprised of two contributions: the term $T(\partial S/\partial V)_T$, which we may call the entropy contribution or the *kinetic pressure*, and the term $-(\partial U/\partial V)_T$, which we may call the internal energy contribution or the *internal pressure*. In certain cases S and U can be calculated as functions of volume and temperature from very simple models and by very simple methods, as will be shown subsequently. This is another procedure for obtaining the equation of state from theoretical considerations.

For any given substance it is also desirable to have a purely experimental approach for evaluating the kinetic pressure and internal pressure from pVT data. This is accomplished by using the well-known thermodynamic relation

2.5
$$\left(\frac{\partial S}{\partial V}\right)_T = \left(\frac{\partial p}{\partial T}\right)_V$$

The kinetic pressure is therefore $T(\partial p/\partial T)_V$, and can be evaluated simply by measuring the variation of pressure with temperature at constant volume.

2.6
$$\text{Kinetic pressure} = T(\partial p/\partial T)_V$$

By subtracting the kinetic pressure from the total pressure one obtains the internal pressure:

2.7   Internal pressure $= p - T(\partial p/\partial T)_V$

Another very useful thermodynamic formula for the kinetic pressure is

2.8 $T(\partial p/\partial T)_V = aBT$

where a is the coefficient of expansion $-(1/V)(\partial V/\partial T)_p$ and B is the bulk modulus. This provides another method for obtaining the kinetic pressure from experimental data.

Experimental studies of the kinetic contribution $T(\partial p/\partial T)_V$ for many substances reveal that there are two limiting cases. (1) If the pressure at constant volume is *proportional* to absolute temperature, that is $p = cT$, then by substituting into equation 2.6 it is clear that the kinetic pressure is also cT. From equation 2.7 the internal pressure is therefore zero. (2) On the other hand, if the pressure at constant volume is *independent* of temperature, then from equation 2.6 it is clear that the kinetic pressure $T(\partial S/\partial V)_T$ is zero.

If the internal pressure $-(\partial U/\partial V)_T$ is zero, then quite obviously U is a function of temperature only. Hence:

2.9 $$p = T\left(\frac{\partial S}{\partial V}\right)_T = T\left(\frac{\partial S}{\partial V}\right)_U$$

(if condition 1 applies and internal pressure is zero).

For an ideal gas maintained at constant volume, the pressure is proportional to absolute temperature according to the law of Charles. Condition 1 applies, the internal pressure is zero, and equation 2.9 obtains.

In order to employ equation 2.9 it is necessary to have an expression for entropy as a function of volume. For an assembly of N molecules maintained at constant energy U and volume V the entropy S is given by the famous equation of Boltzmann,

2.10 $S = \mathbf{k}\ln\Omega(U, V)$

where Ω is the number of quantum states of the assembly consistent with the given values of U, V and N. In classical statistical mechanics Ω is proportional to the volume of the phase space of the assembly. In the very simplest physical terms Ω is the number of microstates that correspond to a given thermodynamic macrostate.

For an ideal gas it can be shown that

2.11 $$\Omega = f(U)V^N$$

where $f(U)$ is a function of internal energy alone. The proportionality of Ω and V^N is intuitively obvious as shown in Appendix B, and this is all that is necessary for our argument.

Combining equations 2.9, 2.10 and 2.11, one readily obtains the equation of state $p = NkT/V$.

The above treatment assumes that the molecules are mass points and that there are no forces acting between the molecules. The pressure exerted on the walls of the confining vessel is truly a kinetic pressure, arising only from the thermal velocities of the molecules and their impacts with the walls.

For a molecular model which is capable of treating real gases, particularly gases at high pressures, one must account for the attractive and repulsive forces between molecules. These forces give rise to deviations of real gases from ideal behavior, especially at high pressures. For *real* gases, the equation of state for one mole of gas at low and moderate pressures can be conveniently expressed by the so-called virial expansion.

2.12 $$\frac{pV}{RT} = 1 + \frac{\gamma_2(T)}{V} + \frac{\gamma_3(T)}{V^2} + \frac{\gamma_4(T)}{V^3} + \cdots$$

The quantities γ_2, γ_3, γ_4, etc., are called the second, third, fourth, etc., virial coefficients of the gas. They may be obtained as functions of temperature by pVT measurements.

From the general laws of statistical mechanics,[1] a simple relation may be written between the second virial coefficient γ_2 and the energy of interaction $u(r)$ between two isolated molecules separated by a distance r.

2.13 $$\gamma_2(T) = 2\pi N \int_0^\infty (1 - \exp\left[-u(r)/kT\right])r^2 \, dr$$

For chemically saturated molecules such as argon, nitrogen, carbon dioxide and methane, the energy of interaction $u(r)$ between a pair of isolated molecules can be expressed in terms of the intermolecular distance r. A very useful approximation is the Lennard-Jones formula.[2]

2.14 $$u(r) = \epsilon^* \left[\left(\frac{r^*}{r}\right)^{12} - 2\left(\frac{r^*}{r}\right)^6 \right]$$

The inverse 12th power describes the repulsive potential between the molecules, and the inverse 6th power expresses the attractive potential.

The quantity ϵ^* represents the minimum potential energy value at a separation r^* between the molecules (see Figure I.1). ϵ^* and r^* should be regarded as fundamental properties of the molecule in question.

If equation 2.14 is substituted in equation 2.13, an explicit relation is obtained [2] among γ_2, ϵ^* and r^*. This relationship has been extensively tabulated for purposes of numerical computation.[3] This means that from the experimentally determined values of the second virial coefficient of gases one can obtain the fundamental quantities ϵ^* and r^*. Table I.2 gives the values of these constants for several molecules.[4]

One can also use the quantities ϵ^* and r^* to derive an equation of state applicable to gases at very high pressures.[5] This equation of state is expressed in terms of reduced variables p/p^*, V/V^* and T/T^*, and in terms of these reduced variables it is the same for all (chemically saturated) substances. The quantities p^*, V^* and T^* are defined as follows:

2.15 $$p^* = 2\epsilon^*/r^{*3}$$

$$V^* = Nr^{*3}/\sqrt{2}$$

$$T^* = \epsilon^*/k$$

Two substances having the same values of p/p^*, V/V^* and T/T^* are

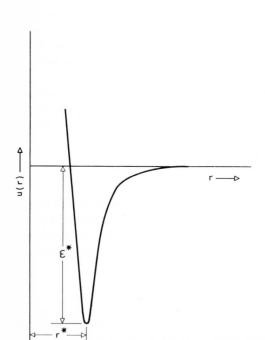

Figure I.1. The Lennard-Jones potential.

Table I.2

CHARACTERISTIC VALUES ϵ^*, r^* FOR SEVERAL CHEMICALLY
SATURATED MOLECULES

Gas	$10^{15}\epsilon^*$, ergs	r^*, Å	T^*, °K	V^*, cm³/mole	p^*, atm
He⁴	1.41	2.87	10.22	10.06	84.5
Ne	4.91	3.09	36.3	13.51	220
A	16.54	3.82	120.3	24.0	415
Kr	23.6	4.04	171	28.3	503
Xe	30.5	4.60	221	41.5	440
H₂	5.11	3.29	37.0	15.12	203
D₂	5.11	3.29	37.0	15.12	203
N₂	13.2	4.17	96.6	31.3	254
O₂	16.3	3.89	118	24.9	390
NO	18.1	3.56	131	19.3	562
CO₂	28.3	4.57	205	40.6	416
CH₄	20.5	4.29	148.5	33.6	364

said to be in corresponding states. Unfortunately the equation of state for gases at very high pressures is of great mathematical complexity, and is further complicated by quantum effects important for light molecules such as H_2, D_2 and He at low temperatures. However, for molecules where the quantum effects are unimportant, the theory predicts the following values for the critical constants p_c, V_c and T_c.

2.16

$$T_c/T^* = 1.33$$

$$V_c/V^* = 2.0$$

$$p_c/p^* = 0.47$$

These predictions compare fairly well with the experimental facts. [4]

It is interesting to note that for liquids at atmospheric pressure both the kinetic pressure and the internal pressure are very large and nearly balance each other.

References I.2

1. J. E. Mayer and M. G. Mayer, *Statistical Mechanics*, Chapter 12, John Wiley & Sons, New York, 1940.
2. J. E. Lennard-Jones, *Proc. Roy. Soc. London*, **A106,** 463 (1924).

3. J. O. Hirschfelder, C. F. Curtiss and R. B. Bird, *Molecular Theory of Gases and Liquids*, John Wiley & Sons, New York, 1954.

4. S. D. Hamann, *Physico-chemical Effects of Pressure*, Chapter III, pp. 42–48, Academic Press, New York, 1957.

5. J. E. Lennard-Jones and A. F. Devonshire, *Proc. Roy. Soc. London*, **A163**, 53 (1937).

3. EQUATION OF STATE FOR MOLECULAR CRYSTALS

Very important from the point of view of understanding the behavior of solids, the quantities ϵ^* and r^* can also be used to calculate the equation of state and the bulk modulus of *molecular crystals*. The calculations are easiest to perform at $0°K$. The formula for $A(T, V)$ of a molecular crystal is

3.1 $\qquad A(T, V) = U_L(V) + U_Z(V) + U_t(V, T) - T S(V, T)$

In equation 3.1, $U_L(V)$ is the lattice energy with each molecule in its equilibrium position, $U_Z(V)$ is the zero-point vibrational energy, $U_t(V, T)$ is the thermal vibrational energy, and $S(V, T)$ is the entropy due to vibration (and in some cases additional configurational entropy). At $0°K$, $U_t(V, T)$ and $-T S(V, T)$ are both zero.

For very light molecules such as hydrogen, helium, and possibly neon the quantal effects relating to the term $U_Z(V)$ are quite important. For other crystals, $U_Z(V)$ can be neglected, and the pressure and the bulk modulus at $0°K$ are given in good approximation by

3.2 $\qquad\qquad p = -dU_L(V)/dV \qquad \text{at } 0°K$

3.3 $\qquad\qquad B = V\, d^2 U_L(V)/dV^2 \qquad \text{at } 0°K$

Using the Lennard-Jones formula, equation 2.14, as the starting point, one can obtain the formula for the molar lattice energy $U_L(V)$ of a molecular crystal (argon, nitrogen, carbon dioxide, methane, etc.). We treat the case of a face-centered cubic lattice. At $0°K$ the N molecules occupy the exact lattice sites of the lattice. The intermolecular distances r_{ij} between any two lattice points i and j are easily computed in terms of the nearest neighbor distance r. The relation between the volume V and the nearest neighbor distance r is

3.4 $\qquad\qquad V = \mathrm{N}r^3/2^{1/2}$

The energy $U_L(r)$ or $U_L(V)$ can be written in terms of the pair interactions $u(r_{ij})$.

3.5 $\qquad\qquad U_L(V) = \tfrac{1}{2}\mathrm{N}\Sigma' u(r_{ij})$

The prime on the summation indicates summation over all points j on the lattice except $j = i$. Equation 3.5 expresses the fact that one first computes the total energy of interaction of the ith molecule with all of its neighbors j. To get the total energy this must be multiplied by $\mathbf{N}$ and then divided by 2, lest all pair interactions be counted twice.

In the face-centered lattice there are 12 nearest neighbors at a distance r, six next nearest neighbors at a distance $2^{1/2}r$, etc. The sum indicated in equation 3.5 can be carried out numerically, considering the contribution from nearest neighbors, next nearest neighbors, etc. Carried out in this fashion the sum converges quite rapidly.

The result of this calculation is [1,2]

$$3.6 \qquad U_L(V) = \mathbf{N}\epsilon^* \left[8.62 \left(\frac{V_0}{V} \right)^4 - 17.24 \left(\frac{V_0}{V} \right)^2 \right]$$

In the above equation V_0 is defined in terms of the quantity r^* appearing in the Lennard-Jones potential as follows:

$$3.7 \qquad V_0 = 0.69\mathbf{N}r^{*3} = 0.916V^*$$

From equation 3.6 and $p = dU_L/dV$ one readily derives the equation of state for a molecular crystal at $0°K$.

$$3.8 \qquad p = 37.64p^* \left[\left(\frac{V_0}{V} \right)^5 - \left(\frac{V_0}{V} \right)^3 \right]$$

$$p = 2^{1/2}(\epsilon^*/r^{*3})$$

We can now see from equation 3.8 that the quantity V_0 introduced in equations 3.6 and 3.7 is in fact the molar volume at $T = 0°K$ and $p = 0$.

The bulk modulus at $0°K$ can be obtained as a function of pressure from equations 3.8 and 1.3.

$$3.9 \qquad B(p) = 1.07 \times 10^2(\epsilon^*/r^{*3}) + 7p$$

At ordinary pressures the second term in equation 3.9 is completely negligible compared to the first, so that at $0°K$ and pressures below 100 atm the bulk modulus B_0 is given by

$$3.10 \qquad B_0 = 1.07 \times 10^2(\epsilon^*/r^{*3})$$

The molar energy of vaporization $E°_{vap}$ at $0°K$ and $p = 0$, is equal to $-U_L(V_0)$. It can be immediately obtained from equation 3.6 by setting $V = V_0$.

$$3.11 \qquad E°_{vap} = 8.62\mathbf{N}\epsilon^*$$

Table I.3

CALCULATED VERSUS EXPERIMENTAL PROPERTIES OF MOLECULAR LATTICES

	Substance								
	Ne	A	Kr	Xe	N_2	O_2	NO	CO_2	CH_4
$10^{15}\epsilon^*$, ergs	4.91	16.54	23.6	30.5	13.2	16.3	18.1	28.3	20.5
r^*, Å	3.09	3.82	4.04	4.60	4.17	3.89	3.56	4.57	4.29
V_0 calc ^{a}	11.4	21.8	25.8	38.0	28.3	23.0	17.6	37.3	30.7
V'_0 expt ^{b}		16.76	32.19	42.94	13.65	25.20		38.16	37.70
E_{vap}, ergs/mole $\times 10^{-10}$ calc ^{c}	2.55	8.58	12.2	15.8	6.86	8.48	9.41	14.7	10.7
E_{vap}, ergs/mole $\times 10^{-10}$ expt ^{b}	1.82	6.47	9.7	13.0	5.6	6.8		25.2	81.9
B_0, dynes/cm$^2 \times 10^{-10}$ calc ^{d}	1.70	3.16	3.83	3.35	1.94	2.99	4.29	3.17	2.78
B, dynes/cm$^2 \times 10^{-10}$ expt ^{b}	1.0	1.6			1.9				
θ, °K calc ^{e}	60	63	49	39	61	69	82	65	98
θ, °K expt ^{b}	63	85			68		119		

^{a} From equation 3.7.

^{b} All experimental values are taken from the literature at the lowest temperatures there recorded, but not extrapolated to 0°K. V'_0 is molar volume at boiling point.

^{c} From equation 3.11.

^{d} From equation 3.12.

^{e} From equation 5.17.

A new expression for the bulk modulus B_0 can therefore be given in terms of the experimentally measurable $E°_{vap}$ and V_0, as can be seen from equations 3.7, 3.10 and 3.11.

$$3.12 \qquad B_0 = 8.04(E°_{vap}/V_0)$$

At higher temperatures it is an experimental fact that the bulk modulus $B(T)$ is approximately B_0. To a slightly better approximation one may postulate the formula

$$3.13 \qquad B(T) = 8.04(E_{vap}/V)$$

where E_{vap} and V are the molar energy of vaporization and the molar volume at the temperature in question.

In Table I.3 values of molar volume, energy of vaporization, bulk modulus, ϵ^* and r^* are presented for some molecular crystals.

References I.3

1. S. D. Hamann, *Physico-chemical Effects of Pressure*, Chapter III, pp. 42–48, Academic Press, New York, 1957.
2. J. E. Lennard-Jones and A. E. Ingham, *Proc. Roy. Soc. London*, **A107**, 636 (1925).

4. ELASTIC BEHAVIOR OF ISOTROPIC BODIES AT SMALL STRAINS

There are three very elementary types of elastic deformation of isotropic bodies: uniform compression, simple tension and simple shear. Uniform compression has been discussed in the first two sections. We now introduce the concepts of tension and shear.

An example of simple tension is shown in Figure I.2. A rectangular prism of isotropic elastic material of dimensions x, y, z is subject to the balanced pair of tensile forces X shown in the figure. Owing to this tensile force, the sample changes its dimensions to $x + dx$, $y + dy$ and and $z + dz$. The strains s_x, s_y and s_z in the x, y and z direction are defined as follows (we confine ourselves to very small strains).

4.1
$$s_x = dx/x$$

$$s_y = dy/y$$

$$s_z = dz/z$$

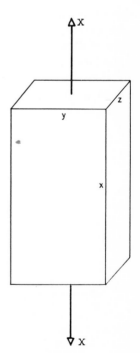

Figure I.2. Simple tension.

The sample will of course have a positive strain in the x direction. For an isotropic body there is contraction in the lateral directions as specified below.

4.2 $s_y = s_z = -\sigma s_x$

The quantity σ is the Poisson ratio, which is an important characteristic of the elastic substance in question. Its value varies from zero (in which case there is no lateral contraction) to 0.5 (in which case the volume does not change during stretching). The value of σ for most rubbery materials is close to 0.5. For most crystals and glasses Poisson's ratio is about 1/4 to 1/3.

The tensile stress f in the simple tension experiment shown in Figure I.2 is

4.3 $f = X/A$

where $A = yz$ is the cross-sectional area of the sample, and X is the tensile force.

For elastic substances in tension the stress and strain are related by Hooke's law

4.4 $f = Es_x$

where E is called Young's modulus.

An example of simple shear is shown in Figure I.3. A rectangular prism of dimensions x, y, z is made to adhere firmly to a rigid support at the face xy. At the opposite face a transverse force is applied in the direction shown, causing the body to deform. The shear strain s is defined as the tangent of the angle γ shown in the figure; for small strains $\tan \gamma \approx \gamma$; hence

4.5 $s = \tan \gamma \approx \gamma$

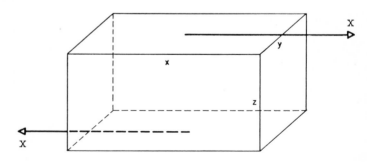

Figure I.3. Simple shear.

The shearing stress f is defined as the force X divided by the area $A = xy$.

4.6 $$f = X/A$$

For elastic substances in shear the stress and strain are related through Hooke's law

4.7 $$f = Gs$$

where G is the shear modulus.

Hooke's law as expressed in equations 4.4 and 4.7 is valid only at very small values of the strain. Many glasses and crystals can be subjected to tensile or shear strains of only 0.001 or less without fracturing, yielding or showing other nonrecoverable nonelastic effects. For these solids, treatment of elastic behavior in shear or tension *must* be restricted to small strains.

The various elastic constants presented in this section are related in the following ways. [1]

4.8 $$E = 3B(1 - 2\sigma) = 2(1 + \sigma)G$$

In other words, only two of the four elastic constants, E, B, G and σ are truly independent. Since we have already derived the bulk modulus B in terms of fundamental molecular parameters, at least for molecular crystals, it is interesting to see how E/B and G/B vary with the Poisson ratio σ. Table I.4 shows these ratios for various permissible values of σ.

Table I.4

E/B, G/B, AND E/G VERSUS POISSON RATIO σ

σ	E/B	G/B	E/G	Remarks
0.00	3	1.50	2	
0.10	2.4	1.09	2.2	
0.20	1.8	0.75	2.4	
0.25	1.5	0.60	2.5	Range for crystalline materials and
0.30	1.2	0.463	2.6	glasses
0.333	1.0	0.375	2.666	
0.40	0.6	0.214	2.8	
0.4996	0.0024	0.008	2.9992	
0.4997	0.0018	0.0006	2.9994	
0.4998	0.0012	0.0004	2.9996	
0.4999	0.0006	0.0002	2.9998	Range for rubbery materials
0.49995	0.0003	0.0001	2.9999	
0.50	0.000	0.000	3.00	

The general definition of stress and strain in three dimensions is an interesting but essentially geometric problem that will not be considered here since it is so adequately treated in many other textbooks.[1] For the most general nonisotropic body, Hooke's law consists of six equations relating each of six components of stress to linear combinations of six components of strain. There are in the most general case 21 independent elastic constants.

The number of independent elastic constants is reduced in crystals having elements of symmetry. However, even a cubic crystal has three independent elastic constants, if we are discussing a *single* crystal. Fortunately from the point of view of simplicity of mathematical treatment most macroscopic samples of crystalline substances exist in a polycrystalline form, i.e. composed of thousands of tiny crystallites randomly oriented with respect to one another. Such a polycrystalline substance can be treated as an isotropic body no matter what the crystal symmetry of its individual crystallites. Similarly inorganic and organic glasses and rubbers are generally isotropic in the unstretched state. All these substances can be regarded as having only two independent elastic constants. The interrelations among B, E, G and σ are given by equation 4.8.

For a substance such as rubber that is reversibly extensible over a wide range of values of length L, one can determine experimentally an equation of state (at atmospheric pressure) relating tensile force X, length L and temperature T. For zero tensile force the substance attains its unstretched length L_u. The equation of state is usually referred to as the "stress-strain law" and is generally nonlinear; i.e., Hooke's law does not apply except for very small values of $(L - L_u)/L_u$. The strain in these cases of high reversible extensibility is more properly defined in differential fashion as dL/L rather than as $(L - L_u)/L_u$.

Reference I.4

1. C. Kittel, *Introduction to Solid State Physics*, 2d ed., Chapter 4, John Wiley & Sons, New York, 1956.

5. ELASTIC CONSTANTS AND LATTICE VIBRATIONS

Consider a crystal lattice composed of **N** lattice points of mass m occupied by atoms, ions or molecules. The volume is related to the nearest neighbor distance as follows:

5.1
$$V = cNr^3$$

$$c = 1/\sqrt{2} \qquad \text{for face-centered cubic lattice}$$

$$c = 1 \qquad \text{for simple cubic lattice}$$

At $0°K$ the lattice energy $U_L(V)$ can be expanded around the volume V_0, which is the equilibrium volume at zero pressure, by means of Taylor's series.

5.2 $\quad U_L(V) = U(V_0) + \Delta V \left(\dfrac{dU}{dV}\right)_{V=V_0} + \tfrac{1}{2}(\Delta V)^2 \left(\dfrac{d^2U}{dV^2}\right)_{V=V_0} + \cdots$

The second term vanishes since $p = -dU/dV$ at $0°K$, and by definition $p = 0$ at $V = V_0$. The following term can be simplified since $B_0 = V_0(d^2U/dV^2)$ at $0°K$. Hence:

5.3 $\qquad U_L(V) = U_L(V_0) + \tfrac{1}{2}(B_0/V_0)(\Delta V)^2$

From equation 5.1 one obtains by differentiation

5.4 $\qquad \Delta V = 3Ncr^2(\Delta r) \approx 3Ncr_0{}^2(\Delta r)$

where r_0 is the value of r when the volume is V_0. Substituting 5.4 into 5.3, one obtains

5.5 $\qquad U_L(V) = U_L(V_0) + (9N/2)cr_0B_0(\Delta r)^2$

Einstein postulated that the real crystal lattice of **N** mass points could be placed in correspondence with a set of **N** three-dimensional harmonic oscillators, or equivalently with a set of 3**N** independent linear oscillators.[1] Each mass point, it must be remembered, has three degrees of freedom because it vibrates in three dimensions.

If the force constant of each of these harmonic oscillators of mass m is taken as k, the energy of this array is

5.6 $\qquad U = U_0 + 3\mathbf{N} \cdot \tfrac{1}{2}k\overline{(\Delta r)^2}$

where U_0 is the energy of the oscillators at their equilibrium positions and $\overline{\Delta r^2}$ is the mean-square displacement of the oscillators from equilibrium. If we take the set of 3**N** oscillators as being an equivalent representation of the actual crystal lattice, we can place the terms of equations 5.6 and 5.5 in correspondence. Hence, we obtain

5.7 $\qquad\qquad B_0 = \dfrac{1}{3c}\dfrac{k}{r_0}$

which is a very simple and edifying relationship.

The vibration frequency ν_E of the oscillators is related to the force constant k and the mass m by the equation

5.8 $$\nu_E = \frac{1}{2\pi}\left(\frac{k}{m}\right)^{\frac{1}{2}}$$

Eliminating between equations 5.8 and 5.7, one obtains

5.9 $$\nu_E = \frac{1}{2\pi}\left(\frac{3cr_0B_0}{m}\right)^{\frac{1}{2}}$$

Substituting equation 5.1 into equation 5.9, there results

5.10 $$\nu_E = 2.33 \times 10^7 B_0^{\frac{1}{2}}v^{\frac{1}{6}}/M^{\frac{1}{3}}$$

for simple cubic lattice

5.11 $$\nu_E = 2.1 \times 10^7 B_0^{\frac{1}{2}}v^{\frac{1}{6}}/M^{\frac{1}{3}}$$

for face-centered cubic lattice

where v is the specific volume (volume per gram), and M is the molecular weight of the molecules, atoms or ions at the lattice points.

Einstein further postulated that the allowed energy values to be associated with each oscillator obeyed Planck's law, $\epsilon_n = nh\nu_E$, where n assumes the integral values $n = 1, 2, 3, \ldots$, etc., and h is Planck's constant $= 6.626 \times 10^{-27}$ erg sec. He thereby obtained the average value for the combined energy of the 3N oscillators, which he took to be the thermal vibrational energy of the crystal.

5.12 $$U_t(V, T) = 3N \sum_{n=1}^{\infty} \epsilon_n \frac{\exp(-\epsilon_n/kT)}{\sum_{n=1}^{\infty} \exp(-\epsilon_n/kT)}$$

$$= \frac{3Nh\nu_E}{\exp(h\nu_E/kT) - 1}$$

From equation 5.12 the specific heat of the crystal (in the Einstein approximation) is immediately obtained by differentiation with respect to T.

5.13 $$C_v = [\partial U_t(V, T)/\partial T]_V$$

$$= \frac{3Nk(h\nu_E/kT)^2 \exp(h\nu_E/kT)}{[\exp(h\nu_E/kT) - 1^2]}$$

Equation 5.13 for the specific heat of a crystal was the first application of quantum theory to the properties of matter. By proper choice of ν_E equation 5.13 provides a reasonable but not perfect fit to the experimental curves of C_V vs. T obtained for monatomic solids.

Of great interest from the point of view of mechanical properties, the best value of the Einstein frequency ν_E obtained from experimental specific heat curves and equation 5.13 also gives a good value for B through equation 5.10 or 5.11. This is illustrated in Table I.5. The Einstein theory for solids provides a self-consistent approximate relation between thermal properties and mechanical properties, which is in no way dependent on the law of force between the atoms at the lattice point of the crystal. The other elastic constants E and G can be obtained from B and the Poisson ratio σ.

As is well known, Debye improved the Einstein theory of the specific heat of solids by considering a distribution of the 3N frequencies characterized by a maximum frequency ν_m (Appendix A). This gives relationships for B and ν_m and C_v and ν_m somewhat more exact but also more complex than the Einstein equations.[2]

The values of ν_m which when inserted into Debye's equation for C_v give the best fit to specific heat data have been widely tabulated for

Table I.5

COMPARISON OF EXPERIMENTAL AND THEORETICAL (EINSTEIN) VALUES OF B

Substance	B experimental, dynes/cm$^2 \times 10^{-12}$	$\dfrac{B \text{ experimental}}{B \text{ calculated }^a}$
Na	0.062	0.61
Al	0.66	0.64
Cu	1.5	0.84
C	5.5	0.33
Au	1.5	1.1
Pb	0.42	1.2
Bi	0.33	0.74
W	3.6	0.59
Ar	0.97	0.89
NaCl	0.30	0.57
KCl	0.21	0.66

^{a} B calculated from equation 5.11; ν_E calculated from equation 5.15.

many substances. Most frequently the tabulations are expressed in terms of the Debye temperature θ_D defined as follows

5.14 $\theta_D = (\mathbf{h}/\mathbf{k})\nu_m$

The Einstein frequency ν_E which gives the best fit to specific heat data is approximately related to the much more widely tabulated Debye temperature θ_D of the solid by

5.15 $\nu_E \approx (3\mathbf{k}/4\mathbf{h})\theta_D \approx (3/4)\nu_m$

From the relation between bulk modulus and Einstein frequency (equation 5.11) and the equations for the bulk modulus and molar volume of molecular lattices (equations 3.7 and 3.10), the author obtains the new relation

5.16 $\nu_E = 2.37(\epsilon^{*\frac{1}{2}}/m^{\frac{1}{2}}r^*)$

where m is the molecular mass. This provides an interesting relation between thermal properties and the molecular constants ϵ^* and r^* for molecular lattices. The validity of this equation is easier to verify when ν_E is replaced by θ_D, using equation 5.15.

5.17 $\theta_D \approx 1.17 \times 10^2(\epsilon^{*\frac{1}{2}}/r^*M^{\frac{1}{2}})$

Experimental values of θ_D have been obtained for some molecular lattices by specific heat measurements. These experimental values are compared in Table I.3 with the predicted values calculated from ϵ^*, r^*, and the molecular weight M by equation 5.17.

The relationships given in this section and in section 3 are nearly sufficient to provide an equation of state valid for molecular crystals not only at 0°K but also at all other temperatures. Such an equation will be developed in Appendix C.

References I.5

1. A. Einstein, *Ann. Physik*, **22**, 180 (1907); *ibid.*, **34**, 170 (1911).
2. J. C. Slater, *Introduction to Chemical Physics*, Chapter 14, especially p. 238, McGraw-Hill Book Co., New York, 1939.

6. THERMODYNAMIC TREATMENT OF SIMPLE TENSION

The combined first and second laws of thermodynamics when applied to tensile strains lead to the following equation,

6.1 $$dU = T\,dS + X\,dL - p\,dV$$

where X is the tensile force, and L is the length. This equation can be rewritten as follows:

6.2 $$X = \left(\frac{\partial U}{\partial L}\right)_{T,V} - T\left(\frac{\partial S}{\partial L}\right)_{T,V}$$

From equation 6.2 the equilibrium tensile force which maintains an elastic substance at a length L is comprised of two contributions, a kinetic tensile force $-T(\partial S/\partial L)_{T,V}$ and an internal tensile force $(\partial U/\partial L)_{T,V}$.

The magnitude of the kinetic tensile force can be computed from the following thermodynamic equation:

6.3 $$-T\left(\frac{\partial S}{\partial L}\right)_{T,V} = T\left(\frac{\partial X}{\partial T}\right)_{V,L}$$

Although equation 6.3 is exact, the coefficient $(\partial X/\partial T)_{V,L}$ is hard to obtain from a simple experiment. To maintain a constant length while varying the temperature is of course easy. However, as the temperature changes under ordinary atmospheric conditions, the volume also changes. In order to compensate for this, a varying hydrostatic pressure would have to be applied, which does not meet the criterion of a simple experiment. Various essentially equivalent theoretical treatments have been made to show how to deal with this situation.[1,2,3] For highly extensible substances that have the physical attributes that are qualitatively described as "rubbery," the simplest expression of the theoretical results, is the following approximate (but highly accurate) equation:[3]

6.4 $$-T\left(\frac{\partial S}{\partial L}\right)_{T,V} \approx T\left(\frac{\partial X}{\partial T}\right)_{p,\alpha}$$

where α is the elongation defined by

6.5 $$\alpha = L/L_u$$

and L_u is the length at zero stress, at pressure p (generally 1 atm) and at the temperature T. The length L_u is a function of temperature because of thermal expansion.

In order to evaluate $(\partial X/\partial T)_{p,\alpha}$ for a rubbery substance, two methods are available: (1) the length L can be adjusted at each temperature so that L/L_u is indeed a constant, and (2) the measurement of force as a function of temperature can be made at constant length, and

the adjustment necessary to refer back to constant elongation can be
introduced as a calculated correction by a knowledge of the coefficient
of thermal expansion and by using the stress-strain curve of the rubbery
substance.[1,4,5] At high elongations where α is in the neighborhood of
two or greater, this correction becomes negligible.

Equation 6.2 can now be recast in the following form:

$$6.6 \qquad \left(\frac{\partial U}{\partial L}\right)_{T,V} \approx X - T\left(\frac{\partial X}{\partial T}\right)_{p,\alpha}$$

If, at constant elongation α, the tension is proportional to absolute
temperature $(X = aT)$ in the temperature interval of rubbery behavior,
then from equation 6.6 the internal tension $(\partial U/\partial L)_{T,V}$ is zero, and the
stress arises from kinetic tension alone. This has been found to be true
for vulcanized natural rubber and for many vulcanized synthetic rubbers,
and this will be taken as the definition of an *ideal rubber*.

For an ideal gas subjected to reversible isothermal compression the
pressure arises from a decrease in entropy with decrease in volume. In
perfect analogy, for an ideal rubber subjected to reversible isothermal
extension, the tension arises from a decrease of entropy with increase
in extension.

$$6.7 \qquad p = T(\partial S/\partial V)_T \qquad \text{for ideal gas}$$

$$6.8 \qquad X = -T(\partial S/\partial L)_{T,V} \qquad \text{for ideal rubber}$$

The fact that the tension in rubber maintained at constant highly
extended length is proportional to the absolute temperature, and that
the length of a rubber sample maintained at constant tension decreases
with increasing temperature were well known for over a century. The
thermodynamic consequences of this result, such as shown in equation
6.8, have also been known for a long time. However, it was only after
the macromolecular chain structure of rubber was established in the
late 1920s, that the underlying meaning of equation 6.8 in terms of
molecular statistics was suggested by Meyer, von Susich and Valko,[6]
and rapidly implemented and developed by many others.

A history of these developments as well as a very thorough treatment
of the molecular statistics of rubber elasticity is given in the treatises of
Flory [7] and Treloar.[8]

In this book we shall discuss the equation of state for ideal rubbers
in the next section and present a molecular statistical treatment in
Chapter II, section 9.

If the tensile force X at constant elongation is *independent* of temperature, then from equation 6.4 the kinetic tension is zero. The tension in this case arises only from the increase of internal energy on stretching. This situation is met in crystals and glasses at absolute zero. It is clear from equation 6.2 (and *à fortiori*, from the third law of thermodynamics) that, as T approaches zero,

6.9 $X = (\partial U/\partial L)_{T,V}$ for crystals and glasses at $0°K$

This is completely analogous to the compression of crystals or of glasses at $0°K$, a subject that has been discussed for molecular crystals in section 3. The contribution of the internal tension $(\partial U/\partial L)_{T,V}$ becomes important for a discussion of the elastic behavior of polymers in their glassy state, which is always attained at sufficiently low temperatures.

References I.6

1. D. R. Elliott and S. A. Lippmann, *J. Appl. Phys.*, **16**, 50 (1945).
2. G. Gee, *Trans. Faraday Soc.*, **42**, 585 (1946).
3. P. J. Flory, *Principles of Polymer Chemistry*, pp. 489–491, Cornell University Press, Ithaca, N. Y., 1953.
4. K. H. Meyer and C. Ferri, *Helv. Chim. Acta*, **18**, 570 (1935).
5. R. L. Anthony, R. H. Caston and E. Guth, *J. Phys. Chem.*, **46**, 826 (1942).
6. K. H. Meyer, G. von Susich and K. Valko, *Kolloid-Z.*, **59**, 208 (1932).
7. P. J. Flory, *Principles of Polymer Chemistry*, Chapter 12, Cornell University Press, Ithaca, N. Y., 1953.
8. L. R. G. Treloar, *The Physics of Rubber Elasticity*, Clarendon Press, Oxford, England, 1949; 2d ed., 1959.

7. THE ELASTICITY OF IDEAL RUBBER NETWORKS

Whereas the Young's modulus of crystalline solids and glasses lies in the range 10^{10} to 10^{13} dynes/cm^2, the Young's modulus of natural rubber and of a tremendous variety of synthetic rubbers lies in the approximate range 10^6 to 10^8 dynes/cm^2. Furthermore, whereas the elastic limit of many crystalline and glassy solids is substantially less than 1%, natural and synthetic rubbers may often be reversibly stretched several hundred per cent. We shall use the word rubber to characterize a state of matter rather than the specific chemical substance obtained from the rubber tree.

A very important clue which led to the elucidation of the stretching mechanism in rubbery materials was the fact that the stress at constant elongation α is proportional to the absolute temperature in the temperature region of rubbery behavior. As discussed in section 6 it is immediately apparent that the tension in a stretched ideal rubber arises from the entropy contribution in equation 6.2.

All the innumerable synthetic rubbers as well as natural rubber have a common molecular morphology. They are formed from long flexible chain-like molecules occasionally cross-linked to form a three-dimensional network. There is approximately one cross link to every few hundred chain atoms in a typical rubber of good properties. Linear polymers of sufficiently high molecular weight also show rubbery properties in a suitable temperature interval. In these cases the "entanglements" between the chains act as transient cross links, but the linear polymer will flow at sufficiently high temperatures. For example, unvulcanized natural rubber is a linear polymer which though rubbery at room temperature has only limited uses as such because it flows at high temperatures. To make a more useful product, natural rubber is mixed with vulcanizing agents such as sulfur or peroxides, molded or extruded into its desired final shape at high temperatures, and finally cured or vulcanized at high temperatures. The last process consists in chemically cross-linking the rubber to form a network. It is mainly these chemically cross-linked networks that we are discussing in this section, recognizing that transient "cross links" can be formed by entanglement, by tiny crystallites and perhaps by exceptionally strong secondary valences.

In the unstretched state the network chain (the portion of the molecular chain between contiguous cross links) is randomly coiled, and in fact is rapidly changing from one conformation to the other, all, however, consistent with the fixed distance between the cross links. When the rubber is stretched, the average distance between the cross links increases, and the number of possible conformations of the flexible chain between its fixed end points (the cross links) is now reduced from Ω_u to Ω. The change in entropy between the stretched state and the unstretched state is related to the number of configurations in the stretched and unstretched states by the relation

7.1 $$S - S_u = \mathbf{k} \ln \Omega/\Omega_u$$

By evaluating the number of configurations Ω_u and Ω by numerous methods fully presented in references 1 and 2, one arrives at the following equation,

7.2 $$S - S_u = -\tfrac{1}{2}N_0\mathbf{k}\left[\left(\frac{L}{L_u}\right)^2 + 2\frac{L_u}{L} - 3\right]$$

where N_0 is the number of network chains in a sample whose initial length and cross-sectional area are L_u and A_u and whose stretched length and cross-sectional area in the stretched state are L and A. It has been experimentally demonstrated that the volume changes only slightly even for twofold extension so that $L_u A_u = LA$.

Equation 7.2 will be derived by an elementary method in Chapter II, section 9.

The tensile force X is obtained from equation 7.2 and the equation

7.3 $$X = -T(\partial S/\partial L)_T$$

from which is readily obtained

7.4 $$X = \frac{N_0 kT}{L_u}\left[\frac{L}{L_u} - \left(\frac{L_u}{L}\right)^2\right]$$

The true stress-strain curve for an ideal rubber is obtained by dividing both sides of equation 7.4 by A, the cross-sectional area of the sample whose length is L.

7.5 $$f = \frac{X}{A} = n\mathbf{R}T\left[\left(\frac{L}{L_u}\right)^2 - \frac{L_u}{L}\right]$$

where n is the number of moles of network chains per unit volume (in cubic centimeters) of rubber and is equal to $N_0/(A_u L_u)\mathbf{N}$.

Quite frequently the equation of state for an ideal rubber is written in terms of the "stress" F, which is defined as X/A_u, the force per unit area of the unstretched sample. From equation 7.4 one obtains

7.6 $$F = \frac{X}{A_u} = n\mathbf{R}T\left[\frac{L}{L_u} - \left(\frac{L_u}{L}\right)^2\right]$$

A new quantity M_c, the number-average molecular weight of the network chains, is often introduced. M_c is defined by the relationship

7.7 $$nM_c = d$$

where d is the density of the rubber (in grams per cubic centimeter).

Equations 7.5 and 7.6 can be expressed in terms of M_c rather than n.

7.8 $$f = \frac{d\mathbf{R}T}{M_c}\left[\left(\frac{L}{L_u}\right)^2 - \frac{L_u}{L}\right]$$

7.9 $$F = \frac{d\mathbf{R}T}{M_c}\left[\frac{L}{L_u} - \left(\frac{L_u}{L}\right)^2\right]$$

The isothermal Young's modulus at any portion of the stress-strain curve may be defined as follows:

7.10 $$E = L(\partial f/\partial L)_T$$

From equations 7.10 and 7.5 one obtains

7.11 $$E = n\mathbf{R}T\left[2\left(\frac{L}{L_u}\right)^2 + \frac{L_u}{L}\right]$$

For very small strains the Young's modulus can be obtained from equation 7.11 by putting $L = L_u$.

7.12 $$E \text{ (at low strains)} = 3n\mathbf{R}T = 3d\mathbf{R}T/M_c$$

At 298°K the value for the Young's modulus E in dynes per square centimeter is

7.13 $$E = 7.43 \times 10^{10}d/M_c = 7.43 \times 10^{10}n$$

If the density of the rubber is unity, the modulus will be 7.43×10^6 when $M_c = 10,000$ or when n is 10^{-4}. Values of M_c between 5,000 and 10,000 are in fact rather typical for many cross-linked natural and synthetic rubbers.

Suppose that the network was produced from originally "infinite" linear molecules by the addition of c moles of tetrafunctional cross-linking agent per cubic centimeter of rubber. From each cross link there emanates four network chains, but each network chain belongs to two cross links. Hence there are $2c$ moles of network chains per cubic centimeter in the cross-linked network.

7.14 $$2c = n = d/M_c$$

If the linear molecular chains before cross linking are of finite number-average molecular weight M_n, the network produced by c moles of cross-linking agent per cubic centimeter of rubber will contain some terminal network chains which are ineffective in supporting stress.

The same theoretical considerations that give rise to equation 7.5 for tensile strains yield the following equation for shear strains,

7.15 $$f_\gamma = n\mathbf{R}T\gamma$$

where f_γ is the shear stress, γ is the shear strain and n is the number of network chains per cubic centimeter of rubber. This equation holds theoretically and experimentally for a very wide range of shear strains. The shear modulus for an ideal rubber network is

7.16 $$G = n\mathbf{R}T = d\mathbf{R}T/M_c$$

References I.7

1. P. J. Flory, *Principles of Polymer Chemistry*, Chapter XI, Cornell University Press, Ithaca, N. Y., 1953.
2. L. R. G. Treloar, *The Physics of Rubber Elasticity*, Clarendon Press, Oxford, England, 1949; 2d ed., 1959.

8. THE VISCOSITY OF LIQUIDS

We may define a liquid as a condensed phase which under normal experimental conditions responds to a shear stress by flowing rather than by exhibiting a fixed shear strain. At sufficiently low shear stresses both liquids and gases obey Newton's law,

$$8.1 \qquad\qquad f = \eta \, ds/dt$$

where f is the shearing stress, ds/dt the rate of shear and η is the coefficient of viscosity. If f is expressed in dynes per square centimeter, and t in seconds, the viscosity coefficient obtained from equation 8.1 is expressed in poises. Viscosity has the dimensions mass/(length $\times$ time).

Viscometers are instruments used for measuring viscosities. These can be of several designs, depending on the range of viscosity which is to be measured. The following types are very common: capillary flow; falling (or rising) ball, bubble or oil drop; rotating concentric cylinders; parallel-plate plastometer.

The range of liquid viscosities is enormous. At room temperature the viscosities of water, castor oil and pitch are approximately 10^{-2}, 10^{1} and 10^{10} poises, respectively. By comparison, the viscosity of air at 23°C is 1.84×10^{-4} poise.

The viscosity of gases at pressures less than 100 atm is satisfactorily derived from the principles of kinetic theory. If, due to an external shearing stress, one plane layer of molecules in the gas is moving faster than an adjacent plane of molecules, each will tend to drag the other so that the state of relative motion will dissipate when the shearing stress is removed. In a gas the viscous drag originates in the following manner: When molecules from the faster-moving plane enter the slower-moving plane, they transfer their extra momentum to molecules in this plane by collision; when molecules from the slower-moving plane enter the faster-moving plane, they lower the momentum of the molecules in this plane by collision. Thus the state of relative motion tends to dissipate. The formula derived from straightforward application of the kinetic theory of gases is

8.2
$$\eta \text{ (gas)} = \frac{1}{3}\left(\frac{2}{\pi}\right)^{3/2}\frac{(m\mathbf{k}T)^{1/2}}{(2r)^2}$$

where m is the molecular mass and $2r$ is the molecular diameter. It should be noted that the viscosity of a gas is independent of pressure and increases with temperature.

In a liquid, adjacent layers are coupled by very strong intermolecular forces. If these two layers are moving relative to each other, the drag will be related to the strong attractive forces between the layers.

Molecular theories of the viscosity of liquids have been developed by Born and Green [1,2] and by Kirkwood [3] et al. The theories are quite complex, and only the results can be presented here. They are applicable to liquids composed of chemically saturated and spherical molecules. The important molecular property that is invoked is the energy of interaction $u(r)$ between a pair of isolated molecules.

8.3
$$u(r) = u_r(r) - u_a(r)$$

In equation 8.3, the term $u_r(r)$ represents the repulsive interaction between the molecules, and $u_a(r)$ represents the attractive interaction between the molecules. For chemically saturated molecules the Lennard-Jones potential is a good approximation, giving

8.4
$$u_r(r) = \epsilon^*(r^*/r)^{12}$$

8.5
$$u_a(r) = +2\epsilon^*(r^*/r)^6$$

The molecular theory of fluid viscosity leads to a tractable result only after numerous approximations. One such result is [1,2,6]

8.6
$$\eta = 0.48\,\frac{r_1}{v_m}\,[mu_a(r_1)]^{1/2}\exp\left(-\frac{u(r_1)}{\mathbf{k}T}\right)$$

where v_m is the volume per molecule, m is the molecular mass and r_1 is some particular value of r which turns out to be somewhat larger than r^*.

At this point it is well to recall the expression for the Einstein frequency for an Einstein solid derived in section 5.

8.7
$$\nu_E = 2.37(\epsilon^{*1/2}/m^{1/2}r^*)$$

By combining the last four equations, one obtains, in order of magnitude,

8.8
$$\eta \approx \frac{m}{r^*} \nu_E \approx \frac{m}{v_m^{1/3}} \nu_E$$

where ν_E is the Einstein frequency of the corresponding solid.

Equation 8.8 is very similar to the formula that was proposed by Andrade [4,5] for the viscosity of liquid metals at their melting points and was found to compare very well with experimental results.

8.9
$$\eta = \frac{m}{v_m^{1/3}} \frac{4\mathbf{k}\theta_D}{3\mathbf{h}} \qquad \text{Andrade's formula}$$

The molecular theory of fluid viscosity in the form of equation 8.6 (and in a more exact expression due to Kirkwood) has been applied to liquid argon and liquid methane and found to give agreement with experimental results within a factor of two.[6]

By making certain simplifying assumptions it is possible to extend the molecular theory to treat the viscosity of more complicated molecules.[6] However, many approximations are required. It is still very useful to treat liquid viscosities from more empirical approaches which serve to correlate many important facts.

Batchinski [7] in an exhaustive experimental study of liquid viscosity concluded that the viscosity at constant specific volume was relatively independent of pressure and temperature. He proposed the equation

8.10
$$1/\eta = c(v - v_0) = cv_f$$

where c is a constant for each liquid, v is the specific volume of the liquid (volume per gram) and v_0 is the specific volume of the liquid extrapolated to 0°K without any change of phase. Several numerical methods for making this extrapolation are discussed by Doolittle.[8] What is really desired is the volume per gram of the "solidly packed" molecules, although the exact mode of packing is somewhat unspecified. The quantity $v_f = v - v_0$ is the specific "free volume" or the specific "empty volume" and this quantity is found to be of great significance in correlating viscosities.

A more accurate empirical equation employing the free-volume concept has been proposed by Doolittle,[8]

8.11
$$\ln \eta = \ln A + B v_0/v_f$$

where A and B depend on the nature of liquid (B is near unity), and v_0 and v_f have been discussed above. It should be emphasized that temperature does not appear in equation 8.11 in any explicit fashion, but appears implicitly through the dependence of v_f (and hence of v) on temperature. It might also be pointed out that the empirical equation 8.11 is good in a range of low specific volumes (and low free volumes) where equation 8.6 obtained from the molecular theory is probably invalid. Equation 8.11 is therefore very useful in treating the viscosity of super-cooled liquids or the viscosity of liquids under high pressures.

Another way of thinking of the behavior of liquids is to consider that the molecules of a liquid form a very imperfect quasi-lattice which has many vacant lattice sites (or holes). The "holes" are not necessarily equal in size to a molecule. In this quasi-lattice the molecules can very readily move from one position to another by surmounting an energy barrier. The ease of this diffusional motion is reciprocally related to the viscosity. This "activated-diffusional model" leads to the following formula, due to Eyring, for the viscosity of liquids,[9]

$$8.12 \qquad \eta = \frac{Nh}{V} \exp \frac{\Delta F^*_{\text{visc}}}{RT}$$

where V is the molar volume of the liquid, and ΔF^*_{visc} is the free energy of activation per mole for the motion of the molecules from one equilibrium position to the other.

For nearly one hundred simple liquids at atmospheric pressure, including associated liquids, it has been found empirically that $\Delta F^*_{\text{visc}} = E_{\text{vap}}/2.45$ where E_{vap} is the molar heat of vaporization of the liquid. Therefore, at atmospheric pressure,[9]

$$8.13 \qquad \eta = \frac{Nh}{V} \exp \frac{E_{\text{vap}}}{2.45RT}$$

Attempts have been made to combine the activated-jump theory and the free-volume theory in order to obtain a more universally valid equation for viscosity. These lead to equations of the form [6]

$$8.14 \qquad \eta = f(v_f) \exp (E^*_{\text{visc}}/RT)$$

where $f(v_f)$ is some function of the free volume and E^*_{visc} represents the activation energy for diffusional motion at constant volume (or constant free volume).

References I.8

1. M. Born and H. S. Green, *Proc. Roy. Soc. London*, **A190**, 455 (1947).
2. H. S. Green, *The Molecular Theory of Fluids*, Interscience Publishers, New York, 1952.
3. J. G. Kirkwood, F. P. Buff and M. S. Green, *J. Chem. Phys.*, **17**, 988 (1949).
4. E. N. da C. Andrade, *Phil. Mag.*, **17**, 497, 698 (1934).

5. E. N. da C. Andrade, *Proc. Roy. Soc. London*, **A215**, 36 (1952).
6. A. Bondi, Chapter 9 in *Rheology: Theory and Applications*, F. R. Eirich (ed.), Academic Press, New York, 1956.
7. A. J. Batchinski, *Z. physik. Chem.*, **84**, 643 (1913).
8. A. K. Doolittle, *J. Appl. Phys.*, **22**, 1471 (1951); **23**, 236 (1952).
9. H. Eyring, K. Laidler and S. Glasstone, *The Theory of Rate Processes*, Chapter IX, McGraw-Hill Book Co., New York, 1941.

9. VISCOELASTICITY: THE MAXWELL MODEL

James Clerk Maxwell was among the first to discuss quantitatively the viscoelasticity of matter. He observed that substances such as pitch or tar could be regarded neither as ideal elastic solids nor as viscous liquids, but seemed instead to partake of the character of both. In fact he proposed an equation, which now bears his name, which he hoped would suffice to explain this type of behavior.[1] For very rapidly applied stresses pitch behaves like an elastic body: It undergoes a deformation proportional to the stress, and it shows a recovery if the stress is very rapidly removed. If the stress is applied slowly or over a long period of time, the pitch behaves like a very viscous liquid: It will show a continued deformation with time, the rate of deformation being proportional to the applied stress, as predicted by Newton's equation. A substance that manifests the phenomenon of viscoelasticity very dramatically is "bouncing putty."

Maxwell attempted to incorporate Hooke's law and Newton's law into the same equation. He proposed

$$9.1 \qquad \frac{ds}{dt} = \frac{1}{G}\frac{df}{dt} + \frac{1}{\tau G}f$$

where s is the shear strain, f the shear stress, G the shear modulus and τ is a quantity called the relaxation time.

The best way to understand the implication of the Maxwell equation 9.1 is to apply it to several types of experiments. Suppose first that at time $t = 0$ a constant shear stress f_0 is suddenly applied to a Maxwell body (a substance which obeys equation 9.1). In the "instantaneous" interval during which f increases from zero to f_0, df/dt is extremely large, and the first term on the right-hand side of equation 9.1 is much larger than the second term; hence

$$9.2 \qquad \frac{ds}{dt} = \frac{1}{G}\frac{df}{dt}$$

(for times much shorter than the relaxation time).

Integration of equation 9.2 gives $s = f_0/G$ at the end of the time interval over which the full stress f_0 is applied. This may be taken as the boundary condition for $t = 0$. Integrating equation 9.1 for $f = f_0$ and inserting this boundary condition, one obtains

9.3 $$s = \frac{f_0}{G} + \frac{f_0}{\tau G} t$$

In other words, under conditions of constant stress f_0, a Maxwell body shows first an instantaneous elastic deformation followed by a viscous flow (a deformation linearly proportional to time). For long times ($t \gg \tau$) the elastic contribution becomes negligible, and

9.4 $$s = (f_0/\tau G)t$$

Newton's law relating shear stress and shear strain in a viscous liquid is

9.5 $$s = f_0 t/\eta$$

Comparing equation 9.4 with equation 9.5, one finds that the viscosity of a Maxwell body is

9.6 $$\eta = \tau G$$

It is probable that all Newtonian liquids, even those such as water and benzene which are very fluid, have elastic as well as viscous behavior. The maximum relaxation time of benzene or water is so short, however (probably less than 10^{-12} sec), that, if we apply a constant stress (either shear or tension), the viscous component of equation 9.3 overtakes the elastic component in importance in immeasurably short times (at least for this type of experiment).

A plot of deformation versus time for a Maxwell body subjected to a constant load is shown in Figure I.4.

Another interesting experiment is to subject a Maxwell body to a constant strain s_0 starting with time $t = 0$. It is assumed that the strain can be instantaneously applied; i.e., the sample can be stretched to a value s_0 at times very short compared with the relaxation time τ. Under these conditions the viscous term is negligible compared with the elastic term in equation 9.1, and the equation can be integrated. In this way one obtains the result that, at time $t = 0$, $f = s_0 G$. Since at constant strain $ds/dt = 0$, the subsequent behavior is obtained by integrating the equation

9.7 $$0 = \frac{1}{G}\frac{df}{dt} + \frac{1}{\tau G}f$$

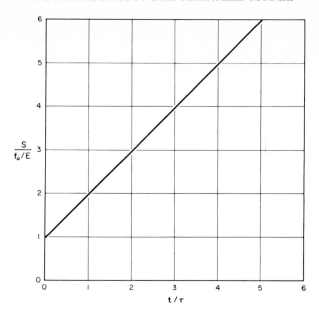

Figure I.4. Maxwell body under constant stress.

Equation 9.7 integrates to

9.8 $$f = s_0 G \exp{(-t/\tau)}$$

This law of exponential decay is of great importance and is known as Maxwellian decay.   Maxwellian decay is plotted in four different ways in Figure I.5.   In (a) is shown a plot of stress versus linear time; in (b) a plot of the logarithm of stress versus linear time; in (c) a plot of stress versus logarithmic time; in (d) a plot of the logarithm of stress versus the logarithm of time.   It is interesting to note the characteristic shape of the curve in (c).   Changing the relaxation time does not change the shape of the curve but merely displaces the curve horizontally along the logarithmic time axis.

Maxwell's equation 9.1 can readily be generalized to behavior in tension as well as shear.   For tensile experiments,

9.9 $$\frac{ds}{dt} = \frac{1}{E}\frac{df}{dt} + \frac{1}{\tau E}f$$

where s is tensile strain, f is tensile stress, E is the tensile modulus, and τ is the relaxation time.   It is assumed that the relaxation time for tension

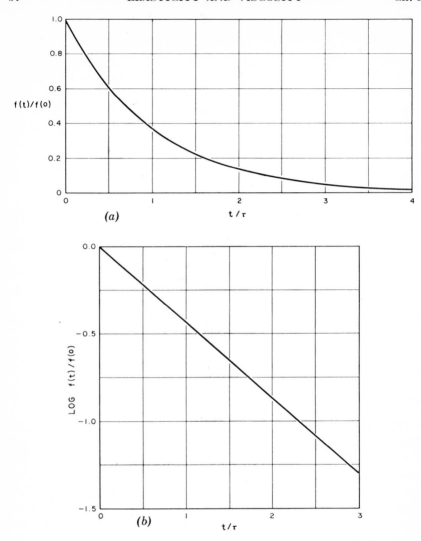

Figure I.5.   Maxwellian decay of stress at constant extension.

is the same as the relaxation time for shear.   All the equations derived from equation 9.1 have analogous solutions derived from equation 9.9. At constant tensile stress, the tensile strain is given by

$$9.10 \qquad s = \frac{f_0}{E} + \frac{f_0}{\tau E} t = \frac{f_0}{E} + \frac{f_0}{\eta^{(t)}} t$$

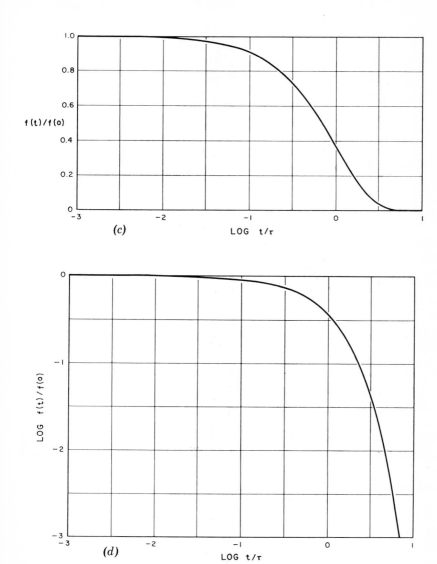

Figure I.5 (*continued*).

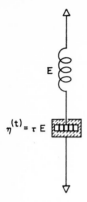

Figure I.6.   The Maxwell model.

The slope of the plot s versus time is $f_0/\tau E$. However, since we are dealing with tensile stress rather than shear stress, the quantity τE is the tensile viscosity $\eta^{(t)}$ rather than the shear viscosity η. The relation among $\eta^{(t)}$, η, and the Poisson ratio σ is

9.11 $$\eta^{(t)} = \tau E$$

$$\eta = \tau G$$

$$\frac{\eta^{(t)}}{\eta} = \frac{E}{G} = 2(1 + \sigma)$$

For an incompressible substance $\sigma = \frac{1}{2}$ and $\eta^{(t)} = 3\eta$.

A mechanical model which represents the Maxwell body is a spring and dashpot in series as shown in Figure I.6. Here the stress is the same on both elements, and the deformation of the total model is the sum of the deformation of the spring and the dashpot. It is assumed that the spring obeys Hooke's law $f = Es_1$ and the dashpot obeys Newton's law $f = \tau E(ds_2/dt)$. Inasmuch as the total deformation is $s = s_1 + s_2$, it follows that

9.12 $$\frac{ds}{dt} = \frac{1}{E}\frac{df}{dt} + \frac{1}{\tau E}f$$

which is identical with equation 9.9.

Reference I.9

1. J. C. Maxwell, *Phil. Trans. Roy. Soc. London*, **157**, 52 (1867); *Scientific Papers*, **2**, 26; Cambridge University Press, 1890.

Aspects of Polymer Physics

1. THE CONFORMATIONS OF A LINEAR POLYMER CHAIN [1]

The basic structure of polymer molecules is that of a flexible linear chain. The most highly idealized version of such a structure is a chain composed of $\mathfrak{N}$ links, each of length l_0, and each hinged to the previous one by a completely freely rotating joint, which allows each link to take any angular position with respect to the previous link. Such a molecular chain when subject to thermal agitation adopts a very large number of conformations. The links are assumed infinitely thin so that steric interference between different portions of the chain can be neglected.

37

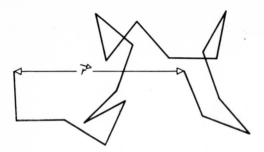

Figure II.1. The freely jointed chain.

If we assume all conformations of the chain equally probable, we can find the mean-square distance between the ends of the chain. Let the successive links of the chain in a given conformation be designated by the vectors $\vec{l}_1, \vec{l}_2, \vec{l}_3, \ldots, \vec{l}_{\mathfrak{N}}$ each of length l_0. The vector distance $\vec{r}$ between the beginning and end of the chain for a particular conformation is (see Figures II.1 and II.2)

1.1 $$\vec{r} = \vec{l}_1 + \vec{l}_2 + \cdots + \vec{l}_{\mathfrak{N}}$$

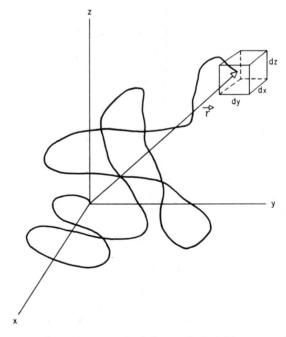

Figure II.2. Spatial configuration of a polymer chain taking one end of the chain as origin.

The square of the distance between chain ends is

1.2 $$r^2 = \vec{r} \cdot \vec{r} = \vec{l}_1 \cdot \vec{l}_1 + \vec{l}_2 \cdot \vec{l}_2 + \cdots + \vec{l}_\mathfrak{N} \cdot \vec{l}_\mathfrak{N} + 2 \sum_{i<j}^{\mathfrak{N}} \vec{l}_i \cdot \vec{l}_j$$

1.3 $$r^2 = \mathfrak{N} l_0{}^2 + 2 \sum_{i<j}^{\mathfrak{N}} \vec{l}_i \cdot \vec{l}_j$$

The first term on the right-hand side of equation 1.3 is the same for all conformations of the chain. The typical term of the summation is equal to $l_0{}^2 \cos \alpha_{i,j}$ where $\alpha_{i,j}$ represents the angle between vector $\vec{l}_i$ and vector $\vec{l}_j$. Since absolutely free rotation is assumed, the angle $\pi + \alpha_{ij}$ is just as likely as the angle α_{ij} when a summation over all conformations is carried out. Since $\cos \alpha_{ij} = -\cos(\pi + \alpha_{ij})$, the second term on the right-hand side of equation 1.3 vanishes. The mean-square end-to-end distance $\bar{r}^2$ for the freely rotating chain is [2,3]

1.4 $$\bar{r}^2 = \mathfrak{N} l_0{}^2 \qquad \text{(freely jointed polymer chain)}$$

If we consider that the neighboring links in the chain make a fixed bond angle θ (where $\theta = \pi - \alpha$) with each other, but rotate freely around that fixed angle, the value of $\bar{r}^2$ is [3]

1.5 $$\bar{r}^2 = \mathfrak{N} l_0{}^2 (1 - \cos \theta)/(1 + \cos \theta)$$

(chain links freely rotating around the valence angle θ)

For the special case of the hydrocarbon chain, as in polymethylene, the valence or bond angle θ is the tetrahedral angle, namely, 109.5°. Equation 1.5 becomes

1.6 $$\bar{r}^2 = 2 \mathfrak{N} l_0{}^2$$

(chain links freely rotating around the tetrahedral bond)

For an actual hydrocarbon chain, rotation is not free around the tetrahedral angle, but instead there are three preferred positions (Figures II.3 through II.5). The jth bond can be in the plane of either the $j - 1$ and $j - 2$ bonds (*trans*), or it can be in two other positions 120° out of the plane (*gauche*). If we take the energy difference between the *gauche* configuration and the *trans* configuration as being ϵ per mole, an exact expression for $\bar{r}^2$ can be derived [4,5] (see Appendix D):

1.7 $$\bar{r}^2 = \left(\frac{2}{3} + \frac{4}{3} \exp \frac{\epsilon}{RT} \right) \mathfrak{N} l_0{}^2$$

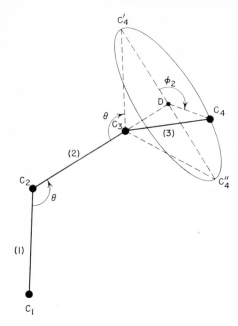

Figure II.3. Spatial representation of a simple singly bonded
carbon-carbon chain. (After P. J.
Flory, *Principles of Polymer Chemistry*, Figure 74.)

If the *trans* position is the one of lowest energy, the chain will tend to assume its extended planar zigzag conformations, and $\bar{r}^2$ will tend to be large. If the *gauche* positions are of lower energy, $\bar{r}^2$ will be smaller than is the case in equation 1.6. If $\epsilon = 0$, $\bar{r}^2$ has the same value as in equation 1.6.

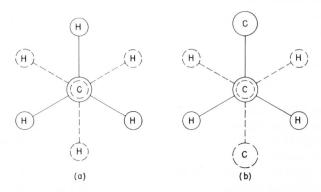

Figure II.4. Minimum energy forms for ethane (*a*) and for a section of a poly-methylene chain (*b*) as viewed along the axis of the C—C bond about which hindrance to rotation is under consideration. Dotted portions in each figure represent atoms or substituents attached to the lower carbon of the bond. (After P. J. Flory, *Principles of Polymer Chemistry*, Figure 80, page 416.)

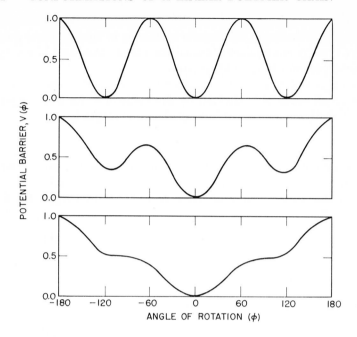

Figure II.5. Potential energy associated with bond rotation as function of angle. [After W. J. Taylor, *J. Chem. Phys.*, **16**, 257 (1948).]

In addition to the difference in the energy of the three potential *minima* corresponding to the three staggered configurations around the carbon-carbon bond, there is also an (average) energy barrier height V_0 separating the potential minima. For restricted rotation around the central carbon-carbon bond in butane, V_0 is 3.3 kcal/mole. The height of this energy barrier is an inverse measure of the rate at which the chain can move from one chain conformation to another [rate $\sim$ exp $(-V_0/RT)$]. Some diagrams of the energy barrier for restricted rotation are shown in Figure II.5.

Because of the finite size of the links in an actual polymer chain there is an important steric or "excluded volume" effect. This effect is not restricted to neighboring elements in a chain, but also involves bonds that are remote from one another in sequence along the chain. This tends to increase $\bar{r}^2$ and also considerably complicates its computation. It has been proposed that, for the case of "excluded volume,"[6]

1.8 $$\bar{r}^2 = 2\mathfrak{N}^\gamma l_0{}^2$$

where γ varies between 1.0 and 2.0.

The actual value of $\bar{r}^2$ can be obtained from experimental measurements such as studies of the angular scattering of light in dilute polymer solutions, or by simultaneous measurements of stress and birefringence on a solid polymer in its rubbery state.

The stiffness Z of a polymer chain may be defined as the square root of the actual value of $\bar{r}^2$ divided by the value of $\bar{r}^2$ for a freely jointed chain of the same number of links of the same length l_0.

1.9 $$Z = (\bar{r}^2/\mathfrak{N}l_0^2)^{\frac{1}{2}}$$

If we take one end of a polymer chain as the origin, we can write a function that expresses the probability that the other end of the chain will be found in the region of space $dx\,dy\,dz$ [7,8,9] (see Appendix E and Figure II.2),

1.10 $$W(x, y, z)\,dx\,dy\,dz = (b/\pi^{\frac{1}{2}})^3 \exp\left[-b^2(x^2 + y^2 + z^2)\right] dx\,dy\,dz$$

where the quantity b^2 is simply related to the actual mean-square distance $\bar{r}^2$ as follows:

1.11 $$b^2 = 3/2\bar{r}^2$$

The probability that the chain has an end-to-end length between r and $r + dr$ *irrespective of direction* is

1.12 $$W(r)\,dr = (b/\pi^{\frac{1}{2}})^3[\exp(-b^2r^2)]4\pi r^2\,dr$$

The most probable end-to-end length $r_{\max}$ is readily obtained by maximizing $W(r)$.

1.13 $$r_{\max} = \frac{1}{b} = \left(\frac{2\bar{r}^2}{3}\right)^{\frac{1}{2}}$$

An actual polymer chain with the complicating effects of bond angle, hindered rotation, steric hindrance, etc., can for purposes of calculation be replaced by an equivalent freely jointed chain of the same end-to-end length.[7] The actual chain of $\mathfrak{N}$ links each of length l_0 having a mean-square end-to-end length $\bar{r}^2$ is replaced by a freely jointed chain of $\mathfrak{N}_e$ "statistical segments," each of length l_e such that

1.14 $$\bar{r}^2 = \mathfrak{N}_e l_e^2$$

Further:

1.15 $$r_{\mathrm{ext}} = \mathfrak{N}_e l_e$$

where r_{ext} is the maximum extended length of the real chain. Equations 1.14 and 1.15 define $\mathfrak{N}_e$ and l_e.

The size of a polymer chain can be described not only in terms of the number of links along the main chain, but also in terms of the number of chemically identical repeating units (degree of polymerization) and in terms of molecular weight. Furthermore, a given mass of polymeric material contains many molecules, which only rarely are all the same size. The question of size distribution (molecular-weight distribution) and matters such as number-average molecular weight $\overline{M}_n$ and weight-average molecular weight $\overline{M}_w$ are discussed in Appendix F.

References II.1

1. P. J. Flory, *Principles of Polymer Chemistry*, Chapter X, Cornell University Press, Ithaca, N. Y., 1953. Contains references to the original literature.
2. F. T. Wall, *J. Chem. Phys.*, **11**, 67 (1943).
3. H. Eyring, *Phys. Rev.*, **39**, 746 (1932).
4. W. J. Taylor, *J. Chem. Phys.*, **16**, 257 (1948); M. W. Wolkenstein, *J. Phys. Chem. U.S.S.R.*, **26**, 1072 (1952).
5. A. V. Tobolsky, *J. Chem. Phys.*, **31**, 387 (1959).
6. P. J. Flory, *J. Chem. Phys.*, **17**, 303 (1949).
7. W. Kuhn, *Kolloid-Z.*, **76**, 258 (1936); **87**, 3 (1939).
8. H. M. James and E. Guth, *J. Chem. Phys.*, **11**, 470 (1943).
9. W. Kuhn and F. Grun, *Kolloid-Z.*, **101**, 248 (1942).

2. AMORPHOUS AND CRYSTALLINE POLYMERS

Polymers can be very sharply divided into two categories, those which are wholly amorphous and those which are partly crystalline. Some polymers are wholly amorphous under *all* conditions; the polymers which are partly crystalline may of course be amorphous under certain conditions (above their melting point, or if quickly quenched from their molten condition).

The two categories are very readily distinguished from each other by X-ray photographs or by Geiger-counter measurements of intensity of scattered X rays versus angle of scatter. The amorphous polymers show the same type of diffuse halo on an X-ray photograph as do simple liquids. The local structure of an amorphous polymer or of a simple liquid does not have the high degree of spatial order that is characteristic of crystals. In fact, from any given point in the structure out to a distance of approximately 15 A, the spatial arrangements of amorphous polymers and those of simple liquids or organic glasses are very similar. From the point of view of longer-range distances, the structure of an amorphous polymer might be considered as comparable to the contents

Figure II.6. Spherulite structure of a crystalline polymer viewed between crossed polaroids. (After F. P. Price, page 466 in *Growth and Perfection of Crystals.*)

of a bowl of cooked spaghetti. The spaghetti-like molecules, of course, are in a state of wriggling motion whose amplitude and speed depend on temperature.

The X-ray diagrams of crystalline polymers show a series of sharp diffraction rings superposed on some diffuse scattering. The diffuse scattering comes from the amorphous regions of the polymer; the sharp rings come from regions of crystalline order (crystallites) embedded in an amorphous matrix. The individual crystallites are small; typical dimensions might be 100 A × 200 A × 200 A. The individual crystallites generally group together in large aggregates called spherulites, which are often of a size easily visible to the naked eye when viewed between crossed polaroids (see Figure II.6).

It is important to bear in mind that in crystalline high polymers the same molecular chain may traverse a crystallite, enter a disordered amorphous region between crystallites, re-enter another crystallite, etc. The linear dimensions of a single crystallite are small compared with the

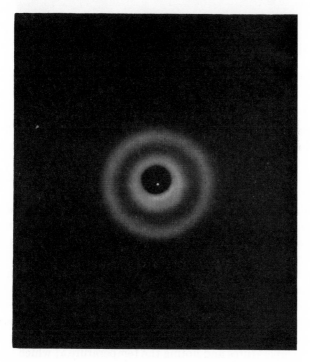

Figure II.7. X-ray photograph of an amorphous polymer. (Atactic polystyrene, courtesy R. L. Miller, Monsanto Chemical Co.)

Figure II.8. X-ray photograph of an unoriented crystalline polymer. (Annealed isotactic polystyrene, courtesy R. L. Miller, Monsanto Chemical Co.)

linear dimensions of a high-polymer chain. In cases where this is not true, i.e., in crystalline polymers of low chain length, the polymer has the physical attributes of a wax.

Typical X-ray photographs of amorphous and crystalline polymers are shown in Figures II.7 through II.9.

Crystalline polymers are characterized by the arrangement of the atoms in the unit cell; by the fraction of crystalline material present; by the size, shape, orientation and aggregation of the crystallites; and by a melting temperature T_m above which *all* crystalline regions disappear.

The melting temperature is often determined by viewing a thin film of the polymer on a heated stage of a polarizing microscope. When the temperature of the heated stage exceeds T_m, no light is transmitted by the film which has been placed between the crossed polaroids.

The temperature T_m can also be determined by taking X-ray diagrams at various temperatures and noting the temperature at which the crystalline diffraction rings completely disappear (see Figure II.10).

The melting temperatures of low-molecular-weight solids (ice, camphor, etc.) are precisely defined at a fixed pressure such as atmospheric pressure. In fact, the melting point of ice at atmospheric pressure is used to define the fixed point of 0° on the centigrade temperature scale. The melting phenomenon for these simple substances is a first-order phase transition. At the melting temperature there is a discontinuous change of volume and a discontinuous change of enthalpy, equivalent to the heat of fusion.

A discontinuous volume change is also observed at the melting temperature T_m of crystalline high polymers, provided that the crystalline polymer is previously properly annealed at temperatures somewhat below the melting temperature, and provided that the rate of heating during the measurement of the specific volume-temperature curve is extremely slow. Under these conditions the abrupt change of volume near the melting temperature is surprisingly sharp, with about 80% of the melting occurring in an interval of 3 to 4°.[1] There is a sharply defined temperature T_m at which the last trace of crystallinity abruptly disap-

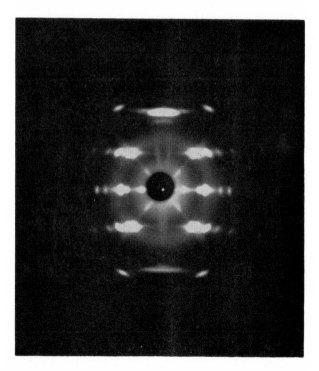

Figure II.9. X-ray photograph of an oriented crystalline polymer. (Oriented annealed isotactic polystyrene, courtesy R. L. Miller, Monsanto Chemical Co.)

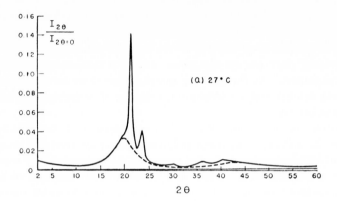

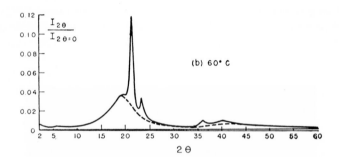

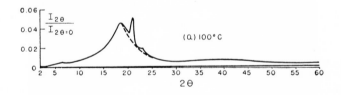

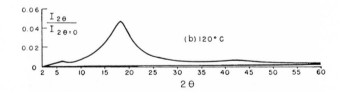

Figure II.10. Scattered X-ray intensity versus angle for low-density polyethylene ($T_m = 110°$) at four different temperatures. [After S. Krimm and A. V. Tobolsky, *J. Polymer Sci.*, **7,** Figures 3 and 4, pp. 62–63 (1951).]

pears. It appears that the fusion in polymers is best described as a diffuse first-order transition. Figure II.15 shows some vT curves in the neighborhood of T_m.

The weight fraction of amorphous material in a crystalline polymer can be obtained from X-ray studies. A Geiger counter is used to give scattering intensity as a function of angle. The integrated intensity of scattering under the amorphous halo is measured; the intensity of scattering under the crystalline peaks is *not* included.

The same polymer is then subjected to X-ray studies above its melting temperature T_m, making sure that it is exposed to the same total quantity of X radiation as in the first case. The integrated scattered intensity is measured again under these new conditions; there is, of course, no crystalline scattering above T_m. The fraction of amorphous material present in the polymer under the conditions of the first experiment is equal to the ratio of the integrated intensities measured in the two experiments.

The specific volume and the temperature coefficient of expansion of the amorphous regions can be established by measurements above the melting temperature. The specific volume and the coefficient of expansion of the crystalline regions can be determined from the lattice distances obtained from the diffraction rings. The measured specific volume $v(T)$ at any temperature is related to the specific volume of the crystalline regions $v_C(T)$ and the specific volume of the amorphous regions $v_A(T)$ by the formula

$$2.1 \qquad v(T) = (1 - \lambda)v_C(T) + \lambda v_A(T)$$

where λ is the volume fraction of the amorphous material in the polymer at the temperature T. From the above equation,

$$2.2 \qquad \lambda = [v(T) - v_C(T)]/[v_A(T) - v_C(T)]$$

Measurements of specific volume therefore provide a simple method for estimating the volume fraction of crystalline material present under any specified conditions.

It is now important to consider the structural features of a polymer that determine whether it will be amorphous or crystalline, and, if crystalline, to consider what determines the fraction of crystalline material.

First and foremost, the ability of the polymer chain to pack in an orderly crystalline array is determined by the regularity of the polymer chain. For example, polystyrene can be prepared in two forms, atactic and isotactic. In the atactic form the configuration of the phenyl groups in the "up" and "down" position along the chain is random. In the isotactic structure the phenyl groups along the chain are all in the "up" position or all in the "down" position.

$$\text{-\!\!\backslash\!\!\backslash\!\!\backslash\!-}CH_2-\underset{\underset{C_6H_5}{|}}{CH}-CH_2-\overset{\overset{C_6H_5}{|}}{CH}-CH_2-\overset{\overset{C_6H_5}{|}}{CH}-CH_2-CH-CH_2-\underset{\underset{C_6H_5}{|}}{CH}-CH_2-\underset{\underset{C_6H_5}{|}}{CH}\text{-\!\!\backslash\!\!\backslash\!\!\backslash\!-}$$

atactic polystyrene

$$\text{-\!\!\backslash\!\!\backslash\!\!\backslash\!-}CH_2-\underset{\underset{C_6H_5}{|}}{CH}-CH_2-\underset{\underset{C_6H_5}{|}}{CH}-CH_2-\underset{\underset{C_6H_5}{|}}{CH}-CH_2-\underset{\underset{C_6H_5}{|}}{CH}-CH_2-\underset{\underset{C_6H_5}{|}}{CH}\text{-\!\!\backslash\!\!\backslash\!\!\backslash\!-}$$

isotactic polystyrene

Atactic polystyrene is completely amorphous; no one has ever succeeded in bringing it into a partly crystalline condition. On the other hand, isotactic polystyrene is generally obtained in a partly crystalline condition (perhaps about 50% crystalline). Its melting point T_m is about 250°C. Occasionally by quick quenching or by casting from certain solvents or by certain polymerization procedures it can be obtained in a completely amorphous condition at room temperature. However, this is a metastable form which *can* be brought to the crystalline state by an appropriate annealing procedure.

Syndiotactic polymers have also been prepared. These have regular alternation of the side groups in the "up"-"down" positions.

Another example of the effect of regularity upon the crystallizing tendency is evidenced by the great propensity of symmetrical vinylidene polymers to crystallize. Two striking examples of this are polyvinylidene cyanide and polyvinylidene chloride. Both these polymers are much more crystalline than the corresponding atactic polyacrylonitrile and atactic polyvinyl chloride.

$$\text{-\!\!\backslash\!\!\backslash\!\!\backslash\!-}CH_2C(CN)_2CH_2C(CN)_2CH_2C(CN)_2\text{-\!\!\backslash\!\!\backslash\!\!\backslash\!-}$$

polyvinylidene cyanide

$$\text{-\!\!\backslash\!\!\backslash\!\!\backslash\!-}CH_2C(Cl)_2CH_2C(Cl)_2CH_2C(Cl)_2\text{-\!\!\backslash\!\!\backslash\!\!\backslash\!-}$$

polyvinylidene chloride

$$\text{-\!\!\backslash\!\!\backslash\!\!\backslash\!-}CH_2CH(CN)CH_2CH(CN)CH_2CH(CN)\text{-\!\!\backslash\!\!\backslash\!\!\backslash\!-}$$

polyacrylonitrile

$$\text{-\!\!\backslash\!\!\backslash\!\!\backslash\!-}CH_2CHClCH_2CHClCH_2CHCl\text{-\!\!\backslash\!\!\backslash\!\!\backslash\!-}$$

polyvinyl chloride

The importance of regularity in the chain structure as predisposing toward crystallization is also evidenced by the disrupting effect of copolymerization on this property. For example, polyvinylidene fluoride and polytrifluorochlorethylene are both highly crystalline polymers.

$$-\text{WW-}CH_2CF_2CH_2CF_2CH_2CF_2-\text{WW-}$$
polyvinylidene fluoride

$$-\text{WW-}CF_2CF(Cl)CF_2CF(Cl)CF_2CF(Cl)-\text{WW-}$$
polytrifluorochlorethylene

The two monomers $CH_2{=}CF_2$ and $CF_2{=}CF(Cl)$ can also be copolymerized over the entire composition range to form random copolymers.

$$-\text{WW-}CH_2CF_2CF_2CF(Cl)CF_2CF(Cl)CH_2CF_2-\text{WW-}$$

Within a certain range of composition centering around the 1:1 composition, the copolymers are completely amorphous (and rubbery at room temperature). At compositions that have a large preponderance of $-CF_2CF(Cl)-$, the copolymers are crystalline but have a lower crystallinity and a lower melting point than that of the pure homopolymer. The same can be said of compositions that have a large preponderance of $-CH_2CF_2-$.

The introduction of an impurity in a pure homopolymer of infinite molecular weight usually lowers the melting point of the polymer. This impurity may be a comonomer unit, a low-molecular-weight diluent or a chain end.

The formula expressing the lowering of the melting point in a copolymer whose repeating structural units are A and B is:

$$2.3 \qquad\qquad \frac{1}{T_m} - \frac{1}{T_m^\circ} = -\frac{\mathbf{R}}{\Delta H_u}\ln X_A$$

where T_m° is the melting point of the pure homopolymer A, T_m the melting point of the copolymer whose mole fraction of A units out of the total of A and B units is X_A (where X_A is close to unity), $\mathbf{R}$ is the gas constant, and ΔH_u is the heat of fusion per structural unit A.

Not only is the melting point T_m lowered by the introduction of an irregularity such as a copolymerizing unit, but the equilibrium volume fraction of crystalline material is lowered as well. This is demonstrated by an examination of the per cent crystallinity of polyethylene prepared by the newer low-pressure processes with heterogeneous ionic catalysts compared with the per cent crystallinity of polyethylene prepared by the older high-pressure (2,000-atm) process with free-radical initiators. The former product is a true linear polymethylene with a melting temperature of 137°C and a degree of crystallinity of about 90%. The latter contains an average of two butyl and one ethyl side groups per 100 carbon-chain atoms, has a melting temperature of 110°C and is about 50% crystalline. The density of the linear polyethylene is 0.97 gram/cm^3; the density of the branched polyethylene is about 0.92.

When the percentage of copolymerizing impurity is sufficiently large, the copolymer becomes completely amorphous, even though each of the constituents might form a crystalline homopolymer. It only requires eight ethyl or butyl groups per 100 carbon-chain atoms to destroy completely the crystallinity of polyethylene.

It must be added that not all copolymerizing units B cause a depression of the melting point of a polymer formed of A units. If B is isomorphous with A and will enter the chain without disrupting the crystal lattice of the pure A chains, and similarly, if A units will enter B chains without disrupting the crystal lattice formed by chains of pure B units, then copolymers of A and B will have melting points linearly intermediate between that of pure A and B. This is analogous to solid-solution formation in low-molecular-weight crystalline substances.

Another factor which governs the tendency to crystallize is the bulk of the side groups. Linear polyethylene is highly crystalline; atactic polyvinyl alcohol is highly crystalline; radical-initiated polyvinyl chloride and polyacrylonitrile are less crystalline and contain very imperfect crystallites. Moreover there is reason to believe that these materials are not entirely atactic, but for short sequences have some slight isotactic or syndiotactic regularity.[2] Atactic polypropylene, atactic polybutene-1 and atactic polystyrene are all completely amorphous because the bulkiness of the side groups does not permit the formation of a crystal lattice unless the side groups are lined up in the same direction.

The geometric conformation of individual polymer molecules in the unit cell of a polymer crystallite depends very much on the details of molecular geometry and energetics. For polymethylene the molecular conformation within the unit cell of the crystal is the planar zigzag conformation (at least for short lengths of the chain). This is due in part to the large positive value of ϵ for n-paraffins (about 600 to 800 cal/mole). For isotactic polypropylene the repulsion of the methyl groups in the planar zigzag conformation is very high. The molecules assume *gauche* rather than *trans* configurations and are therefore found in helical conformations within the unit cell of their crystallites. Many different types of helical structure are possible. The systematization[3] of these structures in terms of molecular geometry is a subject of great beauty and great complexity.

In the case of protein molecules a fairly complicated helical structure called the α-helix has received especial attention.[4]

References II.2

1. L. Mandelkern, *Chem. Revs.*, **56**, 903 (1956).
2. B. D. Coleman, *J. Polymer Sci.*, **31**, 155 (1958).
3. G. Natta and P. Corradino, *J. Polymer Sci.*, **38**, 29 (1959).
4. L. Pauling, R. B. Corey and H. R. Branson, *Proc. Natl. Acad. Sci. U. S.*, **37**, 205 (1951).

3. THERMODYNAMICS OF CRYSTALLIZATION

The statistical thermodynamics of crystallization of crystalline polymers has been extensively developed, mainly by P. J. Flory, and is thoroughly presented in his treatise.[1] In this section the important formulas will be presented without derivation, but their significance will be discussed. Many of the formulas are readily apprehended by analogy.

The melting point of a low-molecular-weight solid A is lowered by the introduction of an impurity soluble in the melt according to the formula

3.1
$$\frac{1}{T_m} - \frac{1}{T_m^\circ} = -\frac{R}{\Delta H_f} \ln a_A$$

where T_m° is the melting point of the pure solid A, T_m is the melting point in the presence of the impurity, ΔH_f is the heat of fusion, R is the gas constant and a_A is the activity of A in the melt in the presence of the dissolved impurity. For sufficiently low concentrations of the impurity, the activity a_A of the impurity is equal to the mole fraction of A present in the melt.

Correspondingly the melting point of a crystalline polymer is depressed by "impurities" such as low-molecular-weight diluents, chain ends, and randomly comonomerized units along the chain. The corresponding formulas analogous to equation 3.1 are [1]

3.2
$$\frac{1}{T_m} - \frac{1}{T_m^\circ} = \frac{R}{\Delta H_u} \frac{V_u}{V_l} \phi_l \left(1 - \frac{B' V_l \phi_l}{R T_m^\circ} \right)$$

3.3
$$\frac{1}{T_m} - \frac{1}{T_m^\circ} = \frac{R}{\Delta H_u} \frac{2}{\overline{P}_n}$$

3.4
$$\frac{1}{T_m} - \frac{1}{T_m^\circ} = -\frac{R}{\Delta H_u} \ln X_A$$

In the above equations ΔH_u is the heat of fusion per mole of the repeating structural units of the polymer chain. In equation 3.2, V_u and V_l are the molar volumes of the polymer structural unit and of the diluent, ϕ_l is the volume fraction of the diluent in the polymer-diluent solution and B' is a constant which characterizes the interaction energy of the polymer-diluent system. In equation 3.3, $\bar{P}_n$ is the number-average degree of polymerization of the polymer, i.e., the number of repeating structural units per chain. In equation 3.4, X_A is the mole fraction of A units in the copolymer consisting of a few B units randomly copolymerized with a preponderance of A units.

All the equations 3.1 through 3.4, inclusive, reduce to a common equation at sufficiently low "impurity" concentration,

$$3.5 \qquad \frac{1}{T_m} - \frac{1}{T_m^\circ} = \frac{R}{\Delta H_u} X_B$$

where X_B is the mole fraction of "impurity," i.e., diluent, chain end or comonomer unit.

The values of ΔH_u for several polymers have been obtained mainly through application of equation 3.2. From ΔH_u and the value of T_m one can obtain ΔS_u by the relation

$$3.6 \qquad T_m = \Delta H_u / \Delta S_u$$

where ΔS_u is the entropy of melting per mole of the repeating structural units of the polymer chain.

Table II.1 gives T_m, ΔH_u, ΔS_u, ΔH_u per bond and ΔS_u per bond for several polymers.[2] ΔH_u per bond is obtained by dividing ΔH_u by the number of single bonds along the main chain of the repeating unit, and similarly for ΔS_u. It is particularly interesting to note that ΔS_u per bond is rather constant for many polymers at an order of magnitude value of R cal/(deg mole).

A value ΔH_u^* can be obtained by calorimetric studies of the heat of fusion of crystalline polymers. This value will generally be lower than ΔH_u calculated from equations 3.2 through 3.5, because polymers contain amorphous regions as well as crystallized regions. For a polymer that is 100% crystalline, ΔH_u^* and ΔH_u should be the same. Otherwise, $\Delta H_u^* / \Delta H_u = 1 - \lambda$, the volume fraction of crystalline material.

Formula 3.6 can be rewritten as follows:

$$3.7 \qquad T_m = \Delta H_u \text{ (per bond)} / \Delta S_u \text{ (per bond)}$$

The value of ΔS_u (per bond) is subject to several molecular interpretations. In the first place, ΔS_u (per bond) $= \Delta S_v$ (per bond) $+ \Delta S_c$ (per bond), where ΔS_v arises from the volume change on melting, and ΔS_c

Table II.1

THERMODYNAMIC QUANTITIES CHARACTERIZING THE FUSION OF POLYMERS [a]

Polymer	T_m, °C	ΔH_u, cal/mole of Repeating Unit	ΔH_u, per bond	ΔS_u, per unit	ΔS_u, per bond
Polymethylene	137	785	785	1.90	1.90
Polyethylene oxide	66	1,980	660	5.85	1.95
Natural rubber	28	1,050	350	3.46	1.15
Gutta-percha	74	3,040	1,013	8.75	2.92
Polychloroprene	80	2,000	667	5.7	1.9
Polychlorotrifluoroethylene	210 [b]	1,200	600	2.50	1.25
Cellulose tributyrate	207	3,000	1,500	6.2	3.1
Polypropylene	176				
Polytetrafluoroethylene	327				
Polyhexamethyleneadipamide	260				
Polyethyleneterephthalate	267				

[a] L. Mandekern, *Chem. Rev.*, **56**, 903 (1956).

[b] Latest value given as 220°–225°; J. D. Hoffman and J. J. Weeks, *J. Research Natl. Bureau of Standards*, **60**, 465 (1958).

arises from a configurational entropy change. For natural rubber ΔS_v (per bond) has been calculated to be 0.60 cal/deg mole, whereas ΔS_c (per bond) is about 0.55 cal/deg mole.[2] It is probable that ΔS_v (per bond) is much the same for most polymers.

In paraffin crystals the molecular chains are frozen in the planar zigzag configuration. Upon melting, each bond can assume the available three staggered configurations with respect to the preceding bond, rather than the one configuration lying in the plane of the other two. The configurational entropy gained per mole of bonds is therefore $R \ln 3$, which is somewhat larger than the value ΔS_c (per bond) = 1.30 cal/deg mole obtained from polymethylene. [The latter value is obtained from ΔS_u (per bond) = 1.90 (Table II.1) and ΔS_v (per bond) = 0.60.]

It is probable that not all three staggered configurations for each bond are completely available even in the molten state, so that the configurational entropy gain per mole of bonds is, in fact, substantially less than $R \ln 3$.

Another interpretation of ΔS_c (per bond) has been that it represents an entropy of mixing with "holes" that enter the polymer structure in the molten state.[2]

One might expect that ΔH_u (per bond) would correlate with the strength of molecular cohesion. This latter quantity may be estimated from the solubility parameter discussed in section 5 of this chapter. Rather surprisingly, however, experimental results have not borne this out. For example, it has been found that polyesters have a higher ΔH_u than corresponding polyamides,[3] although the solubility parameters of polyesters are smaller than those of polyamides.

Inasmuch as the polyamides melt at higher temperatures than the corresponding polyesters, they must also have a much lower entropy of fusion. In fact, it was suggested that high melting points appear to be associated with low entropies of fusion rather than with high heats of fusion. The crystal structure of polyamides seems to allow for more configurational disorder than that of polyesters, and this may account for the low entropies of fusion found in polyamides.[3]

For crystallizable cross-linked networks the melting point depends on the extension ratio $\alpha = L/L_u$ as follows,[1]

$$3.8 \qquad \frac{1}{T_m} - \frac{1}{T_m^\circ} = - \frac{R}{\Delta H_u} \phi(\alpha)$$

$$3.9 \qquad \phi(\alpha) = \left(\frac{6}{\pi}\right)^{\frac{1}{2}} \frac{\alpha}{\mathfrak{N}_e^{\frac{1}{2}}} - \left(\frac{\alpha^2}{2} + \frac{1}{\alpha}\right) \Big/ \mathfrak{N}_e$$

where T_m° is the melting temperature of the unstretched network, T_m the melting temperature of the stretched network and $\mathfrak{N}_e$ the number of statistical segments of the chain between cross links. Formula 3.8 fails at $\alpha = 1$ but should be valid at high extension ratios. The volume fraction of amorphous material in a stretched crystallizable network is [1,2]

$$3.10 \qquad \lambda = \frac{[\frac{3}{2} - \phi(\alpha)]^{\frac{1}{2}}}{[\frac{3}{2} - \theta]^{\frac{1}{2}}}$$

$$3.11 \qquad \theta = \frac{\Delta S_u}{R} - \frac{\Delta H_u}{RT}$$

Formula 3.10 is valid only at fairly high extension ratios.

Oriented crystalline polymer fibers will shrink and lose their orientation at the melting point T_m of the crystallites. External tension applied to the oriented polymer will raise the melting temperature (or the shrink temperature) quite considerably.   This can be treated very simply by a straightforward application of the Clapeyron-Clausius equation.[4,5]

$$3.12 \qquad \left(\frac{\partial X_{eq}}{\partial T_m}\right)_p = -\frac{\Delta S}{\Delta L}$$

where X_{eq} is the tensile force required to maintain equilibrium between the oriented (crystalline) and the shrunk (amorphous) state of the fiber at the temperatures T and pressure p. ΔS and ΔL are the latent changes in entropy and length associated with the melting transformation of the fiber.

Oriented crystalline polymers which are partially cross-linked to form a three-dimensional network show a shrinkage in length as they are brought to temperatures above their melting point.   This shrinkage in length is partially reversible,[6] indicating the presence of oriented incipient nuclei even in the melt.

A first-order crystal-crystal phase change has been reported [7] for at least one synthetic polymer, namely, trans-1,4-polybutadiene.

References II.3

1. P. J. Flory, *Principles of Polymer Chemistry*, pp. 565–576, Cornell University Press, Ithaca, N. Y., 1953.
2. L. Mandelkern, *Chem. Revs.*, **56,** 903 (1956).
3. P. J. Flory, H. D. Bedon and E. H. Keefer, *J. Polymer Sci.*, **28,** 151 (1958).
4. G. Gee, *Quart. Revs.*, **1,** 265 (1947).
5. J. F. M. Oth and P. J. Flory, *J. Am. Chem. Soc.*, **80,** 1297 (1958).
6. L. Mandelkern, D. E. Roberts, A. F. Diorio and A. S. Posner, *J. Am. Chem. Soc.*, **16,** 4148 (1959).
7. G. Natta and P. Corradino, *J. Polymer Sci.*, **38,** 29 (1959).

4. KINETICS OF CRYSTALLIZATION

The rate of growth of crystalline material in polymers is of great importance.   For certain polymers such as natural rubber or isotactic polystyrene, it is possible to quick-chill from the molten state through the range of crystallization into the glassy state without developing any crystallinity.   With other polymers such as polymethylene it has not yet proved possible to quick-chill the polymer into a completely amorphous condition below its melting point T_m.   Nevertheless, the amount of crystallinity and the size of the crystallites and of the crystallite aggregates (spherulites) will, even in the case of polymethylene, depend very much on thermal history and the "annealing" procedure. Since mechanical properties depend so much on these factors, it is well to give a brief discussion of these phenomena.

The over-all rate of formation of crystalline material is proportional to the rate of nucleation and also to the rate of growth around a nucleus.

Figure II.11. Electron micrograph (gold palladium shadowing) of a single paraffin crystal. The paraffin is $C_{13}H_{74}$, and the crystal was formed in a solution of petroleum ether. The spiral staircase effect is due to growth based on a screw dislocation. [After A. J. Forty, *Advances in Physics*, **3**, 1 (1954).]

The nucleation rate, favored by supercooling, has a maximum value which occurs at a temperature appreciably below T_m. The growth rate, largely dependent on diffusion, has a maximum value just very slightly below T_m. The over-all rate of growth of crystalline material, being a product of these factors, also has a definite temperature at which it is maximum. As a rough rule it has been estimated that this temperature is $\frac{8}{9} T_m$.[1]

The temperature range in which the growth of crystalline material occurs at an appreciable rate is not very broad. Thus natural rubber has a maximum rate of crystallization at about $-25°$, and the rates of crystallization become very slow at $-40°$ and at $+10°$.

The polycrystalline texture of crystalline polymers depends on the kinetics of crystallization. By crystallizing from dilute solution under conditions such that nucleation is very slow compared to growth, one can actually grow polymer single-crystals of macroscopic dimensions. In paraffin crystals or polymethylene crystals, these seem to grow by a screw-dislocation mechanism, resulting in a spiral staircase structure of the plate-like crystal (see Fig. II.11 and II.12).

Under normal conditions the crystalline texture of polymers is established during chilling from a hot melt. Very tiny (submicroscopic) crystallites form under these conditions. Each individual crystallite is part of a closely spaced cluster called a spherulite, which may often be of macroscopic dimensions (Figure II.6). The formation of a single nucleus in a polymer cooled below T_m favors the formation of another nucleus in its immediate vicinity by the creation of local stresses. This process of secondary nucleation may be the underlying mechanism of spherulite formation; under many conditions crystal growth may be relatively minor compared with secondary nucleation.

An electron micrograph of polycrystalline polyethylene is shown in Figure II.13.

The nucleation and growth of individual crystallites and of the spherulites depend on the mechanism and kinetics of crystallization, and therefore depend very markedly on the exact thermal history of the quenching operation. Polyethylene film that is fabricated under ordinary conditions of atmospheric cooling is cloudy, indicating the presence of large spherulites. On the other hand, this same film will be nearly clear if quickly quenched by cold water. In the latter case the nucleation process is probably more rapid, leading ultimately to more but smaller spherulites. The physical properties of the film as well as the optical properties depend on microcrystalline texture.

The mechanism and kinetics of the growth of crystalline material in polymers is a subject which is at present experiencing a rapid and far-

Figure II.12.   Electron micrograph of a single crystal of polyethylene.   (After A. Keller, p. 499 in *Growth and Perfection of Crystals*.)

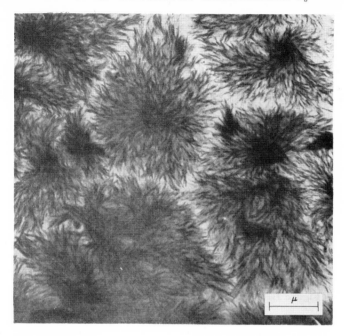

Figure II.13.   Electron micrograph of a thin film of polyethylene showing fine structure of the spherulites.   (Courtesy E. R. Walter.)

reaching development.   The results prior to 1956 are reviewed in reference 1, and later developments (1958) are presented in reference 2.

References II.4

1. L. Mandelkern, *Chem. Revs.*, **56,** 903 (1956).   Contains many references to the original literature.
2. R. H. Doremus, B. W. Roberts and D. Turnbull (eds.), *Growth and Perfection of Crystals*, John Wiley & Sons, New York, 1958.

5. THE GLASS TRANSITION TEMPERATURE T_g

Let us return to the analogy of the structure of an amorphous linear polymer as being similar to the structure of the contents of a bowl of cooked spaghetti.   To make the analogy more complete, one must imag-

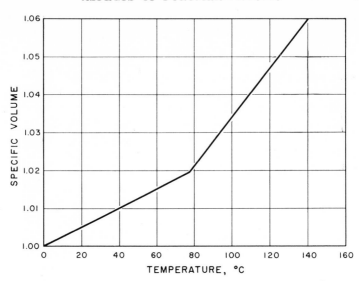

Figure II.14. Specific volume versus temperature near T_g.

ine that at sufficiently high temperatures the spaghetti is in a constant wriggling motion, perhaps more like a tangle of earthworms, although the latter analogy is unpleasant. The wriggling, segmental motion of the linear polymer molecules is due to thermal energy and to the existence of free volume in the polymeric mass. At sufficiently low temperatures, the free volume becomes very small, and the thermal energy kT also becomes small compared to the potential energy barrier heights for rotational and translational jumps of the polymer segments. At these low temperatures the wriggling and diffusional motions of the polymer molecules are "locked in" or "frozen in," and the polymer segments and atomic groups can make only vibrational motions as in an ideal solid. This state of the polymer is called the glassy state.

There appears to be a narrow temperature range, or perhaps a definite temperature T_g, below which the polymer is considered to be in its glassy state. The most usual method for determining T_g is to measure the specific volume $v(T)$ of the polymer as a function of temperature. The measurements give rise to plots such as those schematically shown in Figure II.14. There appears to be a definite bend in these curves (ideally a discontinuity in the derivative dv/dT). The temperature at which this bend occurs is defined as T_g. How sharp the bend is and how dependent on the rate of heating or cooling, considered from both the experimental and theoretical viewpoints, are questions that will not be resolved here.

Suffice it to say that the method described above gives values of T_g that are meaningful and usually defined to well within a few degrees Centigrade.

For comparison, plots of relative volume versus temperature are shown for some crystalline polymers in Figure II.15.

The glass transition temperature is perhaps the most important characteristic parameter of an amorphous polymer.[1, 2]   As will be elucidated later on, amorphous polymers obey a law of corresponding states in which T/T_g or $T - T_g$ is the basic reduced variable.   Inasmuch as T_g is such an important property of a polymer, it is of course very interesting to inquire how T_g depends on the structural and energetic properties of the polymer.

The amorphous tangle of polymer molecules can be defined in terms of certain simple structural parameters.   First, the fractional "free volume" is an intuitively appealing concept.   The free volume per gram v_f is defined as $v - v_s$, where v is the actual specific volume, and v_s is the

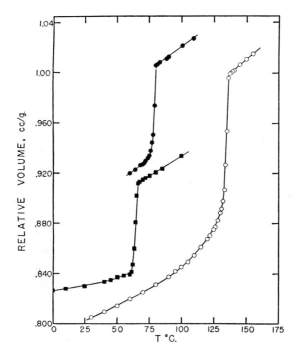

Figure II.15.   Relative volume versus temperature near T_m.   [After L. Mandelkern, *Chem. Revs.*, **56**, Figure 2, p. 911 (1956).]

Table II.2

SOLUBILITY PARAMETER OF SEVERAL LIQUIDS [a, b, c]

Liquid	Solubility Parameter δ	Liquid	Solubility Parameter δ
Linear dimethylsiloxanes		Dimethyl sulfide	9.4
2 to 11 Si atoms	5.90–4.97	Butyl lactate	9.4
Aliphatic fluorocarbons	5.5–6.2	Pentachloroethane	9.4
Aromatic fluorocarbons	7.5–8.2	Methyl acetate	9.6
Neopentane	6.3	Methylene chloride	9.7
n-Hexane	7.3	Ethylene dichloride	9.8
1-Hexene	7.4	Cyclohexanone	9.9
Ethyl ether	7.4	Cellosolve (2-ethoxyethanol)	9.9
Diisobutylene	7.7	Dioxane	9.9
Tricresyl phosphate	8.2	Ethyl lactate	10.0
Cyclohexane	8.2	Ethylamine	10.0
Turpentine	8.1	Acetone	10.0
Dipentene	8.5	Acetic acid	10.1
Butyl acetate	8.5	Methyl formate	10.1
Carbon tetrachloride	8.6	Aniline	10.3
Dioctyl sebacate	8.6	Methyl Cellosolve	10.8
Cellosolve acetate	8.7	Ethylene oxide	11.1
Xylene	8.8	Cyclohexanol	11.4
Toluene	8.9	Butanol	11.4
Ethyl bromide	8.95	Acetonitrile	11.7
Ethyl acetate	9.1	Dimethyl formamide	12.1
Diacetone alcohol	9.2	Nitromethane	12.4
Methyl Cellosolve acetate	9.2	Dimethyl phosphite	12.5
Benzene	9.2	Ethanol	12.7
Ethyl mercaptan	9.25	Methanol	14.5
Methyl ethyl ketone	9.3	Ammonia	16.3
Chlorobenzene	9.3	Water	24.2
Chloroform	9.3		

[a] J. H. Hildebrand and R. L. Scott, *Solubility of Nonelectrolytes*, Rheinhold Publishing Corp., New York 1950.

[b] H. Burell, *Interchem. Rev.*, **14**, 31 (1955).

[c] M. H. Wilt, "Use of Cohesive Energy Density," *Monsanto Chemical Co. Tech. Bull.*, issued July 15, 1955.

volume per gram of the "solidly packed" polymer molecules. This concept has already been discussed in connection with liquid viscosity in Chapter I, section 8.

To describe the energetics of the interaction between segments of polymer molecules, we borrow a concept from the theory of liquid solubility.[3] A quantity known as the cohesive energy density is an important property of liquids. The CED is defined as the molar energy of vaporization divided by the molar volume, both easily measured properties. This quantity measures the cohesion per unit volume of the liquid. The solubility parameter δ is defined as the square root of the cohesive energy density.

5.1 $$\delta = (\text{CED})^{\frac{1}{2}} = (E_{\text{vap}}/V)^{\frac{1}{2}}$$

The values for the solubility parameter of numerous simple liquids are given in Table II.2.

The solubility parameters for polymers cannot be obtained directly from equation 5.1. Instead a slightly cross-linked polymer is prepared,

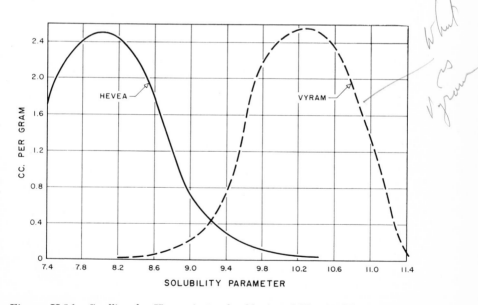

Figure II.16. Swelling for Hevea (natural rubber) and N-5400 (Vyram rubber) versus solubility parameter of the solvent. Ordinate is cubic centimeters of solvent imbibed per gram of rubber. Abscissa is solubility parameter in (calories/cubic centimeters)$^{\frac{1}{2}}$. [After M. H. Wilt, *Monsanto Chemical Co.*, *Tech. Bull.*, Apr. 1, (1954).]

and identical samples are placed in a series of liquids of known δ.[4] The polymer is swollen by all these liquids but not dissolved because of the cross links. The extent of swelling can be plotted versus the solubility parameter of the swelling liquids. This gives rise to a gaussian-shaped curve centering around a certain value of solubility parameter δ_p at which the swelling is maximum. This is shown schematically in Figure II.16. The value δ_p is taken as the solubility parameter of the polymer. Table II.3 gives the solubility parameter of numerous polymers.

An important chain parameter is V_0, the energy barrier impeding rotation around the bonds in the chain. For high values of V_0 the internal

Table II.3

SOLUBILITY PARAMETERS FOR SEVERAL POLYMERS [a, b, c]

Polymer	Solubility Parameter δ_p
Teflon (polytetrafluoroethylene)	6.2
Silicone rubber (polydimethylsiloxane)	7.3
Polyethylene	7.9
Polyisobutylene, Butyl rubber	7.8
Natural rubber	8.1
Polybutadiene	8.1
GR-S (butadiene-styrene 75/25)	8.1
Polystyrene	8.56
Neoprene (polychloroprene)	8.6
Buna-N (budadiene-acrylonitrile 75/25)	8.9
Polymethyl methacrylate	9.08
Polyvinyl acetate	9.4
Polyvinyl chloride	9.53
Ethyl cellulose	10.3
Polymethacrylonitrile	10.7
Polyethyleneterephthalate	10.7
Cellulose diacetate	10.9
Epoxy resin	10.9
Polyvinylidene chloride	12.2
Nylon 66	13.6
Polyacrylonitrile	15.4

[a] H. Burrell, *Interchem. Rev.*, **14**, 3 (1955).

[b] M. H. Wilt, "Use of Cohesive Energy Density," *Monsanto Chemical Co. Tech. Bull.*, reprint issued July 15, 1955.

[c] G. M. Bristow and W. F. Watson, *Trans. Faraday Soc.*, **54**, November (1958).

chain mobility is low. Another chain parameter is the geometric chain stiffness $Z = (\bar{r}^2/\mathfrak{N}l_0{}^2)^{1/2}$ discussed in section 1 of this chapter. Finally, the chain length $\mathfrak{N}$ is also an important chain parameter.

How then does T_g depend on the parameters v_f/v, δ_p, V_0, Z and $\mathfrak{N}$?

1. It is possible that to a first approximation the value of v_f/v at T_g may be the same for all amorphous polymers.[5-8] This value has been estimated as 0.025 by an ingenious method to be described in section 8 of this chapter.

2. Polymers of high δ_p tend to have high values of T_g. For example, polydimethylsiloxane (silicone rubber) has the lowest T_g thus far recorded and also a very low value of δ_p. Polybutadiene also has a very low value of T_g and δ_p. At the other end of the scale, polyacrylonitrile, polymethacrylonitrile and polyacrylic acid with high values of δ_p also have high values of T_g.

3. Polymers of low V_0 (high internal mobility) have low values of T_g. In this connection it is interesting to compare the T_g values of silicone rubber ($-120°C$), polyethylene ($\sim -85°C$), and polytetrafluoroethylene ($>20°C$). All these have low values of δ_p, with the polytetrafluoroethylene having the lowest value. However, rotation around —Si—0— bonds is nearly free, and the barrier to rotation around —CH_2—CH_2— bonds is 3.3 kcal/mole, and around —CF_2—CF_2— bonds is in excess of 4.7 kcal/mole.[10] Amorphous sulfur with a very high value of δ_p nevertheless has a T_g of about $-20°C$ because of the relatively free rotation around —S—S— bonds.

4. Polymer chains which are geometrically stiff (high values of Z) probably have higher values of T_g than more flexible polymers of similar chemical constitution and similar δ_p. For example, the polyvinyl acetals have a much higher T_g value than polyvinyl acetate, and polyacenaphthalene a much higher T_g than polystyrene. (The structures of these latter are shown in Chart II.1.) It is difficult to be certain of the effect of geometric stiffness, however, because those polymers which are geometrically stiff also tend to have high V_0 values, and are therefore less internally mobile as well.[10]

5. T_g depends on the chain length $\mathfrak{N}$ in the following way,

5.2 $$T_g = T_g^° - c'/\mathfrak{N}$$

where c' is a constant for each polymer, and $T_g^°$ is the limiting value of T_g for infinite chain length. Inasmuch as it is observed experimentally that $T_g \approx T_g^°$ for values of $\mathfrak{N} > 500$, one can take $T_g = T_g^°$ for reasonably high polymers.

The value of T_g for an amorphous copolymer can be predicted approximately if the glass transition temperatures $T_g(1)$ and $T_g(2)$ of both

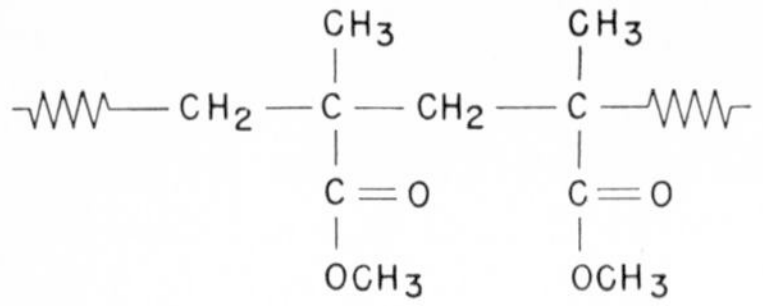

polymethyl methacrylate

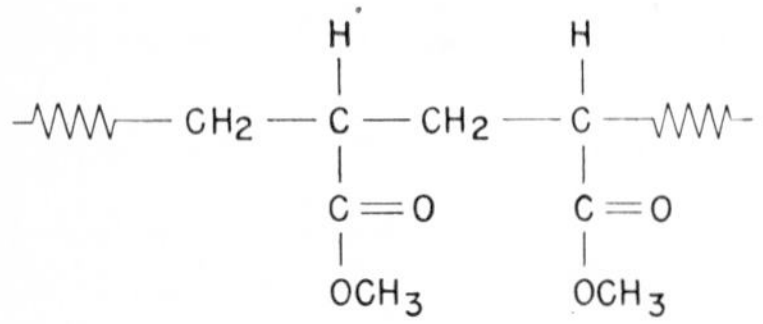

polymethyl acrylate

Chart II.1. Some chain structures.

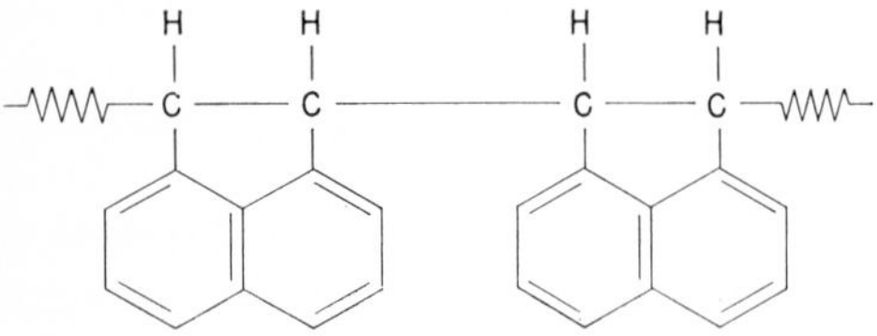

polyacenaphthalene

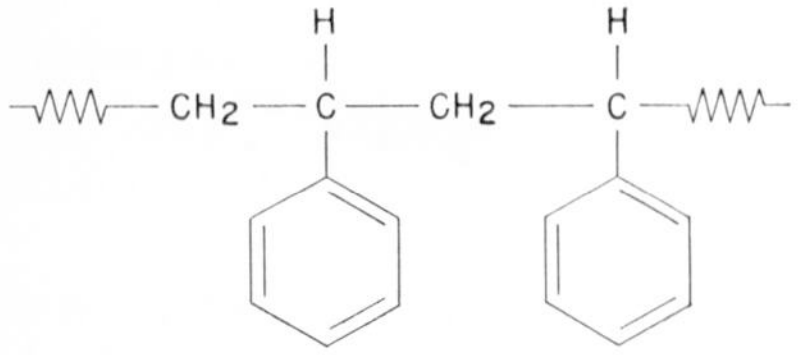

polystyrene

homopolymers are known. One of the empirical formulas that has been found to apply fairly well in many cases is [11]

$$5.3 \qquad \frac{1}{T_g} = \frac{w_1}{T_g(1)} + \frac{w_2}{T_g(2)}$$

where w_1 and w_2 are the weight fractions of each of the components of the copolymer. This formula can be readily generalized to terpolymers, etc. It assumes that the monomer units of each constituent are distributed along the chain in a more or less random fashion. Equation 5.3 is only approximately valid in certain systems, and more general formulas have been proposed.[12]

Formula 5.3 is very useful for obtaining the glass transition temperatures of crystalline polymers. Frequently the vT curves of crystalline polymers show no clearly defined bend that corresponds to T_g. In this case by making a series of amorphous copolymers whose glass transition temperatures can be readily measured, values of $T_g(1)$ and $T_g(2)$ can be calculated. A case in point are the homopolymers and copolymers of trifluorochlorethylene and vinylidene fluoride. Both homopolymers are exceedingly crystalline, but a range of amorphous copolymers can be prepared whose values of T_g can be readily measured. By plotting $1/T_g$ vs. w_1 for these copolymers, a few experimental points can be obtained in the range $0.4 < w_1 < 0.6$. By extrapolating the straight line obtained to the intercept at $w_1 = 0$ and $w_1 = 1$, the values of $T_g(1)$ and $T_g(2)$ are obtained. In this way it turns out that T_g for polytrifluorochlorethylene is approximately 40°C, and T_g for polyvinylidene fluoride is about -39°C.[13] By a similar procedure the value of T_g for polyperfluoropropylene has been estimated as 11°C.[10] By using the known T_g values of polysulfide rubbers such as —CH_2CH_2SSSS— together with the T_g of polyethylene, a value of $T_g \approx -27$°C can be estimated for the linear sulfur chain, in agreement with values obtained on amorphous sulfur.

Some crystalline polymers can be quick-chilled from the melt into an amorphous condition. In these cases a value for T_g can be readily measured on the amorphous polymer. The T_g for crystalline isotactic polypropylene can be obtained by studying the T_g of amorphous atactic polypropylene.

It is interesting to note that for crystalline polymers there appears to be a simple numerical relationship between T_g and T_m.[14]

5.4 $T_g/T_m \sim 0.5$ for symmetrical polymers such as polymethylene or polyvinylidene chloride

5.5 $T_g/T_m \sim 0.67$ for unsymmetrical polymers such as polytrifluorochlorethylene or isotactic polypropylene

It is perhaps safer to state that as a general rule

5.6 $$0.5T_m < T_g < 0.67T_m$$

Table II.4 gives the glass transition temperature of selected polymers. The quantity a_r refers to volume coefficient of thermal expansion in the rubbery state, and a_g refers to volume coefficient of thermal expansion in the glassy state.

The dangers of studying the T_g of highly crystalline polymers by volume-temperature curves or mechanical properties methods is illustrated by the case of polytetrafluoroethylene. By studies of this kind the T_g value was reported as -112°C.[15] In contrast, it is here contended

Table II.4

GLASS TRANSITION TEMPERATURES FOR SELECTED POLYMERS [a]

Polymer	T_g, °C	$a_r \times 10^4$	$a_g \times 10^4$
Silicone rubber	−123	12	2.7
Polybutadiene (emulsion, 50°C)	−85	7.8	2
Polyisobutylene [b]	−70	—	—
Natural rubber	−72	6.16	2.07
Poly(butyl acrylate)	−56	6.0	2.6
Poly(vinylidene fluoride)	−39	—	—
Poly(ethyl acrylate)	−22	6.1	2.8
Poly(methyl acrylate)	9	5.6	2.7
Poly(perfluoropropylene)	11	—	—
Poly-(n-butyl methacrylate)	22	6.3	3.7
Poly(vinyl acetate)	29	5.98	2.07
Poly-(n-propyl methacrylate)	35	5.80	3.51
Poly(chlorotrifluoroethylene)	45	—	—
Poly(ethyl methacrylate)	65	5.40	2.75
Poly(vinyl chloride)	82	5.2	2.1
Poly(styrene)	100	5.5	2.5
Poly(methyl methacrylate)	105	5.0	1.95
Poly(acrylic acid)	106		
Poly(methacrylonitrile) [b]	120		

[a] L. A. Wood, *J. Polymer Sci.*, **28**, 319 (1958).

[b] P. J. Flory, *Principles of Polymer Chemistry*, pp. 52–53, Cornell University Press, Ithaca, N. Y. 1953.

that the true T_g will be found to be in excess of room temperature as predicted by equation 5.6 and from the low internal mobility.[9]

An important practical question is involved: If T_g for tetrafluoroethylene is in fact −112°C, amorphous copolymers of tetrafluoroethylene and perfluoroethylene or similar monomers should make rubbers that are flexible down to quite low temperatures. It is doubtful that this would be found true. In order to obtain good low-temperature properties in the field of fluorine containing elastomers, it is necessary to have flexibility in the chain backbone, such as would be conferred by $CH_2=CF_2$, $CH_2=CH(CF_3)$, $CH_2=CF(CF_3)$, and similar monomers. These must be copolymerized with suitable monomers to produce amorphous copolymers.

References II.5

1. R. F. Boyer and R. S. Spencer, Chapter 1 in *Advances in Colloid Science*, vol. II, Interscience Publishers, New York, 1946.
2. N. Bekkedahl, *J. Research Natl. Bur. Standards*, **13**, 411 (1934).
3. J. H. Hildebrand and R. L. Scott, *Solubility of Nonelectrolytes*, Rheinhold Publishing Corp., New York, 1950.
4. G. Gee, "Thermodynamics of Rubber Solutions and Gels," chapter in *Advances in Colloid Science*, vol. II, Interscience Publishers, New York, 1946.
5. J. D. Ferry and R. F. Landel, *Kolloid-Z.*, **148**, 1 (1956).
6. M. L. Williams, R. F. Landel and J. D. Ferry, *J. Am. Chem. Soc.*, **77**, 3701 (1955).
7. H. Fujita and A. Kishimoto, *J. Colloid Sci.* (in press).
8. T. G. Fox and P. J. Flory, *J. Appl. Phys.*, **21**, 581 (1950); *J. Am. Chem. Soc.*, **70**, 2384 (1948); *J. Phys. Chem.*, **55**, 221 (1951); *J. Polymer Sci.*, **14**, 315 (1954).
9. A. V. Tobolsky, *J. Polymer Sci.*, **35**, 555 (1959).
10. G. J. Janz, *Estimation of Thermodynamic Properties of Organic Compounds*, p. 161, Academic Press, New York, 1958.
11. T. G. Fox, *Bull. Am. Phys. Soc.*, **1**, no. 3, 123 (1956).
12. L. A. Wood, *J. Polymer Sci.*, **28**, 319 (1958).
13. L. Mandelkern, G. M. Martin and F. A. Quinn Jr., *J. Research Natl. Bureau Standards*, **58**, 137 (1957).
14. R. G. Beaman, *J. Polymer Sci.*, **9**, 470 (1952).
15. M. Baccaredda and E. Butta, *J. Polymer Sci.*, **31**, 189 (1958).

6. FIVE REGIONS OF VISCOELASTIC BEHAVIOR FOR LINEAR AMORPHOUS POLYMERS

The simplest way to characterize the elastic properties of a polymer is to measure its elastic modulus as a function of temperature. Since polymers are viscoelastic, the modulus will depend on the time of measurement and the method of measurement. For the moment we shall discuss the relaxation modulus E_r obtained by measuring the stress in a sample maintained at a fixed stretched length. The time of measurement will be standardized at 10 sec, so that the quantity being measured as a function of temperature is $E_r(10)$. Other methods for measuring the modulus will give qualitatively similar conclusions.

The results obtained with a typical linear amorphous polymer, atactic polystyrene, are shown in Figure II.17. Two samples A and C of polystyrene are displayed in this figure, both of quite narrow molecular-weight distribution. The number-average molecular weight $\overline{M}_n$ for sample A is 140,000; $\overline{M}_n$ for sample C is 217,000.

The curves log $E_r(10)$ versus temperature show five regions of viscoelastic behavior,[1] which are indicated for sample C in Figure II.18. The first region below 90°C is the glassy region, in which the modulus is between 10^{10} and $10^{10.5}$ dynes/cm^2. In this region the polymer is truly glassy, hard, and brittle. In the second region, the transition region, the modulus varies between 10^{10} and $10^{6.10}$ dynes/cm^2 in the temperature interval 90 to 120°C. In this region of rapidly changing modulus the physical properties are best described as leathery. In the third region the modulus remains fairly constant with temperature at a value between $10^{6.7}$ and $10^{6.4}$ dynes/cm^2. The temperature interval over which the modulus remains fairly constant depends on the chain length $\mathfrak{N}$ of the polymer. For sample C this interval is 120 to 150°C. This region is called the rubbery plateau, and the behavior of the polymer is truly rubbery in this interval. In the fourth region the modulus ranges from $10^{6.4}$ to $10^{5.5}$ dynes/cm^2. Here the polymer is elastic and rubbery, but also has a marked component of flow. This may be termed the region of rubbery flow which for sample C extends from 150 to 177°C. Finally in the fifth region, with modulus values below $10^{5.5}$ dynes/cm^2, the polymer exhibits very little elastic recovery and manifests an apparent state of liquid flow.

The temperature intervals for these regions of viscoelastic behavior depend on the arbitrarily selected reference time of 10 sec. This is

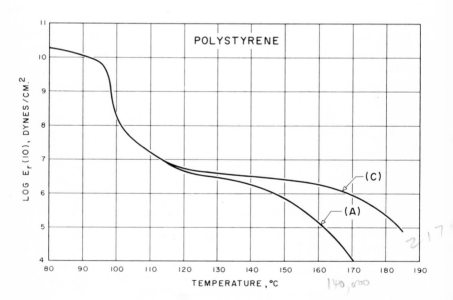

Figure II.17. $E_r(10)$ versus temperature for polystyrene samples A and C.

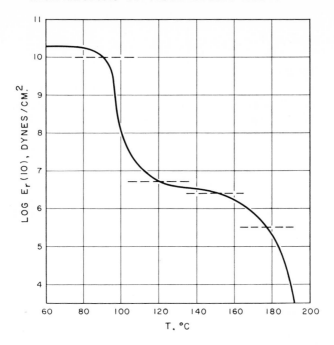

Figure II.18. Five regions of viscoelastic behavior (for polystyrene sample C).

shown in Figure II.19 where modulus data for polystyrene sample C are plotted for measurement times of 5, 10, 100 and 1,000 sec. Actually the regions of viscoelastic behavior are best defined by the modulus values; the temperature intervals corresponding to these viscoelastic regions depend on the time of measurement. In this section we shall specialize our discussion to the temperature intervals based on the 10-sec reference time. A complete discussion of the viscoelastic behavior must await a discussion of time effects, which will be given in Chapter III.

From Figure II.18 several facts emerge in a very clear fashion. The glassy region and the transition region appear to be independent of the chain length (for sufficiently high chain lengths). The value of the modulus in the region of the rubbery plateau is likewise independent of chain length. However the regions of rubbery flow and liquid flow are markedly dependent on chain length.

It is useful to define several parameters which can be obtained directly from the modulus-temperature curve of amorphous polymers. We may readily define E_1, the limiting modulus for the glassy state, and E_2, the modulus for the rubbery-plateau region. In addition we

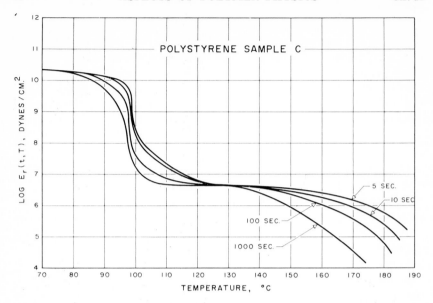

Figure II.19. Modulus at different times versus temperature for atactic polystyrene sample C. [After A. V. Tobolsky and K. Murakami, unpublished; H. Fujita, *J. Colloid Sci.*, **12**, 204 (1957).]

may define the inflection temperature T_i at which the value of $\log E_r(10)$ $= \frac{1}{2}(\log E_1 + \log E_2)$. For polystyrene the values of E_1, E_2 and T_i are $10^{10.35}$ dynes/cm^2, $10^{6.65}$ dynes/cm^2 and 98°C, respectively.

We may also define a flow temperature T_f at which the maximum relaxation time is 10 sec. A discussion of the maximum relaxation time will be given in Chapter IV.

In the glassy region the segments of the polymer chain are frozen in fixed positions on the sites of a disordered quasi-lattice. They vibrate around these fixed positions just as do molecules of a molecular lattice. However, they undergo little if any diffusional motion from one lattice position to another. This type of diffusional motion, characteristic of liquids, sets in only above T_g.

We might expect that the bulk modulus of a polymer in its glassy state can be calculated on the same basis as for a molecular lattice, namely (see section 3 of Chapter I),

6.1 $$B = 8.04(E_{\text{vap}}/V)$$

For the quantity E_{vap}/V we shall substitute the cohesive energy density, or the square of the solubility parameter as discussed in section 5 of this chapter. From Table II.3 the value of CED for polystyrene is 83 cal/cm^3 = 3.47 × 10^9 ergs/cm^3. From equation 6.1, we predict a value of 2.78 × 10^{10} dynes/cm^2 for B. This is in approximate agreement with the experimentally observed value of 3.79 × 10^{10} dynes/cm^2.

In the glassy region the Poisson ratio is expected to be between 0.25 and 0.33. The Young's modulus E_1 in this region is, therefore, of the same order of magnitude as B. One should therefore expect that

6.2 $$E_1 \approx 8.04(E_{vap}/V) \approx 8.04\delta^2$$

The experimental value of E_1 is 2.24 × 10^{10} dynes/cm^2, which again is in approximate accord with equation 6.2.

In the transition region the segments of the polymer chain are undergoing *short-range* diffusional motion. The time for diffusion from one "lattice site" to another is of the order of magnitude of 10 sec (our reference time). In the transition region the modulus is changing very rapidly with time as well as temperature.

The inflection temperature T_i is, of course, dependent on our reference time of 10 sec. Generally T_i for amorphous polymers turns out to be

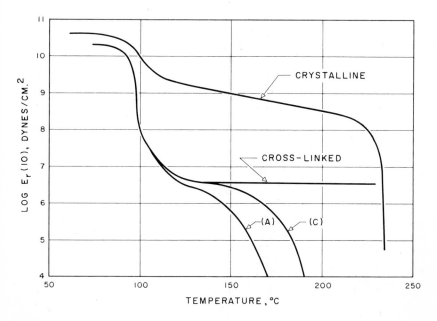

Figure II.20. $E_r(10)$ versus temperature for crystalline isotactic polystyrene, for polystyrene samples A and C, and for lightly cross-linked atactic polystyrene. (After A. V. Tobolsky and H. Yu, unpublished.)

within a few degrees of T_g, the glass transition temperature obtained from vT curves.

In the quasi-static rubbery region the short-range diffusional motions of the polymer segments are very rapid. However the motions of the molecules as a whole, involving the cooperative movement of many chain segments, is retarded, particularly by entanglement between the chains which act as temporary cross links. Using the results of the kinetic theory of rubbery elasticity embodied in equation 7.10, Chapter I, one can calculate the value of M_c, the molecular weight of the network chain between entanglements, from the value of E_2. For example, for polyisobutylene, the first polymer for which the rubbery-plateau phenomenon was noted, the author calculated a molecular weight between entanglements [2] of 8,000. For polystyrene, M_c between entanglements is 20,000.

In the region of rubbery flow the motion of molecules as a whole is becoming important. Major configurational changes of the entire molecule, including the slippage of long-range entanglements, are taking place in times of the order of 10 sec.

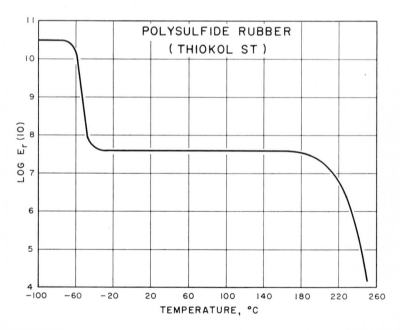

Figure II.21. $E_r(10)$ versus temperature for a cross-linked polysulfide rubber (Thiokol ST).

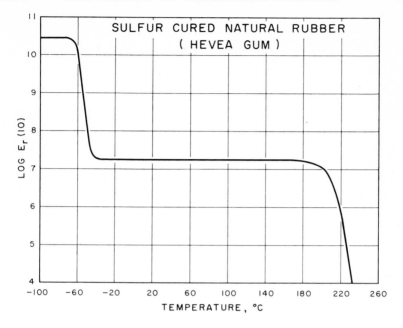

Figure II.22. $E_r(10)$ versus temperature for natural rubber lightly cross-linked by sulfur.

Finally in the region of liquid flow the long-range configurational changes of the molecules are occurring in less than 10 sec. Elastic recovery is nearly completely negligible here for stresses or strains which are maintained for longer than 10 sec.

The regions of rubbery flow and liquid flow can be completely suppressed if chemical cross links are introduced to serve as permanent network junctions in place of the temporary molecular entanglements. Figure II.20 shows the modulus-temperature curve of polystyrene cross-linked by copolymerization with 0.25 mole per cent of divinylbenzene (sample D).

For very small amounts of chemical cross linking the magnitude of the rubbery modulus for the cross-linked polymer is the same as that for the linear polymer, the cross linking merely serving to prevent flow. For higher degrees of cross linking the rubbery modulus for the cross-linked polymer is larger than E_2 for the linear polymer, in accordance with the predictions of equation 7.10 of Chapter I.

In principle, the rubbery modulus E_2 will here be proportional to absolute temperature and independent of time up to the highest temperatures, so that, on a log $E_r(10)$ vs. T plot, the rubbery plateau will look quite flat for an enormous temperature interval as shown in Figure II.20. This is actually true for cross-linked polystyrene, because this polymer resists network interchange, network destruction, scission by molecular oxygen, and depolymerization up to quite high temperatures. For most cross-linked rubber networks, however, the log $E_r(10)$ vs. T curve will show a sharp drop of the rubbery modulus to zero at temperatures at which the rubber network manifests changes in its chemical structure. This is shown for a polysulfide rubber network in Figure II.21 and for vulcanized natural rubber in Figure II.22.

For the polysulfide rubber network the chemical change at high temperatures is disulfide interchange. For the vulcanized natural rubber the chemical change at high temperatures is due to cleavage by molecular oxygen. A fuller discussion will be given in Chapter V.

References II.6

1. A. V. Tobolsky and J. R. McLoughlin, *J. Polymer Sci.*, **8**, 543 (1952).
2. H. Mark and A. V. Tobolsky, *Physical Chemistry of High Polymeric Systems*, p. 344, Interscience Publishers, New York, 1950.

7. MODULUS-TEMPERATURE CURVES FOR AMORPHOUS AND CRYSTALLINE POLYMERS

The quickest way of apprehending the viscoelastic properties of a polymer is through a modulus-temperature curve at a fixed reference time—our reference time being 10 sec. The log modulus versus temperature curves in the transition region for a number of emulsion-prepared butadiene-styrene copolymers (some lightly cross-linked) are shown in Figure II.23. The compositions are given in weight per cent butadiene-styrene. All these polymers are completely amorphous, even when stretched.

It is interesting to note that these curves are approximately equivalent if translated horizontally along the temperature axis so that the T_i (or T_g) values coincide. There are for amorphous polymers differences in the values of the slope s of the log $E_r(10)$ versus temperature curves at T_i (values generally in the range $s = 0.125$ to $s = 0.333$), but in general the transition region extends over approximately 30°C. Essentially the same type of log modulus-temperature curve is obtained with nearly all amorphous polymers.

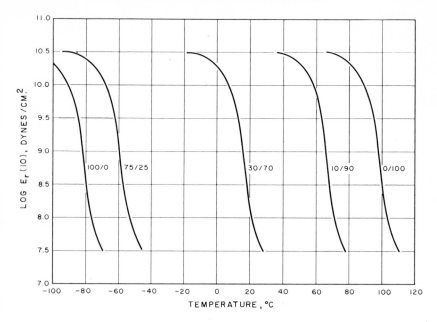

Figure II.23. $E_r(10)$ versus temperature for butadiene-styrene copolymers.

This leads very naturally to a most important *qualitative* concept regarding the mechanical properties of linear amorphous polymers: The author has postulated that two linear amorphous polymers of the same chain-length distribution (or the same distribution of values of $\bar{r}^2$) are mechanically nearly equivalent at *corresponding temperatures*.[1,2] The same concept holds for amorphous cross-linked polymers of the same degree of cross linking and the same concentration of terminal chains. The "equivalent" behavior is valid not only for viscoelastic properties but also for properties such as tensile strength, elongation at break, impact strength, etc.[2] It applies only to polymers that are completely amorphous *even when stretched.*

We are now faced with the problem of defining the concept of corresponding temperatures. This can be done by introducing a reduced temperature T/T_c or $T - T_c$, where T_c is a characteristic temperature of the polymer. We have already introduced two temperatures, T_g and T_i, which are likely candidates for this characteristic temperature. If the principle of corresponding viscoelastic states is regarded as a qualitative principle, either T_g or T_i will serve very adequately as the characteristic temperature since these are only a few degrees different. For more quantitative results other means of selecting a characteristic temperature have been suggested, as will be discussed in Chapter IV. For a truly quantitative application of this principle, however, it must be recognized that factors such as chain stiffness, side-chain mobility, etc., will produce fairly important deviations from the principle of corresponding temperatures.

A corollary of this law of corresponding temperatures is that two amorphous polymers are mechanically "equivalent" for practical purposes if they have the same T_g and chain length.

The butadiene-styrene copolymer series nearly covers the range of practical use of amorphous polymers. At one end of the scale is vulcanized polybutadiene, $T_g = -85°C$, used as a low-temperature rubber, particularly in the Arctic and Antarctic. The vulcanized 75/25 copolymer with 75 parts by weight of butadiene, 25 parts by weight of styrene is at present the most widely used rubber for passenger car tires in the United States, and hence the most widely used all-purpose rubber. It has a T_g value of $-57°C$. The 30/70 copolymer, $T_g = 18°C$, is used in emulsions (with pigment added) as a water-based paint, or (without pigment) as a primer sealer for various surfaces. At room temperature it forms a tough flexible film. The 10/90 polymer, $T_g = 68°C$ is a rigid glass-like plastic, used as a moldable thermoplastic for sheets and for numerous molded objects. It is a hard plastic but has a certain degree of internal flexibility, as indicated by a modest degree of impact strength. Atactic polystyrene, $T_g = 100°C$, is also used as a moldable thermoplastic. It produces a hard clear glass-like plastic of excellent electrical properties, but of poor impact resistance. In addition, various blends of these copolymers are produced and sold, as will be discussed later.

It must be pointed out that the T_g values for styrene-butadiene copolymers obey the empirical equation 7.1 (below) more accurately than the commonly used empirical equation 5.3.

7.1 $$T_g = x_1 T_{g,1} + x_2 T_{g,2}$$

where x_1 and x_2 are the mole fractions of styrene and butadiene in the copolymer, and $T_{g,1}$ and $T_{g,2}$ are the T_g values for polystyrene and polybutadiene.

It is not surprising in view of the principle of mechanical equivalence at corresponding temperatures that the other two major tire rubbers, natural rubber and Butyl rubber have values of T_g close to that of the 75/25 copolymer. Practical latex paints based on copolymers of ethyl acrylate and methyl methacrylate, on the one hand, or vinyl acetate–dibutyl fumarate, on the other hand, have values of T_g close to that of the 30/70 copolymers of butadiene-styrene, namely, 18°C. Polymethyl methacrylate with T_g = 105°C has many uses similar to those of polystyrene with T_g = 100°C. To obtain products that are mechanically similar to the 10/90 butadiene-styrene copolymer, methyl methacrylate is copolymerized with suitable amounts of ethyl acrylate or butyl methacrylate to obtain copolymers of $T_g \approx 68$°C.

In a sense the principle of corresponding viscoelastic states for amorphous polymers limits the mechanical applications of these materials. For many uses it is desirable to have a material of high modulus and also of fairly high impact strength. Amorphous polymers show this desirable behavior in the temperature interval between T_g and $T_g + 20$°. Above $T_g + 20$°, the modulus becomes too low; below T_g, the polymer becomes brittle and has low impact strength.

To extend the temperature range of high-modulus–high-impact-strength behavior, one must resort to the blending of amorphous polymers.[3] Proper blending may produce a polymer whose modulus-temperature curve shows the existence of two transition regions. This type of blending, called polyblending, is a very sensitive process. If the two polymers are completely compatible, the blend behaves like an ordinary amorphous polymer with a single transition region and an intermediate glass transition temperature, and obeys the law of corresponding viscoelastic states. If the polymers to be blended are quite incompatible, the polymers do not wet each other, and essentially cannot be blended even in a grossly homogeneous fashion. Favorable effects are obtained if the polymers are on the border line of incompatibility-compatibility, so that a system of two finely divided continuous phases is formed, one phase being rubbery (at room temperature), the other being rigid.

A polyblend widely used in shoe soles is composed of two parts 75/25 butadiene-styrene copolymer and one part of 10/90 butadiene-styrene copolymer. Another widely used polyblend is composed of one part 75/25 copolymer and three parts of polystyrene. These latter produce materials of nearly the same rigidity as polystyrene but also show a substantial resistance to impact because of the presence of the rubbery phase. These physical characteristics of polyblends may also be achieved by block and graft copolymers. Block copolymers have long sequences of A units followed by long sequences of B units. Graft copolymers have long sequences of B units as branches along a main chain of A units.

Modulus-temperature curves for polyblends are shown in Figure II.24. The polymers being blended in this case are polystyrene and a 30/70 butadiene-styrene copolymer.

A very wide temperature range in which high modulus and high impact strength coexist is encountered in crystalline polymers in the very wide temperature region between T_g and T_m. For linear polyethylene

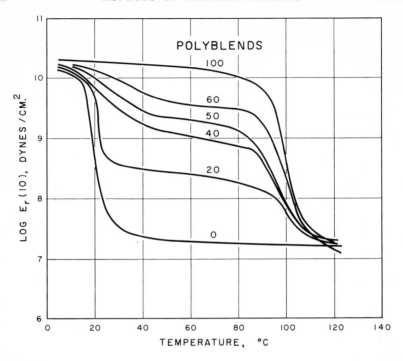

Figure II.24. $E_r(10)$ versus temperature for polyblends of polystyrene and a 30/70 butadiene-styrene copolymer. Numbers on the curves refer to the weight per cent of polystyrene in the blend.

T_m is 137°C and T_g is approximately −85°C (this latter figure is in some dispute).* In this relatively enormous temperature range, linear polyethylene has high rigidity (high modulus) and good impact strength. For low-density polyethylene (3 branches per 100 carbon atoms), the corresponding temperature range is −85 to 110°C, but at room temperature and thereabout branched polyethylene is less rigid than linear polyethylene because it is less crystalline. Empirically, a linear relation between log modulus of polyethylene and degree of crystallinity is valid over a limited range of crystallinity.

Isotactic polystyrene when obtained in a crystalline form has a T_g of 100°C and a T_m of about 250°C. In this temperature region crystalline isotactic polystyrene has the desirable combination of high impact resistance and high rigidity. The $E_r(10)$ vs. T curve for crystalline isotactic polystyrene as compared with atactic linear and atactic cross-linked polystyrene (both, of course, amorphous) is shown in Figure II.20.

* See Appendix K.

It is interesting to note the $E_r(10)$ behavior in the interval between T_g and T_m for the crystalline polymer. The exact shape of the curve depends on the thermal history of the sample, particularly how it was cooled from the melt. By extremely rapid chilling from the melt isotactic polystyrene can be obtained in a completely amorphous condition, in which case it has the same modulus-temperature curve and the same X-ray diagram as atactic polystyrene.

Two crystalline polymers are mechanically "equivalent" for practical purposes if they have the same values of T_g, T_m, chain length, per cent crystallinity and crystalline texture. These seem like very restrictive conditions. However, if one examines existing crystalline polymers which are competitively used for the same mechanical application, whether film, fiber or molding, it is surprising to see how frequently this "equivalence" of structural properties does approximately obtain.

References II.7

1. A. V. Tobolsky and E. Catsiff, *J. Am. Chem. Soc.*, **76**, 4204 (1952).
2. A. V. Tobolsky, *Rubber Chem. Tech.*, **30**, 437–438 (1957). See also A. M. Borders and R. D. Juve, *Ind. Eng. Chem.*, **38**, 1066 (1946).
3. R. Buchdahl and L. Nielsen, *J. Polymer Sci.*, **15**, 1 (1955).

8. THE FLOW VISCOSITY OF LINEAR AMORPHOUS POLYMERS [1]

The flow viscosity of a homologous series of linear polymers of increasing molecular weight shows an enormous increase in viscosity values. This is strikingly manifested in polyisobutylene, which can be obtained in a tremendous range of molecular weights. At room temperature, diisobutylene is a very mobile liquid whose viscosity is of the order of 10^{-2} poise. As one proceeds up the scale to molecular weights of 10^3, 10^5, 10^7, one encounters viscous liquids, sticky rubbers, and finally rubbery materials that behave at room temperature in practically the same fashion as if they were vulcanized, with viscosities in excess of 10^{13} poises.

It has been found that the viscosity of a homologous series of linear polymers can be expressed in the equivalent forms

8.1 $$\log_{10} \eta = \Phi^*(T) + F(\mathfrak{N}) + D^*$$

8.2 $$\eta = \phi^*(T)\, f(\mathfrak{N}) \cdot d^*$$

where $\Phi^*(T)$ is a function of the temperature alone, $F(\mathfrak{N})$ is a function of chain length only, and D^* is a constant [the reason why D^* is not grouped together with $\Phi^*(T)$ will appear shortly]. The fact that the viscosity can be written as a product of a temperature-dependent term and a chain-length-dependent term gave rise to the concept that the flow of polymer molecules involves an activated diffusional jump of polymer segments. This segmental "jump" is common to all members of a homologous series and explains the common temperature-dependent factor for chains of all sizes. The chain-length-dependent factor indicates that for flow to take place there must be a coordinated sequence of segmental jumps. This coordination becomes progressively more difficult with increasing chain length. When the chain length is sufficiently great to produce entanglement, this coordination becomes very difficult indeed, because cooperative motion of segments of various chains is now involved.

A plot of $\log_{10} \eta$ versus $\log \mathfrak{N}$ shows that for sufficiently high chain lengths ($\mathfrak{N} > 500$) a straight line is obtained whose slope is 3.4. For smaller values of $\mathfrak{N}$, the slope is approximately unity. The chain length at which the viscosity approaches the 3.4 slope on the log-log plot is deemed by Bueche to be the chain length at which network formation through entanglement becomes important.[2]

For sufficiently high values of $\mathfrak{N}$, therefore,

8.3 $$F(\mathfrak{N}) = 3.4 \log \mathfrak{N} \qquad \mathfrak{N} > 500$$

In order to utilize the law of corresponding viscoelastic states discussed in the last section, it is desirable to express the temperature dependence of η in terms of $T - T_c$ or T/T_c, where T_c is some characteristic temperature for each polymer. When expressed in one of these forms, equation 8.1 becomes (for polymers of sufficiently large $\mathfrak{N}$)

8.4 $$\log \eta = \Phi(T - T_c) + 3.4 \log \mathfrak{N} + D^*$$

A very useful expression for $\Phi(T - T_c)$ was proposed by Williams, Landel and Ferry,[3] using T_g as the characteristic temperature of the polymer. These authors start with the Doolittle equation (8.14 of Chapter I):

8.5 $$\ln \eta = \ln A + B \, v_0/v_f$$

Since polymers are generally highly supercooled liquids (remember that $0.5T_m < T_g < 0.67T_m$ for crystalline polymers), the quantity v_0 can be replaced by v, the specific volume of the polymer. Hence equation 8.5 can be expressed in the following ways at the temperatures T and T_g:

8.6 $$\ln \eta \, (T) = \ln A + B \, v(T)/v_f(T)$$

8.7 $$\ln \eta \, (T_g) = \ln A + B \, v(T_g)/v_f(T_g)$$

Subtracting equation 8.7 from equation 8.6 and setting B equal to unity, which is its experimentally observed order of magnitude value, one obtains

8.8
$$\log \frac{\eta(T)}{\eta(T_g)} = \frac{1}{2.303} \left(\frac{1}{f} - \frac{1}{f_g} \right)$$

$$f = \frac{v_f(T)}{v(T)} \qquad f_g = \frac{v_f(T_g)}{v(T_g)}$$

In equation 8.8 the quantity f is the fractional free volume at temperature T, and the quantity f_g is the fractional free volume at T_g.

The dependence of free volume on temperature is taken to be the difference between the thermal expansion coefficients a_r and a_g above and below the glass transition temperature. Therefore,

8.9 $$f = f_g + (a_r - a_g)(T - T_g) = f_g + a_2(T - T_g)$$

If equation 8.9 is substituted into equation 8.8, one obtains

8.10
$$\log \frac{\eta(T)}{\eta(T_g)} = - \frac{1}{2.303 f_g} \left(\frac{T - T_g}{f_g/a_2 + T - T_g} \right)$$

Empirical data on numerous organic polymers and some inorganic glasses established the approximate empirical validity of the equation [2]

8.11
$$\log \frac{\eta(T)}{\eta(T_g)} = \frac{-17.44(T - T_g)}{51.6 + T - T_g}$$

Equating the constants of equations 8.10 and 8.11, one obtains

8.12 $$f_g = 0.025 \qquad a_2 = a_r - a_g = 4.8 \times 10^{-4} \, \deg^{-1}$$

This is the best evidence that the glass transition temperature for different polymers is a state of constant fractional free volume; the value of a_2 found is in reasonable agreement with experimental results on numerous polymers.

A better empirical formula for the variation of η with temperature was obtained when T_c in equation 8.4 was obtained in another manner (we shall call this new characteristic temperature T_s). T_s was chosen arbitrarily for polyisobutylene as equal to 298°K. The values of T_s for other polymers were then arbitrarily selected so that $\Phi(T - T_s)$ in equation 8.4 was a universal function for all. It was found that a good approximation for $\Phi(T - T_s)$ was [2]

8.13 $$\Phi(T - T_s) = \frac{-8.86(T - T_s)}{101.6 + T - T_s}$$

A list of T_s values for several polymers is given in Table II.5. The value of T_s is roughly $50°$ larger than the T_g value of the polymer. Presumably T_s is the temperature at which a given polymer has the same fractional free volume as does polyisobutylene at $298°K$.

The empirical formula for viscosity of polymers of sufficiently long chain length is

8.14 $$\log_{10} \eta(T) = 3.4 \log \mathfrak{N} - \frac{8.86(T - T_s)}{101.6 + T - T_s} + D$$

In order to obtain a perfect fit of experimental data it is necessary to allow the "constant" D to vary slightly with temperature, especially for $T > T_g + 100$.

So far we have not considered the effect of polydispersity, i.e. the formulas have implicitly assumed a polymer composed of molecules of a single chain length $\mathfrak{N}$. In the general case the polymer is composed of molecules of varying chain length, the weight fraction of molecules of chain length i is w_i, and the number of i-mers is N_i. The weight average chain length $\overline{\mathfrak{N}}_w$ is defined as

8.15 $$\overline{\mathfrak{N}}_w = \sum_{i=1}^{\infty} iw_i = \frac{\sum_i i^2 N_i}{\sum_i i N_i}$$

The other commonly used average chain length is the number average $\overline{\mathfrak{N}}_n$ defined as

8.16 $$\overline{\mathfrak{N}}_n = \sum_i iX_i = \frac{\sum_i i N_i}{\sum_i N_i}$$

where

$$X_i = \frac{N_i}{\sum_i N_i}$$

is the mole fraction of i-mers.

It has been found empirically that the formulas in this section which were developed for monodisperse polymer apply for polydisperse polymer if $\mathfrak{N}$ is replaced by $\overline{\mathfrak{N}}_w$. Hence formula 8.14 can be written for polydis-

Table II.5

T_s VALUES FOR SEVERAL POLYMERS [a]

Polymer	T_s, °K	T_g, °K
Polyisobutylene	243	202
Polymethyl acrylate	378	324
Polyvinyl acetate	349	301
Polystyrene	408	373
Polymethyl methacrylate	433	378
Polyvinylacetal	380	—
Butadiene-styrene		
75/25	268	216
60/40	283	235
50/50	296	252
30/70	328	291

[a] T. G. Fox, S. Gratch and S. Loshaek, Chapter 12 in *Rheology: Theory and Applications*, vol. I, F. R. Eirich (ed.), Academic Press, New York, 1956.

perse polymer as follows:

$$8.17 \qquad \log_{10} \eta = 3.4 \log \overline{\mathfrak{N}}_w - \frac{8.86(T - T_s)}{101.6 + T - T_s} + D$$

Empirical formulas expressing the temperature dependence of viscosity of numerous polymers in alternate but more explicit form are given in reference 1.

The quantity D in equation 8.17 differs considerably from one polymer to another. This is perhaps best exemplified by comparing the viscosity of molten polyethylene and molten polypropylene. Although the T_g value of polyethylene is considerably lower than that of polypropylene, and hence the T_s value is undoubtedly also lower, the viscosity of polyethylene is higher than that of polypropylene at the same temperature and at the same chain length. This is probably because the polyethylene chain is a stiffer chain than the polypropylene chain.

The author suggests that the following equation for the viscosity of long-chain polymers might be useful:

$$8.18 \qquad \log_{10} \eta = \beta \log \frac{\overline{r^2}}{l_0^2} - \frac{17.44(T - T_g)}{51.6 + T - T_g} + B$$

In equation 8.18 $\overline{r^2}$ is the mean square length of the polymer chain (as determined by light scattering measurements or intrinsic viscosity measurements in a suitable solvent) and l_0 is the bond length. The quantity β will vary between 3.0 and 3.4 depending on whether the measurements of $\overline{r^2}$ are done in a good or a poor solvent. It is suggested that the quantity B in equation 8.18 might be more nearly the same for different polymers than is the quantity D in equation 8.17.

Equation 8.18 could obviously be expressed in terms of T_s as well as T_g.

References II.8

1. T. G. Fox, S. Gratch and S. Loshaek, Chapter 12 in *Rheology: Theory and Applications*, F. R. Eirich (ed.), Academic Press, New York, 1956. This chapter contains numerous references to the original literature.
2. F. Bueche, *J. Chem. Phys.*, **20**, 1959 (1952).
3. M. L. Williams, R. F. Landel and J. D. Ferry, *J. Am. Chem. Soc.*, **77**, 3701 (1955).

9. THE KINETIC THEORY OF RUBBER ELASTICITY

The conception of the stress in a stretched sample of rubber as arising from a kinetic tension has been discussed in Chapter I, sections 7 and 8. The calculation of this kinetic tension on the basis of a molecular model of the rubber network must be adjudged as one of the important creative contributions of polymer science. Many valuable theoretical treatments of the problem have been made, each of which has yielded added insight. Among the important contributors were Kuhn, Guth, Mark, James, Wall, Treloar and Flory. The history of these developments and the various theoretical treatments are given in references 1, 2 and 3.

In this section we present a somewhat different calculation of the kinetic tension,[4, 5] which is mathematically quite elementary but which focuses attention on a problem in rubber elasticity which is not completely resolved.

For a hydrocarbon chain of $\mathfrak{N}$ links for which the jth bond can be in three positions with respect to the j-1st bond and the j-2nd bond (one *trans* and two *gauche* configurations), the total number of conformations is

$$9.1 \qquad\qquad \omega = 3^{\mathfrak{N}-2}$$

In Appendix E, equation E.9, there is developed the following expression for the normalized probability of a polymer chain in free space having the vectorial end-to-end distance r:

9.2
$$\omega(r) = (b/\pi^{1/2})^3 \exp(-b^2 \vec{r}^2)$$

$$b^2 = 3/2\bar{r}^2$$

For the idealized hydrocarbon chain, taking all three positions around the C—C bond as having equal energy, $\bar{r}^2 = 2\Re l_0^2$; hence $b^2 = \frac{3}{4}\Re l_0^2$. The number of conformations of a hydrocarbon chain in free space consistent with the vectorial end-to-end distance $\vec{r}$ is

9.3
$$\omega(\vec{r}) = 3^{\Re-2}(b/\pi^{1/2})^3 \exp(-b^2 \vec{r}^2)$$

In equation 9.3 it is assumed that all values of $\vec{r}$ are allowed. A more general expression is

9.4
$$\omega(r) = c \exp(-b^2 \vec{r}^2)$$

Equation 9.4 is not necessarily restricted to hydrocarbon chains but would be applicable to any type of polymer chain by proper choice of b and c. In equation 9.4 we can also imagine c to be a proper normalizing constant, even if only a point set of $\vec{r}$ values is allowed. (The latter is true, for example, if we imagine our hydrocarbon chain as being the physical equivalent of a random walk on a diamond lattice as in Appendix D.)

Consider a rubber network of N_0 network chains such that (1) the juncture points are relatively fixed, and there is comparatively free motion of the portions of the molecular chains connecting network junctures; (2) the internal energy and the volume of the network do not change with strain (no compressibility); (3) the stresses arising from a given strain are due to a change of configurational entropy only.

We further assume that the network in the unstrained state is specified by N_0 network vectors $\vec{r_i}$, where $\vec{r_i}$ is the vector between the network junctures of the ith network chain.

We assume that the number of conformations of the ith network chain is given by

9.5
$$W(\vec{r_i}) = c_i \exp(-b_i^2 \vec{r_i}^2)$$

where c_i depends on b_i but is independent of r_i. The quantity b_i^2 ($= 3/4\Re_i l_0^2$ for the idealized hydrocarbon chain) will depend on the chain length $\Re_i$ between network junctures.

The total number Ω of conformations in the unstrained state is

$$9.6 \qquad \Omega = \prod_{i=1}^{N_o} \omega(\vec{r}_i)$$

By Boltzmann's equation, the conformational entropy S_c of the network is

$$9.7 \qquad S_c = \mathbf{k} \ln \Omega = \mathbf{k} \sum_{i=1}^{N_0} \ln c_i - \mathbf{k} \sum_{i=1}^{N_0} b_i{}^2 \vec{r}_i{}^2$$

The Helmoltz free energy A of the network in the unstrained state, with a total of N_0 network chains, is

$$9.8 \qquad A(T,\,V) = A_0(T,\,V) - \mathbf{k}T \sum_{i=1}^{N_0} \ln c_i + \mathbf{k}T \sum_{i=1}^{N_0} b_i{}^2 \vec{r}_i{}^2$$

where $A_0(T,\,V)$ is the free energy of the network exclusive of the conformational free energy. It includes the internal energy, the vibrational energy and entropy, etc.

In order to obtain the actual values of $\vec{r}_i$ in the unstrained state, it is necessary to minimize $A(T,\,V)$ with respect to all of the variations of the $\vec{r}_i$ which do not break any of the junctions of the network. It is clear that a knowledge of the b_i values alone are insufficient to specify these distances and that a detailed knowledge of $A_0(T,\,V)$ is also required. It will become apparent, however, in the development below that it is merely necessary to know N_0 and the mean value of $b_i{}^2 \vec{r}_i{}^2$ in the unstretched state (if the unstretched state is isotropic) in order to obtain the equation of state.

In a strained condition, the Helmholtz free energy A' is

$$9.9 \qquad A'(T,\,V) = A_0(T,\,V) - \mathbf{k}T \sum_{i=1}^{N_0} \ln c_i + \mathbf{k}T \sum_{i=1}^{N_0} b_i{}^2(\vec{r}_i{}')^2$$

where $\vec{r}_i{}'$ is the vector between network junctures of the ith network chain in the strained condition.

According to assumption 2, $A_0(T,\,V)$ and the volume V do not change under any allowable strain.

Let us treat the simple case of a tensile strain, where a rectangular strip of rubber is stretched from length L_u to length L in the x direction. The over-all dimensions x, y, z of the sample change to new dimensions

x', y', z' as follows:

9.10
$$x' = \alpha x$$
$$y' = \alpha^{-\frac{1}{2}} y$$
$$z' = \alpha^{-\frac{1}{2}} z$$

where
$$\alpha = L/L_u$$

It is assumed that the coordinates x, y, z describing one end of a network chain with respect to the other end (which is taken as the origin) are also transformed during the stretching process to x', y', z' as described by equation 9.10. This is because the network junctures are assumed to be relatively fixed points. Figure II.25 shows how the spherically symmetrical array of network vectors in the unstretched state are transformed by equation 9.10 into an array of elliptical symmetry.

The network vectors $\vec{r_i}$ in the unstretched state are distributed in a spherically symmetrical fashion because the sample is isotropic in the unstretched state. If the network vectors $\vec{r_i}$ in the unstrained state are drawn from a common origin, those of the same magnitude r and the same value of b_i will form a spherical surface in space of uniform density. The transformation 9.10 transforms such a spherical surface of radius r

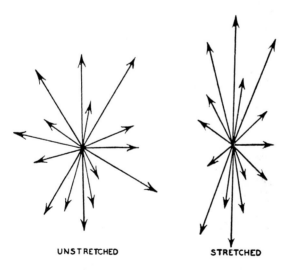

UNSTRETCHED   STRETCHED

Figure II.25.   Affine transformation of network vectors under the effect of a tensile strain.

into an ellipsoid of axes αr, $\alpha^{-\frac{1}{2}}r$, $\alpha^{-\frac{1}{2}}r$. It is easy to show that the average value of $(\vec{r}')^2$ over the surface of the ellipsoid is (see Appendix G)

9.11 $$(\vec{r}')^2 = \frac{r^2(\alpha^2 + 2/\alpha)}{3}$$

Therefore

9.12 $$\sum_{i=1}^{N_0} b_i^2(\vec{r_i'})^2 = \sum_{i=1}^{N_0} b_i^2 \vec{r_i}^2 \frac{\alpha^2 + 2/\alpha}{3}$$

$$= \frac{N_0(\overline{b^2 r^2})}{3}\left(\alpha^2 + \frac{2}{\alpha}\right)$$

where $\overline{b^2 r^2}$ is the average value over all the network chains. Substituting equation 9.12 into equation 9.9, one obtains

9.13 $$A'(T, V) = A_0(T, V) - kT \sum_{i=1}^{N_0} \ln c_i + \frac{kTN_0(\overline{b^2 r^2})}{3}\left(\alpha^2 + \frac{2}{\alpha}\right)$$

The tensile force X is given by

9.14 $$X = \left(\frac{\partial A'}{\partial L}\right)_{T,V} = \frac{1}{L_u}\left(\frac{\partial A'}{\partial \alpha}\right)_{T,V}$$

The force per unit area of original cross section A_u is

9.15 $$F = X/A_u$$

Combining the last three equations, one obtains

9.16 $$F = NkT \frac{2(\overline{b^2 r^2})}{3}\left[\alpha - \left(\frac{1}{\alpha}\right)^2\right]$$

where $N = N_0/V$ is the number of network chains per unit volume.

A more detailed consideration of $2(\overline{b^2 r^2})/3$ is given in the formula below:

9.17 $$2\frac{\overline{b^2 r^2}}{3} = \frac{2}{3}\frac{\sum\limits_{\substack{\text{all} \\ \text{values} \\ \text{of } b_i}} b_i^2 \sum\limits_{\substack{\text{all conforma-} \\ \text{tions } j \text{ for} \\ \text{given } b_i}} \vec{r}^2_{ij}}{N_0}$$

If the network chains in the unstressed network have the same conformational distribution as a similar array of molecular chains in free space, then a comparison of equations 9.17 and 9.2 shows that $2(\overline{b^2r^2})/3$ is unity. In this case, which we term the free-chain approximation, equation 9.16 would reduce to equation 7.6 of Chapter I. This is the equation actually derived in most treatments of the kinetic theory of rubber elasticity.[1, 2, 3] For a real network the distribution of distances $\vec{r_i}$ does not necessarily obey equation 9.2.

As stated before, the *actual* distances $\vec{r_i}$ in the unstrained state of the network can only be obtained by minimizing $A(T, V)$ in equation 9.8 with respect to all of the variations of $\vec{r_i}$ which do not break the network junctures, so that a knowledge of the b_i is insufficient to specify the r_i. If this contention is true, then $2(\overline{b^2r^2})/3$ is not necessarily unity under all conditions, and equation 7.6 of Chapter I which is so widely accepted [1-3] at the present time is only true under special circumstances. This is a minority viewpoint held by the author for very many years.[4, 5] This same conclusion has also been reached by James and Guth by a quite different theoretical approach.[6]

The value of $2(\overline{b^2r^2})/3$ will, in fact, depend on the exact nature of the cross-linking process: i.e., was the network in a strained or a relaxed position when a given cross link was formed? Was the cross linking carried out in the presence of solvent, which may or may not be evaporated afterward? Was the polymer in a partly crystalline condition during cross linking?

For an amorphous network cross-linked under completely relaxed conditions $2(\overline{b^2r^2})/3$ *may* be close to unity if the cross-linking density is low. At very high cross-link densities unusual steric requirements control the situation, since four space-filling polymer chains emanate from each cross link. One may here encounter situations where the spatially nearest cross link *must* also be a contiguous cross link in the network; i.e., interpenetration of network elements becomes impermissible. Here $2(\overline{b^2r^2})/3$ cannot be unity.

To evaluate $2(\overline{b^2r^2})/3$ in the network by approximations other than the free-chain approximation would require some further postulates. It is conceivable that one might replace all the $b_i{}^2$ by $\overline{b^2}$, where $\overline{b^2}(= 3/4\overline{\mathfrak{N}}l_0{}^2$ for the idealized hydrocarbon chain) corresponds to the average number of chain links $\overline{\mathfrak{N}}$ between network junctures. The quantity $\overline{\mathfrak{N}}$ can be readily computed from the cross-link density. In this case equation

9.17 can be simplified as follows (this simple result used in 1944): [5]

$$9.18 \qquad \frac{2(\overline{b^2 r^2})}{3} \approx \left(\frac{2}{3}\right) b^2 \frac{\sum_{i=1}^{N_0} \overrightarrow{r_i}^2}{N_0}$$

$$\approx \frac{\overline{r^2} \ (\text{in network})}{\overline{r^2} \ (\text{in free space})}$$

We now consider the very important problem of relating the concentration of cross links in the network to the concentration of network chains. Suppose that the network was produced from originally "infinite" linear molecules by the addition of c moles of tetrafunctional cross links per cubic centimeter of rubber. From each cross link there emanates four network chains, but each network chain belongs to two cross links. Hence there are $2c$ moles of network chains per cubic centimeter in the cross-linked network. We recall the definition of M_c as being the number-average molecular weight of the network chains. Hence d/M_c is also equal to n, the moles of network chains per cubic centimeter of rubber.

$$9.19 \qquad n = \frac{N}{\mathbf{N}} = \frac{d}{M_c} = 2c$$

If the linear molecular chains are of finite number-average molecular weight M_n before cross linking, the network produced by c moles of cross links per cubic centimeter of rubber will contain some terminal network chains, i.e., network chains that lead from a cross link to a chain end instead of to another cross link. Such a network is an imperfect network, and not all the network chains will contribute to the stress.

Flory [7] suggested that to solve this problem one should first imagine that a portion of the cross links was first used to tie the finite linear molecules into a single "infinite molecule." Since there are d/M_n moles per cubic centimeter of linear polymer to begin with, it requires d/M_n moles of cross links per cubic centimeter (more precisely $d/M_n - 1/\mathbf{N}$) to produce a single "infinite molecule" from these. However, such an infinite molecule is still not a network in the sense of being able to support a stress. It is only the cross linking that proceeds after this that produces a true network. The moles of *effective* cross links per cubic centimeter is, therefore,

$$9.20 \qquad c_e = c - d/M_n$$

By the reasoning by which equation 9.19 was derived, there are two effective network chains per effective cross link,

9.21 $$n_e = 2c - 2d/M_n$$

We retain the definition for M_c

9.22 $$d/M_c = 2c$$

Hence substituting n_e for n in equation 7.6 of Chapter I, one obtains

9.23 $$F = \frac{dRT}{M_c}\left(1 - \frac{2M_c}{M_n}\right)\left[\frac{L}{L_u} - \left(\frac{L_u}{L}\right)^2\right]$$

Equation 9.23 accurately predicts that, when $M_n = 2M_c = d/c$, a true network structure is not formed and the equilibrium modulus of the network is zero. However, the correction factor, $1 - 2M_c/M_n$, though widely accepted,[1] is, in the author's opinion, theoretically invalid where $M_n/M_c \gg 1$.

Consider a network (of cross-link density characterized by M_c) which was formed from infinite molecules. Further consider that a small number of cuts (q moles per cubic centimeter) are randomly introduced. Each cut produces two chain ends. This network can be placed in correspondence with a network (of the same cross-link density M_c) formed from the random cross linking of molecules of finite number-average molecular weight M_n. The correspondence is quantitative if $q = d/M_n$, for, in this case, both networks have the same number of chain ends.

However for small degrees of cleavage, each cut reduces the number of effective network chains by one. The moles of effective network chains per cubic centimeter is therefore $d/M_c - q = d/M_c - d/M_n$. The equation of state for this approximation is

9.24 $$F = \frac{dRT}{M_c}\left(1 - \frac{M_c}{M_n}\right)\left[\frac{L}{L_u} - \left(\frac{L_u}{L}\right)^2\right]$$

approximation for $M_n/M_c \gg 1$

The correction factor $1 - 2M_c/M_n$ is probably accurate for $M_n/M_c \approx 2.0$ whereas the correction factor $1 - M_c/M_n$ is probably accurate for $M_n/M_c \gg 1$. Both factors yield the correct expression for $M_n/M_c \to \infty$. An exact theory which would encompass both of these expressions as limiting formulas has yet to be developed.

The validity of equation 9.23 can be checked by experiment. The value of M_n of the original non-cross-linked polymer can be determined by osmotic-pressure measurements in dilute solution. The number of moles c of cross-linking agent can be controlled at will, if it is possible to find a cross-linking agent that reacts quantitatively with the linear polymer substrate. Knowing M_n and M_c, where $M_c = d/2c$, the "stress" at any value of L/L_u should be predetermined by equation 9.23.

In those few cases where the validity of the correction factor $1 - 2M_c/M_n$ has been tested, very good accord between theory and experiment was obtained,[8] although a possible deviation at large values of M_n/M_c was not particularly examined.

So far as predicting the absolute magnitude of F from M_c and M_n and L/L_u is concerned, the results are different with different rubbers. The experimental values of F invariably tend to exceed the theoretical prediction of equation 9.23, with a mean discrepancy of about 50%. Chain entanglements locked in by permanent chemical cross links have been presented as one possibility for explaining this discrepancy.[7] Perhaps the "front factor" $2(\overline{b^2 r^2})/3$ discussed earlier in this section provides another way to explain this discrepancy.

The success of the kinetic theory of rubber elasticity is nonetheless remarkable. Equation 9.23 can be employed to great advantage to *calculate* (approximately) the number of moles of cross links per cubic centimeter of rubber by the very simple procedure of measuring the value of F necessary to maintain a rubber sample of original length L_u in a stretched state of length L. Since most rubber networks are produced by chemical cross-linking procedures that are not quantitative, these equations provide a very important method for characterizing rubber networks. When cross linking is produced by high-energy radiation, such a procedure is the only way to obtain c (or M_c).

The kinetic theory of rubber elasticity developed in this section is based on the assumption that all conformations of a polymer chain have equal energy. This assumption is valid for many types of polymer chains. However, certain polymer chains show a marked tendency to favor extended conformations, whereas others show a tendency to favor folded conformations. In these cases it can no longer be assumed that the internal energy of an isolated chain is independent of its end-to-end distance or that the internal energy of a rubber network is unaffected by stretching. These very important matters and applications to several polymers are treated in Appendix H.

References II.9

1. T. Alfrey, *Mechanical Behavior of High Polymers*, Chapter C, Interscience Publishers, New York, 1948.
2. L. R. G. Treloar, *The Physics of Rubber Elasticity*, Clarendon Press, Oxford, England, 1949.

3. P. J. Flory, *Principles of Polymer Chemistry*, Chapter XI, Cornell University Press, Ithaca, New York, 1953.

4. M. Green and A. V. Tobolsky, *J. Chem. Phys.*, **14**, 80 (1946).

5. A. V. Tobolsky, Ph.D. thesis, Princeton University, 1944.

6. H. M. James and E. Guth, *J. Chem. Phys.*, **11**, 455 (1943); *ibid.*, **21**, 1039 (1953); *ibid.*, **15**, 669 (1947).

7. P. J. Flory, *Chem. Revs.*, **35**, 51 (1944).

8. P. J. Flory, *Ind. Eng. Chem.*, **38**, 417 (1946).

CHAPTER III

Mathematical Treatment of Linear Viscoelasticity

1. VISCOELASTIC MEASUREMENTS

If an *ideal elastic body* is stretched to a certain value of length L_0, and maintained at that length indefinitely, the equilibrium tensile force X required to maintain that length will be constant with time. The strain s_0 is $(L_0 - L_u)/L_u$, where L_u is the unstretched length; the stress f is X/A, where A is the cross-sectional area. The Young's modulus E is independent of the time at which X is measured and is given by

1.1 $$E = f/s_0$$

Throughout this chapter we are in general confining our mathematical discussion to the case of small strains. For the rare cases where the stress-strain relation is linear up to high strains (i.e., ideal rubbers in shear), this restriction can probably be removed. Large strain behavior will be briefly discussed in section 2.

For any real elastic body stretched to a certain value of length L_0 and maintained at that length indefinitely, the equilibrium tensile force required to maintain that length will not be constant but will be a decreasing function of time $X(t)$. [In certain rare cases $X(t)$ may increase.] The strain s_0 is again equal to $(L_0 - L_u)/L_u$; the stress at any time t is $f(t) = X(t)/A$. A new quantity, the relaxation modulus $E_r(t)$ is defined by the following equation

$$1.2 \qquad\qquad E_r(t) = f(t)/s_0$$

The experiment described above is called relaxation of stress at constant extension;[1] it is the method of viscoelastic measurement most extensively used in this book.

If, on the other hand, a viscoelastic substance is subjected to a constant tensile stress f_0, its length will in general be an increasing function of time $L(t)$. The strain at any time is defined as $s(t) = (L(t) - L_u)/L_u$, where L_u is the unstretched length. A creep modulus $E_c(t)$ can be defined as follows:

$$1.3 \qquad\qquad E_c(t) = f_0/s(t)$$

The measurement of $s(t)$ under constant stress f_0 is called a creep experiment.[2] In practice, most creep experiments are carried out under constant tensile load X_0. Since cross-sectional area changes during extension, this is only approximately a constant-stress experiment.

Relaxation of stress experiments or creep experiments can in principle be carried out in shear rather than tension. Time-dependent shear moduli $G_r(t)$ and $G_c(t)$ would be defined in a manner exactly analogous to equations 1.2 and 1.3.

Very frequently tensile creep experiments are discussed in terms of an elastic compliance $Y(t)$. Under constant stress, f_0, the strain as a function of time, is given by

$$1.4 \qquad\qquad s(t) = Y(t)f_0$$

For a material obeying Hooke's law, the compliance in tension is equal to the reciprocal of the Young's modulus. The shear compliance is denoted by $J(t)$.

A third type of viscoelastic experiment is the study of forced or free vibrations. Suppose for the moment that the viscoelastic body can be described as a classical damped harmonic oscillator; a more penetrating analysis will be given later. Consider a sample of viscoelastic body in the form of a rectangular parallelepiped of area A, height h, rigidly at-

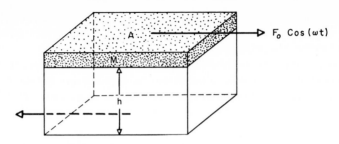

Figure III.1. Forced vibration experiment.

tached to an external mass M, subjected to external forced shear oscillations $F_0 \cos wt$ of force amplitude F_0 and of angular frequency w (see
Figure III.1). The equation of motion is

1.5
$$M \frac{d^2x}{dt^2} + \frac{A}{h} \eta_{\mathrm{dyn}} \frac{dx}{dt} + \frac{A}{h} G_{\mathrm{dyn}} \, x = F_0 \cos wt$$

where x [considered as a function of time $x(t)$] is the transverse displacement of the sample in the direction of the applied force $F_0 \cos wt$.

Equation 1.5 can be rewritten in terms of the strain $s(t) = x(t)/h$, the
stress $f_0 \cos wt = (F_0/A) \cos wt$, and the corrected mass $m = (M/A)h$

1.6
$$m \frac{d^2s}{dt^2} + \eta_{\mathrm{dyn}} \frac{ds}{dt} + G_{\mathrm{dyn}} s = f_0 \cos wt$$

The quantities η_{dyn} and G_{dyn} are defined as the dynamic viscosity and
the dynamic shear modulus of the viscoelastic body.[3] The latter quan-
tities are functions of the angular frequency of oscillation w, but at a
fixed value of w they may be regarded as constants in equations 1.5 and
1.6.

Equation 1.6 may also be regarded as the equation of motion for a
unit cube of the viscoelastic material attached to mass m. We assume
that $s(t)$ is of the form $s_0 \cos (wt - \varphi)$, where φ is often called the phase
angle.

The solution for $s(t)$ in equation 1.6 is

1.7
$$s(t) = \frac{f_0 \cos (wt - \varphi)}{[(G_{\mathrm{dyn}} - mw^2)^2 + w^2 \eta^2_{\mathrm{dyn}}]^{\frac{1}{2}}}$$

$$\tan \varphi = w\eta_{\mathrm{dyn}}/(G_{\mathrm{dyn}} - mw^2)$$

If the periodic exciting force is maintained at $f_0 \cos wt$ but the external
mass m is varied, the response $s(t)$ given by equation 1.7 shows a maxi-

mum amplitude (resonance) at a certain value of the mass m_{res} given by

1.8 $$G_{dyn} = m_{res}w^2$$

Inasmuch as m_{res} is an experimentally determinable quantity, equation 1.7 is a method by which the dynamic modulus G_{dyn} can be obtained. For any actual viscoelastic body, the value of G_{dyn} determined by the method described above will vary with the value of the forcing frequency w.

At resonance the actual value of the amplitude s_0 of $s(t)$ will be

1.9 $$s_0 = f_0/w\eta_{dyn}$$

Equation 1.9 provides a method by which η_{dyn} can be measured. It can also be determined from the shape of the plot of s_0 versus mass m from equation 1.7, or by a direct experimental determination of the phase angle φ.

The energy W dissipated as heat per unit volume per cycle during forcing oscillations $f_0 \cos wt$ is readily obtained by integrating $f_0 \cos wt \cdot ds(t)$ over the time interval zero to $2\pi/w$.

1.10 $$W = \pi w \eta_{dyn} s_0^2 = \frac{\pi w \eta_{dyn} f_0^2}{(G_{dyn} - mw^2)^2 + w^2 \eta^2_{dyn}}$$

where s_0 is the strain amplitude and f_0 is the stress amplitude.

A unit cube of viscoelastic material attached to an external mass m can be set into free vibration by initially imposing a shear strain s_0. The equation of motion is

1.11 $$m \frac{d^2 s}{dt^2} + \eta_{dyn} \frac{ds}{dt} + G_{dyn} s = 0$$

The solution of this equation is

1.12 $$s = s_0[\exp(-\eta_{dyn}/2m)t] \cos wt$$

where

1.13 $$w = \left[\frac{G_{dyn}}{m} - \left(\frac{\eta_{dyn}}{2m} \right)^2 \right]^{1/2} \approx \left(\frac{G_{dyn}}{m} \right)^{1/2}$$

If the damping is not excessive, $w = (G_{dyn}/m)^{1/2}$. The ratio of the amplitude of successive vibrations in this case is

1.14 $$\text{Amplitude ratio} = \exp(-\pi w \eta_{dyn}/G_{dyn})$$

The ratio of elastic energies of successive damped vibrations is equal to the square of the amplitude ratios.

The dynamic modulus and dynamic viscosity can, therefore, be obtained from the frequency of free vibrations, the ratio of successive amplitudes, and the mass. From a practical experimental standpoint, free-vibration experiments are generally carried out on a simple torsion pendulum system.

Harmonic oscillations are elegantly treated by use of the complex periodic function $e^{iwt} = \cos wt + i \sin wt$. Suppose the applied force was equal to the real part of $f_0 e^{iwt}$.

Equation 1.6 becomes

1.15
$$m \frac{d^2 s}{dt^2} + \eta_{\text{dyn}} \frac{ds}{dt} + G_{\text{dyn}} s = f_0 e^{iwt}$$

If the periodic solution $s = s_0^{iwt}$ is inserted in equation 1.15 (with s_0 a complex number), one obtains

1.16
$$m(d^2 s/dt^2) + iw\eta_{\text{dyn}} s + G_{\text{dyn}} s = f_0 e^{iwt}$$

1.17
$$-w^2 m s_0 + iw\eta_{\text{dyn}} s_0 + G_{\text{dyn}} s_0 = f_0$$

The physical solution to the problem is the real part of $s_0 e^{iwt}$.

The vibrational behavior of a viscoelastic body is often described in terms of the complex dynamic modulus $G' + iG''$; G' refers to "in-phase" response; G'' refers to "out-of-phase" response.[4] The equation of motion for a unit cube of material is

1.18
$$m \frac{d^2 s}{dt^2} = f_0 e^{iwt} - f_{\text{el}}$$

The first term on the right hand side of equation 1.18 represents the externally applied oscillating forces; the second term on the right represents the opposing viscoelastic stresses. The relation between f_{el} and the strain $s = s_0 e^{iwt}$ (both s_0 and f_{el} being regarded as complex numbers) is

1.19
$$f_{\text{el}} = (G' + iG'')s$$

If equation 1.19 is substituted in equation 1.18, one obtains

1.20
$$m(d^2 s/dt^2) + iG'' s + G' s = f_0 e^{iwt}$$

By comparing equation 1.20 with equation 1.16, the following identities result:

1.21
$$G' = G_{\text{dyn}}$$

1.22
$$G'' = w\eta_{\text{dyn}}$$

An exactly analogous treatment can be given for tensile vibrations or for compressional vibrations with the corresponding introduction of the complex moduli $E' + iE''$ and $B' + iB''$.

The quantities G' and G'' are widely used in the literature of viscoelasticity. Both G' and G'' are functions of the angular vibration frequency w. More frequently we shall consider G' and G'' as functions of $1/w$, because $1/w$ has the dimensions of time.

It might be expected, and it is actually true in practice, that the moduli $E_r(t)$, $E_c(t)$ and $E'(1/w)$ are reasonably close in value; that is, the type of viscoelastic measurement does not matter too much, provided that the time at which the measurement is made is the same.[5] The same naturally holds true for $G_r(t)$, $G_c(t)$ and $G'(t)$. The exact interrelationships among these quantities and the limitations of the above approximation will be the subject of the subsequent sections. Relaxation and creep measurements are very suitable for viscoelastic studies in the time scale of 1 to 10^6 sec; dynamic measurements are suitable for the time scale of 1 to 10^{-6} sec.

References III.1

1. A. V. Tobolsky, *J. Appl. Phys.*, **27**, 673 (1956).
2. H. Leaderman, *Elastic and Creep Properties of Filamentous Materials*, The Textile Foundation, Washington, D.C., 1943.
3. S. D. Gehman, *J. Appl. Phys.*, **13**, 402 (1942); M. Mooney and R. H. Gerke, *Rubber Chem. Tech.*, **14**, 35 (1941); J. H. Dillon and S. Gehman, *India Rubber World*, **115**, 61 (1946).
4. J. D. Ferry, Chapter VI in *Die Physik der Hochpolymeren*, vol. IV, H. A. Stuart (ed.), Springer, Berlin (1956).
5. T. Alfrey and P. M. Doty, *J. Appl. Phys.*, **16**, 700 (1945).

2. LINEAR VISCOELASTICITY AND THE BOLTZMANN PRINCIPLE

Consider an ideal elastic material obeying Hooke's law subjected to a series of tensile strains $s_0, s_1, s_2, \ldots, s_{n-1}, s_n$ at times $t_0 = 0, t_1, t_2, t_3, \ldots, t_{n-1}, t_n$. The stress at the end of this loading history is

2.1 $f = Es_0 + E(s_1 - s_0) + E(s_2 - s_1) + E(s_3 - s_2) + \cdots$

$\qquad + E(s_n - s_{n-1})$

$\quad = Es_n$

If the material is viscoelastic, the stress produced by each of these successive strains shows a time dependence expressed by the relaxation modulus $E_r(t)$. The definition of linear viscoelastic behavior is expressed by the following equation, due to Boltzmann:[1]

$$2.2 \quad f(t) = E_r(t)[s_0] + E_r(t - t_1)[(s_1 - s_0)] + E_r(t - t_2)[(s_2 - s_1)]$$
$$+ E_r(t - t_3)[(s_3 - s_2)] + \cdots + E_r(t - t_n)[(s_n - s_{n-1})]$$

For a continuous strain history, the Boltzmann principle can be expressed as an integral equation,

$$2.3 \qquad f(t) = \int_0^t E_r(t - \theta)\, \dot{s}(\theta)\, d\theta$$

where θ is the "current time" during the strain history, $\dot{s}(\theta)$ is written for $ds(\theta)/d\theta$ and t, the present time, is considered as a constant in the integration. It is assumed that "current time" θ starts at zero, the time of initial strain.

Exactly analogous equations to 2.2 and 2.3 can be written for a linearly viscoelastic body subject to successive stresses f_0, f_1, f_2, $\cdots$, f_{n-1}, f_n at times $t_0 = 0$, t_1, t_2, t_3, $\ldots$, t_{n-1}, t_n. For these equations we use the time-dependent elastic compliance defined in equation 1.4.

$$2.4 \quad s(t) = Y(t)[f_0] + Y(t - t_1)[(f_1 - f_0)] + \cdots + Y(t - t_n)[(f_n - f_{n-1})]$$

For continuous loading, the definition of linear viscoelasticity can be expressed in terms of another integral equation:

$$2.5 \qquad s(t) = \int_0^t Y(t - \theta)\dot{f}(\theta)\, d\theta$$

where θ is "current time" during the loading history, $\dot{f}(\theta)$ is written for $df(\theta)/d\theta$ and t is considered as a constant in the integration.

One inherent consequence of equations 2.2 and 2.5 which define linear viscoelasticity is that stress-relaxation curves $f(t)/s_0$, or creep curves $s(t)/f_0$ are independent of the constant extension or the constant stress at which they are carried out. This is also inherent in the definitions of $E_r(t)$, $E_c(t)$ and $Y(t)$ given in section 1.

It was shown by Volterra [2,3] that equations 2.5 and 2.3 are necessary consequences each of the other.

If a body exhibits linear viscoelastic behavior as defined in equations 2.2 through 2.5, its behavior can also be described by an infinite set of linear differential equations.[3-7] There are innumerable ways of specifying these sets of linear differential equations, all of which are equivalent, an important consideration that was emphasized by Alfrey and Doty.[5]

Two of these ways of specifying linear viscoelasticity are described in the following two sections.

The history of the development of the theories of linear viscoelasticity before 1943, from the point of view of both the integral equations of Boltzmann and the differential formulations of Wiechert and others, was fascinatingly and creatively reviewed by Leaderman.[3] Interesting experimental and mathematical contributions to the subject had been made by many distinguished physicists and mathematicians over a period of one hundred years. The mathematical problems encountered stimulated important developments in applied mathematics.[2]

Further developments between 1943 and 1948, with especial reference to early attempts to develop molecular theories and phenomenological theories of the linear viscoelastic properties of polymers, are comprehensively and perspicuously discussed in the treatise of Alfrey.[4]

The generalized mathematical structure of linear viscoelasticity is discussed by Sips[6] and very thoroughly developed by Gross.[7]

Linear viscoelastic behavior might be expected to be valid for substances whose basic structure is not changing with time during the viscoelastic experiment.

Boltzmann and his students showed that the superposition principle in the form of equation 2.4 was valid for glass. Leaderman[3] carried out some very careful experiments to check the validity of equation 2.4 for rayon, silk, nylon 66 and mohair, all oriented crystalline fibers. He found marked deviations from the Boltzmann principle under many experimental conditions. This was correctly attributed to the fact that crystalline substances when subject to load often show orientation and further crystallization, and at the end of loading experiments they are very different substances structurally speaking from what they were at the beginning. The Boltzmann principle could apply to these only under special conditions, such as extremely small loads, and at temperatures where crystallization does not occur at an appreciable rate.

On the other hand, it was found that the Boltzmann principle exemplified by equation 2.2 holds true for polyisobutylene, an amorphous polymer[8] and for GR-S.[9] It undoubtedly holds true for all other amorphous polymers.

A somewhat more general definition of "generalized linear viscoelastic behavior" can be couched in terms of stress-relaxation experiments carried out at various extension ratios $\alpha = L_0/L_u$. The material exhibits "generalized linear viscoelastic behavior" if at constant extension ratio

2.6
$$\frac{f(t)}{\alpha - 1} = E_r(t)\ \phi(\alpha)$$

where $\phi(\alpha)$ reduces to unity for very small values of $\alpha - 1 = (L_0 - L_u)/L_u = s_0$. In the limit of small strains, equation 2.6 is identical with equation 1.2.

For a linear polymer in the region of rubbery flow, $\phi(\alpha)$ is given by

$$2.7 \qquad \phi(\alpha) = \frac{\alpha^2 - 1/\alpha}{3(\alpha - 1)}$$

according to the equation of state for ideal rubbers.

The point of equation 2.6 is that the effect of changing the elongation at which a stress relaxation is made is merely to multiply the stress-decay curve by a constant factor; there is no change in *shape* of the decay curve. The effect of the stress-strain relationship at "zero" time is separable from the time-dependent relaxation phenomenon.

It was found by Tobolsky and Andrews that equation 2.6 holds true for vulcanized GR-S [9] in the lower portion of the transition region for values of α up to 2.0 and for linear polyisobutylene [8] in the rubbery-flow region for values up to 2.0. The same undoubtedly holds true for other amorphous polymers in these regions.

This result is a very great experimental convenience which enhances the value of the stress-relaxation technique.

An equation comparable to equation 2.6 does not hold for tensile creep experiments: The *shape* of the creep curves depend on the tensile load down to loads which produce very small initial tensile strains. If such small loads are utilized, the weight of the sample has a complex and non-negligible effect for samples of polymer in the region of rubbery flow.

References III.2

1. L. Boltzmann, *Pogg. Ann. Physik*, **7**, 624 (1876).
2. V. Volterra, *Theory of Functionals*, Dover, 1959.
3. H. Leaderman, *Elastic and Creep Properties of Filamentous Materials and Other High Polymers*, The Textile Foundation, Washington, D.C., 1943.
4. T. Alfrey, *Mechanical Behavior of High Polymers*, Interscience Publishers, New York, 1948.
5. T. Alfrey and P. M. Doty, *J. Appl. Phys.*, **16**, 700 (1945).
6. R. Sips, *J. Polymer Sci.*, **5**, 69 (1950).
7. B. Gross, *Mathematical Structure of the Theories of Viscoelasticity*, Hermann, Paris, 1953.
8. R. D. Andrews, N. Hofman-Bang and A. V. Tobolsky, *J. Polymer Sci.*, **3**, 669 (1948); also extensive unpublished experiments of A. V. Tobolsky and R. D. Andrews.
9. A. V. Tobolsky and R. D. Andrews, *J. Chem. Phys.*, **13**, 3 (1945).

3. THE MAXWELL-WIECHERT MODELS

A differential formulation of linear viscoelastic behavior particularly apt for describing stress-relaxation experiments was first presented by Wiechert [1] as a generalization of Maxwell's equation (Chapter I, section 8). The mechanical models corresponding to the Wiechert formulation are shown in Figures III.2 and III.3. Figure III.2 consists of a very large (or infinite) number of Maxwell elements coupled in parallel. Figure III.3 consists of a very large (or infinite) number of Maxwell elements coupled in parallel *plus* a spring without a dashpot.

The mathematical equations corresponding to these models are

3.1
$$\frac{ds}{dt} = \frac{1}{E_1}\frac{df_1}{dt} + \frac{1}{\tau_1 E_1}f_1$$

$$\frac{ds}{dt} = \frac{1}{E_2}\frac{df_2}{dt} + \frac{1}{\tau_2 E_2}f_2$$

$$\cdots \cdots \cdots \cdots \cdots$$

$$\frac{ds}{dt} = \frac{1}{E_m}\frac{df_m}{dt} + \frac{1}{\tau_m E_m}f_m$$

$$f = f_1 + f_2 + \cdots + f_m$$

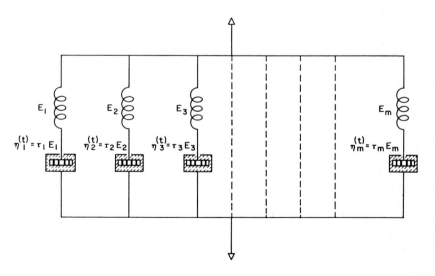

Figure III.2. The Wiechert model III.2.

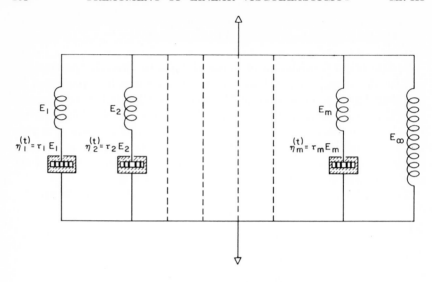

Figure III.3. The Wiechert model III.3.

3.2
$$\frac{ds}{dt} = \frac{1}{E_1}\frac{df_1}{dt} + \frac{1}{\tau_1 E_1}f_1$$

$$\frac{ds}{dt} = \frac{1}{E_2}\frac{df_2}{dt} + \frac{1}{\tau_2 E_2}f_2$$

. . . .

$$\frac{ds}{dt} = \frac{1}{E_m}\frac{df_m}{dt} + \frac{1}{\tau_m E_m}f_m$$

$$\frac{ds}{dt} = \frac{1}{E_\infty}\frac{df_\infty}{dt}$$

3.3
$$f = f_\infty + f_1 + f_2 + \cdots + f_m$$

In equations 3.1 and 3.2, f_i is the partial stress in the ith element, E_i and τ_i are the modulus and relaxation time, respectively, of the ith element, f is the over-all stress, and s is the strain. The single spring E_∞ in Figure III.3 may be regarded as an element with an infinite relaxation time.

Actually, when the mechanical models shown in Figures III.2 and III.3 or the equations 3.1 and 3.2 are used to describe the properties of matter, it must be remembered that the only observables are the external

strains s and the over-all stress f. The partial stresses f_i and the quantities E_i and τ_i are not macroscopically observable, but must be deduced
from the viscoelastic data.

Figure III.2 and equation 3.1 are suitable models for a non-cross-
linked or linear polymer, because at constant strain this model will show
decay to zero stress. At constant strain s_0, from equation 3.1 (boundary
condition $f_i = s_0 E_i$ at $t = 0$),

$$3.4 \qquad f(t) = s_0 \sum_{i=1}^{m} E_i \exp\left(-t/\tau_i\right)$$

$$3.5 \qquad E_r(t) = \frac{f(t)}{s_0} = \sum_{i=1}^{m} E_i \exp\left(-t/\tau_i\right)$$

If a constant stress f_0 is applied for a period of time very long compared with the longest relaxation time τ_m, all the terms $(1/E_i)(df_i/dt)$ in
equations 3.1 become vanishingly small. One therefore obtains

$$3.6 \qquad f_0 = \sum_{i=1}^{m} f_i = (\Sigma \tau_i E_i) \frac{ds}{dt}$$

Hence for sufficiently long times under constant stress the Wiechert
model III.2 behaves like a Newtonian fluid and approaches a constant
rate of strain $f_0/\Sigma \tau_i E_i$. The constant $\Sigma \tau_i E_i$ is $\eta^{(t)}$, the viscosity in tension, related to the shear viscosity η and the Poisson ratio σ as follows:

$$3.7 \qquad \eta^{(t)} = \Sigma \tau_i E_i = 2(1 + \sigma)\eta$$

For linear polymers in the rubbery state $\sigma = \frac{1}{2}$, so that $\eta^{(t)} = 3\eta$.

If the values of the τ_i and E_i can be obtained by an analysis of the
stress-relaxation curve, the viscosity $\eta^{(t)}$ can be obtained from equation
3.7. This is a specific example where one type of viscoelastic experiment
can be used to predict the results of another, in this case stress relaxation
being used to predict the flow behavior under constant stress after very
long times. Many other examples will be given in section 7.

Figure III.3 and equation 3.2 provide a suitable model for a cross-
linked polymer, because at constant strain this model will decay to a
finite stress. At constant strain s_0, from equation 3.1

$$3.8 \qquad f(t) = s_0 E_\infty + s_0 \sum_{i=1}^{m} E_i \exp\left(-t/\tau_i\right)$$

$$3.9 \qquad E_r(t) = E_\infty + \Sigma E_i \exp\left(-t/\tau_i\right)$$

If a constant stress f_0 is applied for a period of time, very long compared to the largest relaxation time, a constant strain is ultimately reached.

3.10 $s_\infty = f_0/E_\infty$

This type of substance exhibits delayed elasticity, but no true viscous flow.

The equations 3.1 and 3.2 can be generalized (or approximated) by a continuous set of differential equations. For all values of τ between zero and infinity we define the continuous functions $E(\tau)$ and $f(t, \tau)$ so that the following equations are valid for the viscoelastic body:

3.11 $$\frac{ds}{dt} = \frac{1}{E(\tau)} \frac{\partial f(t, \tau)}{\partial t} + \frac{1}{E(\tau)} f(t, \tau)$$

$$f_\infty = E_\infty s$$

$$f(t) = f_\infty + \int_0^\infty f(t, \tau)\, d\tau$$

where E_∞ and hence f_∞ may be zero.

Equations 3.5 and 3.9 become

3.12 $$E_r(t) - E_\infty = \int_0^\infty E(\tau) \exp\left(-t/\tau\right) d\tau$$

where E_∞ may be zero (for model III.2). The function $E(\tau)$ is called the distribution of relaxation times. Although the integral in equation 3.12 is taken for all values of τ between zero and infinity, $E(\tau)$ may vanish for values of τ below a minimum value τ_1 and for values of τ above a maximum value τ_m. Note that the quantities having the dimensions of stress are $f(t, \tau)\, d\tau$ rather than $f(t, \tau)$, and that $E(\tau)\, d\tau$ also has the dimensions of modulus or stress.

In principle, if $E_r(t) - E_\infty$ is known for all values of t, equation 3.12 can be solved for $E(\tau)$. This type of equation is known as the Laplace transformation.

Equations exactly analogous to 3.1 through 3.11 can be written for viscoelastic behavior in shear. The relaxation times are identical for shear and tension. The moduli E_i or $E(\tau)$ must be replaced by G_i or $G(\tau)$, where $G_i = E_i/2(1 + \sigma)$ and $G(\tau) = E(\tau)/2(1 + \sigma)$.

For model III.2 and a continuous distribution of relaxation times, equation 3.7 becomes

3.13 $$\eta^{(t)} = \int_0^\infty E(\tau)\, d\tau$$

For the relaxation distribution *in shear*,

3.14
$$\eta = \int_0^\infty G(\tau)\, d\tau$$

The function $E(\tau)$ if known can in principle be used to predict the result of any other type of mechanical experiment: such for example as applying a strain s_1 between $t = 0$ and $t = t_1$, a strain s_2 for the time interval t_1 to t_2, etc. From $E(\tau)$ the complex dynamic modulus can be obtained by quadrature, and the creep modulus by a completely defined but complicated mathematical relationship, as shown subsequently.

One can readily show [2] the identity of the Wiechert formulation (equation 3.11) and the Boltzmann formulation (equation 2.3). Equation 3.11 for a given value of τ is a linear equation of the first order and can be integrated directly. If for simplicity we take $f(t) = 0$ at $t = 0$, the result is

3.15
$$f(t, \tau) = E(\tau) \int_0^t \exp\left(-\frac{t - \theta}{\tau}\right) \dot{s}(\theta)\, d\theta$$

One obtains $f(t)$ as follows (taking $E_\infty = 0$ for simplicity):

3.16
$$f(t) = \int_0^\infty f(t, \tau)\, d\tau$$

$$= \int_0^t \left[\int_0^\infty E(\tau) \exp\left(-\frac{t - \theta}{\tau}\right) d\tau\right] \dot{s}(\theta)\, d\theta$$

Now define $E_r(t - \theta)$ as follows:

3.17
$$E_r(t - \theta) = \int_0^\infty E(\tau) \exp\left(-\frac{t - \theta}{\tau}\right) d\tau$$

whereupon

3.18
$$f(t) = \int_0^t E_r(t - \theta)\dot{s}(\theta)\, d\theta$$

which is identical with equation 2.3.

The applicability of the Wiechert model specifically to the mechanical behavior of polymers was indicated by W. Kuhn in 1939 [3] and shortly thereafter developed by R. Simha [4] and many others, a foreshadowing of the very extensive developments to come.

References III.3

1. E. Wiechert, *Wied. Ann. Physik*, **50**, 335, 546 (1893).
2. R. Sips, *J. Polymer Sci.*, **69** (1950).
3. W. Kuhn, *Z. physik. Chem.*, **B42**, 1 (1939); K. Bennewitz and H. Rötger, *Physik. Z.*, **40**, 416 (1939); W. Holzmuller and E. Jenckel, *Z. physik. Chem.*, **A186**, 359 (1940)
4. R. Simha, *J. Appl. Phys.*, **13**, 201 (1942).

4. THE GENERALIZED VOIGT MODEL

A differential formulation of linear viscoelastic behavior particularly apt for describing creep experiments is the generalized Voigt-Kelvin formulation.[1] The corresponding mechanical models (two variations) are shown in Figures III.4 and III.5.

The mathematical equations corresponding to the model shown in Figure III.4 are

4.1
$$f = E_q s_q$$

$$f = E_1 s_1 + \tau_1 E_1 \dot{s}_1$$

$$f = E_2 s_2 + \tau_2 E_2 \dot{s}_2$$

$$\cdot \ \cdot \ \cdot \ \cdot \ \cdot \ \cdot \ \cdot$$

$$\cdot \ \cdot \ \cdot \ \cdot \ \cdot \ \cdot \ \cdot$$

$$f = E_m s_m + \tau_m E_m \dot{s}_m$$

$$s = s_q + s_1 + s_2 + \cdots + s_m$$

where $\dot{s}_i$ is written for ds_i/dt.

The equations corresponding to Figure III.5 are

4.2
$$f = E_q s_q$$

$$f = E_1 s_1 + \tau_1 E_2 \dot{s}_1$$

$$f = E_2 s_2 + \tau_2 E_2 \dot{s}_2$$

$$\cdot \ \cdot \ \cdot \ \cdot \ \cdot \ \cdot \ \cdot$$

$$f = E_m s_m + \tau_m E_m \dot{s}_m$$

$$f = \eta^{(t)} \dot{s}_\eta$$

$$s = s_q + s_1 + s_2 + \cdots + s_m + s_r$$

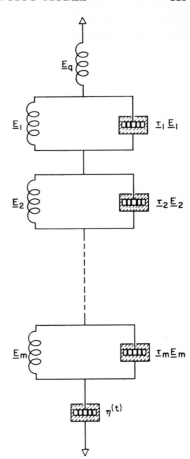

Figure III.4.   The Voigt-Kelvin model
III.4.

In these equations E_i represents the modulus (or spring constant) of the ith element, and τ_i represents the retardation time of the ith element ($\tau_i E_i$ being the tensile viscosity of the ith dashpot). The over-all strain is clearly the sum of the partial strains in all these elements. The quantity $\eta^{(t)}$ appears instead of η because we are dealing with tension instead of shear. Equations exactly analogous to 3.1 and 3.2 can be written for viscoelastic behavior in shear except that E_i would be replaced by G_i and $\eta^{(t)}$ would be replaced by η. The retardation times for shear and tension are assumed identical.

Under constant stress the creep curve for equation 4.1 is

4.3
$$s = \frac{f_0}{E_q} + \sum_{i=1}^{m} \frac{f_0}{E_i} [1 - \exp{(-t/\tau_i)}]$$

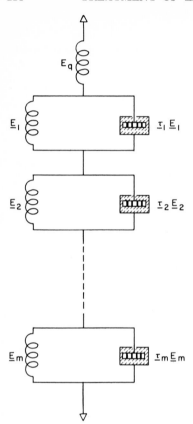

Figure III.5. The Voigt-Kelvin model III.5.

The first term on the right-hand side of equation 4.3 represents the instantaneous elastic response; the second term represents the delayed elasticity.

Under constant stress f_0 the creep curve for equation 4.2 is

$$4.4 \qquad s = \frac{f_0}{E_q} + \sum_{i=1}^{m} \frac{f_0}{E_i} [1 - \exp(-t/\tau_i)] + \frac{f_0 t}{\eta^{(t)}}$$

The third term on the right-hand side represents the limiting flow of the material under constant tensile load.

Equation 4.3 describes a material which under constant stress finally attains a limiting elastic response; equation 4.4 describes a substance which under constant stress shows instantaneous elasticity, delayed elasticity, and finally a state of flow. Equation 4.3 is suitable for cross-linked amorphous polymers; equation 4.4 is suitable for linear amorphous polymers.

The instantaneous elastic modulus E_q of the generalized Voigt models III.4 and III.5 are related to the partial moduli of the generalized Maxwell models III.2 and III.3 as follows,

$$4.5 \qquad E_q = E_\infty + \sum_{i=1}^{m} E_i$$

where E_∞ may be zero (as in model III.2).

Equations 4.1 through 4.4 can be written in terms of elastic compliances rather than elastic moduli. For example, equation 4.4 can be written as

$$4.6 \qquad s = f_0 Y_q + \sum_{i=1}^{m} Y_i \left[1 - \exp\left(-t/\tau_i\right)\right] + \frac{f_0 t}{\eta^{(t)}}$$

A continuous distribution of retardation times can also be defined in terms of a function $Y(\tau)$ such that

$$4.7 \qquad s(t) = f_0 Y_q + f_0 \int_0^\infty Y(\tau)\left[1 - \exp\left(-t/\tau_i\right)\right] d\tau + \frac{f_0 t}{\eta^{(t)}}$$

where $Y(\tau)$ may be zero for values of τ smaller than τ_1 or larger than τ_m.

The generalized Voigt model to explain creep of polymers was used by Aleksandrov and Lazurkin as early as 1940.[2]

References III.4

1. W. Voigt, *Abhandl. Gottingen Ges. Wiss.*, **36** (1899).
2. A. P. Aleksandrov and I. U. S. Lazurkin, *Acta Physicochim. URSS*, **12,** 647 (1940).

5. DYNAMIC MODULUS AND THE GENERALIZED MAXWELL MODEL

Suppose that a cube of viscoelastic material of unit dimensions was attached to an external mass m and the whole system subjected to forced shear oscillations of magnitude $f_0 e^{iwt}$. We further suppose that the viscoelastic material is a generalized Maxwell model (see Figure III.2). The equation of motion is (see equations 1.5, 1.6 and 1.18)

$$5.1 \qquad m \frac{d^2 s}{dt^2} = f_0 e^{iwt} - f_{el}$$

where f_{el} is the viscoelastic stress set up in the material, and s is the tensile strain. The viscoelastic stress is determined by the equations

5.2
$$\dot{s} = \frac{\dot{f}_1}{G_1} + \frac{f_1}{\tau_1 G_1}$$

$$\dot{s} = \frac{\dot{f}_2}{G_2} + \frac{f_2}{\tau_2 G_2}$$

$$\cdot \quad \cdot \quad \cdot \quad \cdot \quad \cdot \quad \cdot \quad \cdot \quad \cdot \quad \cdot \quad \cdot$$

$$\dot{s}_m = \dot{f}_m/G_n + f_m/\tau_m G_m$$

$$f = f_{\mathrm{el}} = f_1 + f_2 + \cdots + f_m$$

We assume that under the effect of the externally applied alternating stress $f_0 e^{iwt}$ all the partial stresses have a steady-state solution $f_i = f_{i,0} e^{iwt}$, $f_{\mathrm{el}} = f_{\mathrm{el},0} e^{iwt}$, and $s = s_0 e^{iwt}$, where $f_{i,0}$, $f_{\mathrm{el},0}$, and s_0 are complex numbers.

From equations 5.2 we find

5.3
$$f_{i,0} = \frac{s_0 i w \tau_i G_i}{1 + i w \tau_i}$$

$$f_{\mathrm{el},0} = \Sigma f_{i,0} = s_0 \left(\sum \frac{G_i w^2 \tau_i^2}{1 + w^2 \tau_i^2} + i \sum \frac{G_i w \tau_i}{1 + w^2 \tau_i^2} \right)$$

The viscoelastic stress set up in the material can be defined in terms of the complex dynamic modulus

5.4
$$f_{\mathrm{el},0} = s_0[G'(w) + i\, G''(w)]$$

Equating the real and imaginary parts of equations 5.4 and 5.3, one obtains the following relation, first given by Tobolsky and Eyring [1] in terms of the notation G_{dyn} and η_{dyn}.

5.5
$$G' = \sum \frac{G_i w^2 \tau_i^2}{1 + w^2 \tau_i^2} = \int_{\tau_1}^{\tau_m} \frac{G(\tau) w^2 \tau^2}{1 + w^2 \tau^2}\, d\tau$$

5.6
$$G'' = \sum \frac{G_i w \tau_i}{1 + w^2 \tau_i^2} = \int_{\tau_1}^{\tau_m} \frac{G(\tau) w \tau}{1 + w^2 \tau^2}\, d\tau$$

Exactly the same treatment can be given for a continuous set of relaxation times, in which case the sums in equations 5.5 and 5.6 can be replaced by integrals in the manner shown. Also the same treatment can be given for alternating tensile stresses. The only changes in the equations would be to replace the G_i by E_i.

If the solutions $s = s_0 e^{iwt}$, $f_{\text{el}} = f_{\text{el},0} e^{iwt}$, and equation 5.3 for $f_{\text{el},0}$ are all substituted in equation 5.1, one obtains the following equations.

5.7 $\qquad -mw^2 s_0 + i \sum \dfrac{G_i w \tau_i}{1 + w^2 \tau_i^2} + \sum \dfrac{G_i w^2 \tau_i^2}{1 + w^2 \tau_i^2} = f_o$

Upon substitution of equations 5.5 and 5.6, there results

5.8 $\qquad -mw^2 s_0 + i G'' s_0 + G' s_0 = f_o$

If one compares equation 5.7 with equation 1.17, the validity of $G'' = w\eta_{\text{dyn}}$ and $G' = G_{\text{dyn}}$ is again apparent.

Reference III.5

1. A. V. Tobolsky and H. Eyring, *J. Chem. Phys.*, **11**, 125 (1943).

6. DISTRIBUTION OF RELAXATION TIMES FROM STRESS-RELAXATION DATA

The relationship between the experimentally obtained stress-relaxation modulus $E_r(t)$ and the distribution of relaxation times $E(\tau)$ was already given in section 3,

6.1 $\qquad E_r(t) = \displaystyle\int_0^\infty E(\tau) \exp\left(-t/\tau\right) d\tau$

where $E(\tau)$ may be zero for values of τ below τ_1 and above τ_m.

The relationship expressed in equation 6.1 is known in mathematics as a Laplace transformation. If $E_r(t)$ is known for all values of t from zero to infinity, $E(\tau)$ can be obtained in principle; many analytic functions $E_r(t)$ have known and tabulated Laplace transforms $E(\tau)$. Examples will be given later.

On the other hand, $E_r(t)$ is obtained experimentally in the form of a graph; even if the graphical data can be expressed as an analytic function, the analytic function may not have any known Laplace transform. It is therefore very desirable to obtain a graphical method for obtaining $E(\tau)$, at least approximately, from $E_r(t)$.

Furthermore, to use the Laplace transform one must know $E_r(t)$ over the entire time scale from $t = 0$ to $t = \infty$. In Chapter IV we shall show how this can be accomplished by the construction of "master curves" obtained from stress-relaxation data at various temperatures. Frequently, however, $E_r(t)$ is known only over a limited time interval. It is not possible to obtain a solution of equation 6.1 in this case, but the graphical approximations are still valid.

For a first approximation we shall replace the function exp $(-t/\tau)$ in equation 6.1 with a step function which is unity for $\tau \geq t$ and zero for $\tau \leq t$. Hence

6.2 $$E(t) \approx \int_t^\infty E(\tau)\, d\tau$$

By differentiating equation 6.2 one obtains

6.3 $$E'(\tau) \approx -[dE(t)/dt]_{t=\tau}$$

We may define a new function $E_1(\tau)$, called the first approximation of the relaxation distribution by

6.4 $$E_1(\tau) = -[dE(t)/dt]_{t=\tau}$$

Formula 6.3 was first proposed by Alfrey.[1] Second and higher approximations have been proposed by Ferry and Williams,[2] Andrews,[3] and Schwarzl and Staverman,[4] and will be detailed later in the section.

The distribution of relaxation times may be expressed in terms of another function $H(\tau)$ defined as follows:

6.5 $$H(\tau) = \tau\, E(\tau)$$

The property H is often expressed in terms of the independent variable $\ln \tau$ instead of τ, with $H(\ln \tau) \equiv H(\tau)$, in the sense that the two functions are equal for a given value of τ. The function $H(\ln \tau)\, d(\ln \tau)$ represents the partial modulus of those elements of the Maxwell model having a relaxation time between $\ln \tau$ and $\ln \tau + d(\ln \tau)$. Clearly from equation 6.5 it follows that

6.6 $$H(\ln \tau)\, d(\ln \tau) = E(\tau)\, d\tau$$

The first approximation for $H(\tau)$, denoted as $H_1(\tau)$, follows from

6.7 $$H_1(\tau) = \tau\, E_1(\tau) = -[dE_r(t)/d \ln t]_{t=\tau}$$

Since $E_r(t)$ is often plotted against $\log_{10} t$, or $\log_{10} E_r(t)$ is often plotted versus $\log_{10} t$, the following definitions are useful (henceforward log will be used without the subscript 10).

6.8 $$H_1(\tau) = -\frac{1}{2.303}\left[\frac{dE_r(t)}{d \log t}\right]_{t=\tau}$$

$$= -E_r(t)\left[\frac{d \log E_r(t)}{d \log t}\right]_{t=\tau}$$

The second approximation according to the method of Andrews [3] is

$$6.9 \qquad H_{2a}(\tau) = -\frac{1}{2.303}\left[\frac{dE_r(t)}{d\log t}\right]_{t=\tau} + 0.109\left[\frac{d^2E_r(t)}{d\log t^2}\right]_{t=\tau}$$

The second approximation according to the method of Ferry and Williams is [2]

$$6.10 \qquad H_{2b}(\tau) = \frac{H_1(\tau)}{\Gamma(1+m)}$$

where

$$6.11 \qquad m = -\frac{d\log H_1(\tau)}{d\log\tau}$$

and Γ is the well-known gamma function (for integral values of m, $\Gamma(1+m) = m!$).

It must be pointed out that in papers from this laboratory through January 1, 1959, the notation $H(\tau)$ was used somewhat differently from the way it is defined here. The previous use of $H(\tau)$ will now be denoted as $\overline{H}(\tau)$. $\overline{H}(\tau)$ will be used in all the figures of this book except Figure III.9, where $H(\tau)$ is plotted.

The definition of $\overline{H}(\tau)$ is as follows:

$$6.12 \qquad \overline{H}(\log\tau)\,d\log\tau = E(\tau)\,d\tau$$

Hence the relation among $\overline{H}(\tau)$, $H(\tau)$ and $E(\tau)$ is

$$6.13 \qquad \overline{H}(\tau) = 2.303H(\tau) = 2.303\tau\,E(\tau)$$

Again we are using the notation $\overline{H}(\log\tau)$ and $\overline{H}(\tau)$ with $\overline{H}(\log\tau) \equiv \overline{H}(\tau)$ in the sense that the functions are equal for a given value of τ. In the same manner we will use the notation $E'(w)$ and $E'(1/w)$ interchangeably in the sense that the two functions are equal for a given value of w.

The introduction of both $H(\tau)$ and $\overline{H}(\tau)$ is desirable in order to prevent confusion when comparisons are made with the nomenclature of other authors.

A method for obtaining a *discrete* distribution of relaxation times from experimental stress-relaxation data was developed by Tobolsky and Murakami and is discussed in Chapter IV, section 9.

References III.6

1. T. Alfrey, *Mechanical Behavior of High Polymers*, Appendix II, p. 533, Interscience Publishers, New York, 1948.
2. J. D. Ferry and M. L. Williams, *J. Colloid Sci.*, **7**, 347 (1952); M. L. Williams and J. D. Ferry, *J. Polymer Sci.*, **11**, 169 (1953).
3. R. D. Andrews, *Ind. Eng. Chem.*, **44**, 707 (1952).
4. F. Schwarzl and A. J. Staverman, *Physica*, **18**, 791 (1952); *Appl. Sci. Research*, **A4**, 127 (1953).

7. TRANSFORMATION OF $E_r(t)$ TO OTHER VISCOELASTIC FUNCTIONS

Suppose that experimental stress-relaxation data yielded a master curve $E_r(t)$ over the entire time scale. How would this master curve be used to obtain other important viscoelastic properties?

We recall the relations among $\eta^{(t)}$, $E'(w)$, $E''(w)$ and $H(\tau)$.

$$7.1 \qquad \eta^{(t)} = \int_0^\infty H(\tau)\, d\tau$$

$$7.2 \qquad E'(w) = \int_{-\infty}^\infty H(\tau)\, \frac{w^2\tau^2}{1 + w^2\tau^2}\, d\ln\tau$$

$$7.3 \qquad E''(w) = \int_{-\infty}^\infty H(\tau)\, \frac{w\tau}{1 + w^2\tau^2}\, d\ln\tau$$

In the above equations one can replace H by H_1, H_{2a} or H_{2b}, the approximations discussed in the previous section, and carry out the integrations by graphical or numerical computations.

It is possible, however, to make some simpler approximations. These are necessary in those cases where $E_r(t)$ and $H(\tau)$ are known only in a limited time interval.

For example, in the case of $E''(w)$, inasmuch as $w\tau/(1 + w^2\tau^2)$ is a function with a maximum at $\tau = 1/w$, the following approximation is valid.

$$7.4 \qquad E''(w) \approx [H(\tau)]_{\tau=1/w} \int_{-\infty}^\infty \frac{w\tau}{1 + w^2\tau^2}\, d\ln\tau$$

$$= \frac{\pi}{2}\, [H(\tau)]_{\tau=1/w}$$

In equation 7.4 we can again substitute H_1, H_{2a} or H_{2b} for H.

For the flow viscosity $\eta^{(t)}$ given by equation 7.1, it is most important that H, H_1, H_{2a} or H_{2b} should be very accurately known in the region of τ_m. However, the contribution to $\eta^{(t)}$ from $H(\tau)$ for values of $\tau < \tau_m/10$ is fairly small, and can often be neglected if not accurately known.

To a crude approximation $E_r(t)$, $E_c(t)$ and $E'(1/w)$ are equal; for a given value of t (or $1/w$), $E_c(t)$ is slightly smaller than $E_r(t)$ which is slightly smaller than $E'(1/w)$. These approximations are valid if $E_r(t)$

Table III.1 [a]

THE FUNCTION $\Upsilon_{(m)}$

			0	1	2	3	4	5	6	7	8	9
−m	0.0	0.2	51	53	56	58	61	64	67	70	74	77
	1		80	84	88	91	95	99	*03	*07	*12	*16
	2	0.3	20	25	30	35	40	46	52	58	64	70
	3		77	83	90	98	*05	*13	*20	*29	*38	*47
	4	0.4	57	67	77	87	98	*10	*22	*35	*48	*61
	5	0.	575	590	606	622	640	658	676	696	718	740
	6		763	788	814	841	872	902	935	970	*008	*048
	7	1.	090									
+m	0.0	0.2	51	48	46	44	42	40	38	35	33	31
	1		29	28	26	24	22	21	20	18	17	15
	2		14	13	12	11	10	08	07	06	05	05
	3		04	03	02	01	01	00	*99	*99	*98	*98
	4	0.1	97	97	97	97	96	96	96	96	95	95
	5		95	95	95	95	95	96	96	96	96	96
	6		97	97	97	98	98	99	99	*00	*01	*01
	7	0.2	02	03	04	04	05	06	07	08	09	10
	8		12	13	14	16	17	18	20	21	23	25
	9		27	28	30	32	35	37	39	41	44	46
	1.0		48	51	53	56	59	62	65	68	71	74
	1		78	81	85	88	92	96	*01	*05	*10	*14
	2	0.3	18	23	28	34	39	45	51	57	63	69
	3		76	83	90	98	*05	*13	*22	*31	*40	*49
	4	0.4	59	69	79	90	*02	*13	*25	*38	*51	*65
	5	0.	580	595	612	628	646	665	685	706	727	750
	6		774	798	825	855	885	917	950	986	*023	*064
	7	1.	108									

[a] E. Catsiff and A. V. Tobolsky, *J. Colloid Sci.*, **10**, 375 (1955).

* The asterisks denote that the digits which they precede belong to the following row.

has a nonzero asymptote E_∞ when t approaches infinity. If $E_r(t)$ approaches zero, these approximations are valid if $t < \tau_m$, where τ_m is the maximum relaxation time.

The complex dynamic modulus $E'(1/w)$ can be computed quite accurately from the equation [1]

7.5 $E'(1/w) - [E_r(t)]_{t=1/w} = [\Upsilon(m)H_{2b}(\tau)]_{\tau=1/w}$

$$\Upsilon(m) = \left(\frac{\pi}{2}\right)\csc\left(\frac{m\pi}{2}\right) - \Gamma(m)$$

In equation 7.5, m is the quantity defined by equation 6.11. The function $\Upsilon(m)$ is tabulated in Table III.1. Similarly

7.6 $E''(1/w) = \dfrac{\pi}{2}\sec\dfrac{m\pi}{2}\,H_{2b}(\tau)$

The relations between creep and relaxation moduli are more complex. A distribution of retardation times $L(\tau)$ exactly analogous to $H(\tau)$ can be defined for creep data. The relation between $L(\tau)$ and $H(\tau)$ as given by Gross is [2]

7.7 $L(\tau) = \dfrac{H(\tau)}{\left\{E_\infty - \displaystyle\int_0^\infty [H(v)/(\tau - v)]\,dv\right\}^2 + \pi^2[H(\tau)]^2}$

If the primary experimental data are obtained from creep data or dynamic data, similar types of approximations to those used in this section can be utilized. It is convenient to introduce other types of distribution functions [such as $L(\tau)$], depending on the primary viscoelastic data. A convenient summary is given in reference.[3]

References III.7

1. E. Catsiff and A. V. Tobolsky, *J. Colloid Sci.*, **10**, 375 (1955).
2. B. Gross, *Mathematical Structure of the Theories of Viscoelasticity*, Hermann, Paris (1953); see also R. Simha, *J. Appl. Phys.*, **13**, 201 (1942).
3. H. Leaderman, in *Rheology: Theory and Applications*, vol. II, F. R. Eirich (ed.), Academic Press, New York, 1956. See Chapter I, especially Table III, p. 49.

8. SOME EMPIRICAL DISTRIBUTIONS OF RELAXATION TIMES

In order to gain a deeper insight into the methods of linear visco-elasticity, it is desirable to examine a few distributions of relaxation times $H(\tau)$ which have proved useful in studying the viscoelastic properties of polymers.

In discussing the hysteretic properties of ferromagnetic materials, Becker and Doring [1] introduced a distribution of relaxation times which we shall call the "box" distribution.

Kuhn, Kunzle and Preismann introduced this same distribution into the Wiechert treatment of viscoelastic properties of polymers.[2] Using this distribution, they showed that, if the creep curve of a material is given by the empirical equation

$$8.1 \qquad E_c(t) = (a + \ln t)/b$$

then the complex dynamic modulus in the same range of time scale is

$$8.2 \qquad E''\left(\frac{1}{w}\right) = \frac{\pi b^2}{2a^2}$$

The mathematical treatment necessary to obtain this relation was quite complicated, and several approximations had to be introduced since the Wiechert model is difficult to apply to creep data. Nevertheless this supplied the first truly numerical correlation of actual creep data and dynamic data.

Tobolsky, Andrews, Dunell and McLoughlin used the box distribution [3] to achieve the first actual numerical correlations between stress-relaxation data and dynamic data,[4,5] stress-relaxation data and flow-viscosity data,[6] and also to obtain the first approximate calculation of the complete relaxation spectrum of an amorphous polymer (the latter for the case of polymethyl methacrylate).[7] Inasmuch as the Wiechert model is natural for stress-relaxation data, the calculations were very straightforward.

The box distribution is defined by the equation

$$8.3 \qquad H(\tau) = E_0 \qquad \tau_3 < \tau < \tau_m$$

$$H(\tau) = 0 \qquad \tau < \tau_3 \qquad \tau > \tau_m$$

One obtains $E_r(t)$, $E'(w)$, $E''(w)$ and $\eta^{(t)}$ from the equations

8.4
$$E_r(t) = \int_{-\infty}^{\infty} H(\tau) \exp(-t/\tau) \, d\ln \tau$$

8.5
$$E'(w) = \int_{-\infty}^{\infty} H(\tau) \frac{w^2 \tau^2}{1 + w^2 \tau^2} \, d\ln \tau$$

8.6
$$E''(w) = \int_{-\infty}^{\infty} H(\tau) \frac{w\tau}{1 + w^2 \tau^2} \, d\ln \tau$$

8.7
$$\eta^{(t)} = \int_{0}^{\infty} H(\tau) \, d\tau$$

This gives

8.8
$$E_r(t) = E_0 \left[Ei \left(-\frac{t}{\tau_3} \right) - Ei \left(-\frac{t}{\tau_m} \right) \right]$$

8.9
$$E'(w) = \frac{E_0}{2} \ln \frac{1 + w^2 \tau_m^2}{1 + w^2 \tau_3^2}$$

8.10
$$E''(w) = E_0 (\arctan w\tau_m - \arctan w\tau_3)$$

8.11
$$\eta^{(t)} = E_0(\tau_m - \tau_3) \approx E_0 \tau_m$$

In equation 8.8 the function Ei is the well-known and carefully tabulated exponential integral function.[8]

In Figure III.6 is shown a plot of $E_r(t)$ vs. log t, $E'(1/w)$ vs. log $(1/w)$, $E''(1/w)$ vs. log $(1/w)$ and $H(\tau)$ vs. log τ for the functions 8.3 and 8.8 through 8.10. In this case E_0 was taken as 7.2×10^5 hr, τ_3 was taken as $10^{-4.34}$ hr and τ_m as $10^{1.70}$ hr. The "plateau" modulus is $E_0 \ln (\tau_m/\tau_3)$.

If log τ_3 and log τ_m differ by more than unity, as is true in this case, then the central portion of the $E_r(t)$ vs. log t plot is a straight line whose slope is equal to

8.12
$$\left[-\frac{d(E_r(t))}{d \log t} \right]_{t=\tau} = 2.303 E_0$$

$$= 2.303 H(\tau) = \overline{H}(\tau)$$

where $2.303 E_0$ is, of course, the height of the box in the $\overline{H}(\tau)$ vs. log τ plot.

Equation 8.12 is equivalent to equation 6.8, the first approximation result discussed in section 6. It is derivable from the properties of the exponential integral function.

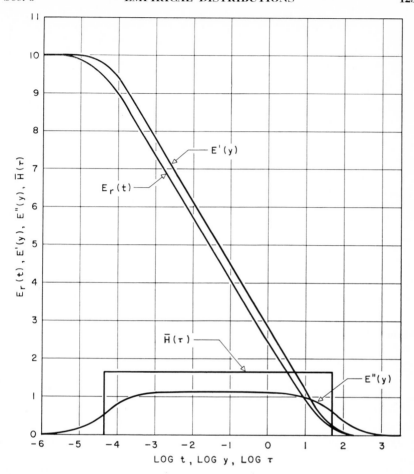

Figure III.6. $E_r(t)$, $E'(1/w)$, $E''(1/w)$ and $H(\tau)$ for the box distribution: a linear-log plot. ($y = 1/w$.) [After A. V. Tobolsky, B. A. Dunell and R. D. Andrews, *Textile Research J.*, **21**, 404 (1951).]

In Figure III.7 we again show the relaxation function $E_r(t)$ plotted in the form $E_r(t)$ vs. $\log t$. The straight-line portion of the curve is prolonged to the points A and B shown in the figure. It can be shown from the properties of the exponential integral function that the time values of the intercepts A and B are related to τ_3 and τ_m as follows: [5]

8.13
$$\frac{\tau_3}{\tau_A} = \frac{\tau_m}{\tau_B} = 1.781$$

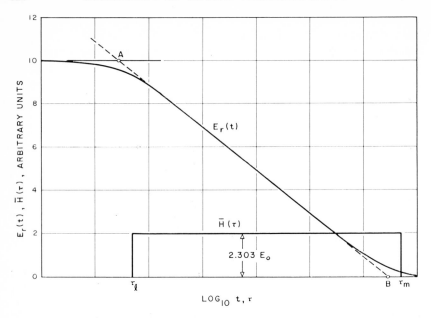

Figure III.7. Constants for the box distribution. [After A. V. Tobolsky, B. A. Dunell and R. D. Andrews, *Textile Research J.*, **21**, 404 (1951).]

Equations 8.12 and 8.13 are very useful because experimental stress-decay curves plotted in the form of $E_r(t)$ vs. $\log t$ are frequently linear for many decades of time. This is especially true for linear amorphous polymers in the transition region of rubbery flow and frequently true for crystalline polymers. In the time interval where $dE_r(t)/d \log t$ is a constant, whose value we can for convenience call $2.303E_0$, the corresponding portion of the relaxation function $\bar{H}(\tau)$ can be approximated by a box whose height is $2.303E_0$. In favorable cases (rubbery-flow region of linear amorphous polymers), τ_m and sometimes even τ_3 can be obtained by equation 8.13.

The flow viscosity $\eta^{(t)}$ can then be obtained from equation 8.11.

In the time region where $dE_r(t)/d \log t$ is constant, $E''(1/w)$ is also approximately constant, as can readily be seen from equation 8.10 and from Figure III.7.

$$8.14 \qquad E''\left(\frac{1}{w}\right) = \frac{\pi}{2} E_0 = \frac{\pi}{4.606} \frac{dE_r(t)}{d \log t}$$

In this same time interval, $E'(1/w) \approx E_r(t)$, as can be seen in Figure III.7.

In 1952 an idealized distribution of relaxation times $H(\tau)$ for the *entire* relaxation spectrum of linear polyisobutylene was proposed.[9] This consisted of a "wedge" and a "box" when plotted in the form of $\log H(\tau)$ vs. $\log \tau$. The wedge is the short-end part of the relaxation-time spectrum (associated with the transition region) and is independent of molecular weight. The "box" is for the long-time end of the relaxation-time spectrum (associated with the rubbery-flow region), and the entire "box" is shifted along the logarithmic time scale by a change in the molecular weight of the polymer. For sufficiently high molecular weights the wedge and box are separated. At low molecular weights the wedge and box fuse together.

At 25°C the wedge-box function for polyisobutylene whose distribution of molecular weights is random (see Appendix F) is as follows:

8.15   Wedge: $H(\tau) = M/\tau^{1/2}$ $\tau_1 < \tau < \tau_2$

8.16   Box: $H(\tau) = E_0$ $\tau_3 < \tau < \tau_m$

The function $H(\tau)$ is zero for other values of τ.

If the relaxation modulus is expressed in terms of dynes per square centimeter, and the unit of time is hours, the constants in the above equations have the following values:

8.17 $M = 8.9 \times 10^3$ $E_0 = 7.2 \times 10^5$

$\tau_1 = 10^{-12.5}$ $\tau_2 = 10^{-5.4}$

$\tau_3 = 9.65 \times 10^{-26} \overline{M}_w{}^{3.30}$

$\tau_m = 1.06 \times 10^{-20} \overline{M}_w{}^{3.30}$

In equations 8.17 $\overline{M}_w$ is the weight-average molecular weight.

In Figure III.8 is plotted the idealized wedge-box distribution $\overline{H}(\tau)$ at 25°C for a sample of "randomly distributed" polyisobutylene, for which $\tau_3 = 10^{-4.34}$ hr and $\tau_m = 10^{1.70}$ hr. This is compared to the actual distribution $\overline{H}_{2b}(\tau)$ obtained on a nonfractionated sample of polyisobutylene distributed by the Bureau of Standards (NBS polyisobutylene). The weight-average molecular weight of this sample was reported as $\overline{M}_w = 1.6 \times 10^6$. If this value of $\overline{M}_w$ is inserted in equations 8.17, it gives values of τ_3 and τ_m very close to but not identical with those selected in Figure III.8 as a "best fit." The idealized wedge-box distribution does, in fact, give a very useful approximation to the true distribution.

Shown as a dotted "box" in Figure III.8 is the idealized box function for the rubbery-flow region of *monodisperse* polyisobutylene of the same τ_m. For "monodisperse" polymers it was found [6] that $E_0 = 1.06 \times 10^6$,

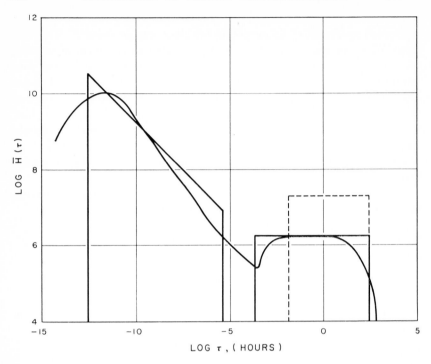

Figure III.8. The idealized wedge-box distribution $\overline{H}(\tau)$ for NBS polyisobutylene ($\overline{M}_w = 1.60 \times 10^6$) at 25°C. The dotted box represents the idealized distribution in the rubbery region for a sharp fraction of the same $\overline{M}_w$. The distribution $H_{2b}(\tau)$ obtained from $E_r(t)$ is shown for comparison. [After A. V. Tobolsky, *J. Am. Chem. Soc.*, **74**, 3786 (1952); *J. Appl. Phys.*, **27**, 673 (1956).]

that τ_m is the same as for samples of random distribution of the same $\overline{M}_w$, and that the rubbery-plateau modulus is the same as for samples of random distribution. From this last, one concludes that the area under the dotted box and the solid box are the same.

Equation 8.15 for the "wedge" gives rise to simple functions for $E_r(t)$, $E'(w)$, $E''(w)$ and $\eta^{(t)}$

$$8.18 \qquad E_r(t) = Mt^{-\frac{1}{2}}[\Gamma_{t/\tau_1}(\tfrac{1}{2}) - \Gamma_{t/\tau_2}(\tfrac{1}{2})]$$

$$8.19 \qquad E'(w) = M\left(\frac{w}{2}\right)^{\frac{1}{2}}\left[\frac{1}{2}\ln\frac{w\tau + (2w\tau)^{\frac{1}{2}} + 1}{w\tau - (2w\tau)^{\frac{1}{2}} + 1}\right.$$

$$\left. + \arctan\frac{(2w\tau)^{\frac{1}{2}}}{w\tau - 1}\right]_{\tau_1}^{\tau_2}$$

8.20
$$E''(w) = M \left(\frac{w}{2}\right)^{1/2} \left[\arctan \frac{(2w\tau)^{1/2}}{w\tau - 1}\right.$$

$$\left. - \frac{1}{2} \ln \frac{w\tau + (2w\tau)^{1/2} + 1}{w\tau - (2w\tau)^{1/2} + 1}\right]_{\tau_1}^{\tau_2}$$

8.21
$$\eta^{(t)} = 2M(\tau_2^{1/2} - \tau_1^{1/2})$$

The function $\Gamma(\frac{1}{2})$ is the extensively tabulated incomplete gamma function.[10]

The contributions of the box and wedge as given in equations 8.8 through 8.11 and 8.18 through 8.21 are additive.

In Figure III.9 is shown a plot of $\log E_r(t)$ vs. $\log t$, $\log E'(1/w)$ vs. $\log (1/w)$, $\log E''(1/w)$ vs. $\log (1/w)$ and $\log H(\tau)$ vs. $\log \tau$ for the wedge-box distribution according to equations 8.8 through 8.11 and 8.18 through 8.21. The constants used were those given in equation 8.17, with $\tau_3 = 10^{-4.34}$ hr, and $\tau_m = 10^{1.70}$ hr.

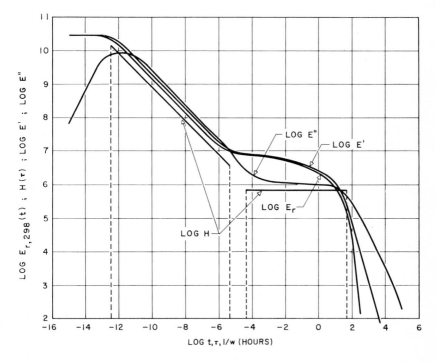

Figure III.9. $E_r(t)$, $E'(1/w)$, $E''(1/w)$ and $H(\tau)$ for the wedge-box distribution: a log-log plot. [After A. V. Tobolsky, *J. Am. Chem. Soc.*, **74**, 3786 (1952).]

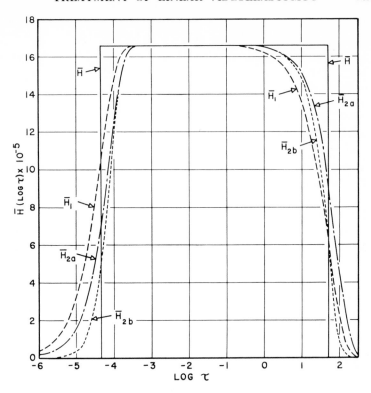

Figure III.10. Comparison of actual distribution $\bar{H}(\tau)$ with first and second approximations for the case of the box distribution. (After E. Catsiff and A. V. Tobolsky, *Tech. Rept. RLT-5* to the ONR, 1953.)

The box distribution for the rubbery-flow region of polyisobutylene has been further developed by Ninomiya and Fujita to consider the problem of other general molecular-weight distributions.[11]

A modified wedge function has also been proposed for the transition region:[12]

8.22 $$H(\tau) = \frac{(E_1 E_2)^{\frac{1}{2}}}{\Gamma(n)} \tau^{-n} \exp\left(- \frac{(E_2 E_1)^{\frac{1}{2}n}}{\tau} \right)$$

This gives rise through equation 8.4 to the following relaxation modulus:

8.23 $$E_r(t) = \frac{(E_1 E_2)^{\frac{1}{2}}}{[t + (E_2/E_1)^{\frac{1}{2}n}]^n}$$

Equations 8.22 and 8.23 will be applied to the transition region of amorphous polymers in Chapter IV.

One very interesting possibility that is afforded by the exact knowledge of $H(\tau)$ and $E_r(t)$ provided by these idealized distributions (the box, wedge and modified wedge) is that one can test the validities of the approximation methods used for obtaining $H_1(\tau)$, $H_{2a}(\tau)$ and $H_{2b}(\tau)$ from $E_r(t)$ through equations 6.8, 6.9 and 6.10. Starting with the known relaxation functions $E_r(t)$ for the box, wedge and modified wedge, the values of $\bar{H}_1(\tau)$, $\bar{H}_{2a}(\tau)$ and $\bar{H}_{2b}(\tau)$ were computed and compared with the known true values of $H(\tau)$.[13] This is shown for the box in Figure III.10, the wedge in Figure III.11, and the modified wedge in Figure III.12. The approximations are good in the center of the distributions, but fail to some extent at the cutoffs.

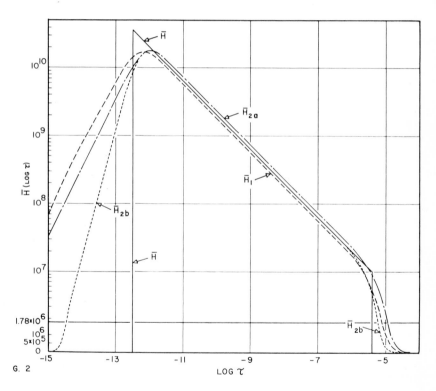

Figure III.11. Comparison of actual distribution $\bar{H}(\tau)$ with first and second approximations for the case of wedge distribution. (After E. Catsiff and A. V. Tobolsky, *Tech. Rept. RLT-5* to the ONR, 1953.)

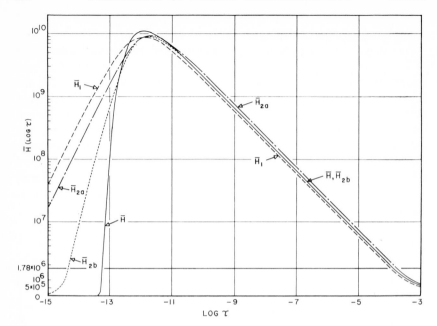

Figure III.12. Comparison of actual distribution $\bar{H}(\tau)$ with first and second approximations for the case of the modified wedge distribution. (After E. Catsiff and A. V. Tobolsky, *Tech. Rept. RLT-5* to the ONR, 1953.)

As will be shown in Chapter IV, if a distribution function is valid for an amorphous polymer at one temperature (i.e., 25°C) it will be essentially valid at other temperatures merely by shifting the entire distribution horizontally along the log time axis. This is called the time-temperature superposition principle. By use of this principle one can, by measurements at several temperatures, greatly extend the time scale of viscoelastic data.

Recently T. L. Smith has derived [14] the exact distribution of *retardation times* corresponding to the wedge relaxation distribution and the box relaxation distribution, using the formula of Gross given in equation 7.7.

References III.8

1. R. Becker and W. Doring, *Ferromagnetismus*, p. 254, Springer, Berlin, 1939.
2. W. Kuhn, O. Kunzle and A. Preissman, *Helv. Chim. Acta*, **30**, 307, 464, 839 (1947).

3. R. D. Andrews, N. Hofman-Bang and A. V. Tobolsky, *J. Polymer Sci.*, **3**, 669 (1948).
4. B. A. Dunell and A. V. Tobolsky, *J. Chem. Phys.*, **17**, 1001 (1949).
5. A. V. Tobolsky, R. D. Andrews and B. A. Dunell, *Textile Research J.*, **21**, 404 (1951).
6. R. D. Andrews and A. V. Tobolsky, *J. Polymer Sci.*, **7**, 221 (1951).
7. J. R. McLoughlin and A. V. Tobolsky, *J. Colloid Sci.*, **7**, 555 (1952).
8. *Tables of Sine, Cosine and Exponential Integrals*, 2 vols., WPA Tables, New York, 1940.
9. A. V. Tobolsky, *J. Am. Chem. Soc.*, **74**, 3786 (1952).
10. Karl Pearson, *Tables of the Incomplete Γ Function*, His Majesty's Stationery Office, London, 1922.
11. K. Ninomiya and H. Fujita, *J. Colloid Sci.*, **12**, 204 (1957); *J. Polymer Sci.*, **24**, 233 (1957).
12. A. V. Tobolsky and J. R. McLoughlin, *J. Polymer Sci.*, **8**, 543 (1952).
13. E. Catsiff and A. V. Tobolsky, *Tech. Rept. RLT-5* to the Office of Naval Research, Contract N6-onr-27021, Project N6 onr-27021, 1953.
14. T. L. Smith, *Trans. Soc. Rheol.*, **2**, 131 (1958).

9. VISCOELASTIC PROPERTIES OF A MAXWELL BODY

Inasmuch as the approximation methods discussed in the previous section are most accurate for a slowly varying distribution function $H(\tau)$, it is interesting to consider the viscoelastic properties of a Maxwell body, in which $H(\tau)$ is a sharply discontinuous function. For a Maxwell body

9.1
$$H(\tau) = \tau E = \tau_p E \qquad \text{at } \tau = \tau_p$$

$$H(\tau) = 0 \qquad \text{at } \tau \neq \tau_p$$

The various viscoelastic functions are

9.2
$$E_r(t) = E \exp\left(-t/\tau_p\right)$$

9.3
$$E_c(t) = \frac{E}{1 + t/\tau_p}$$

9.4
$$E'(y) = \frac{E}{1 + (y/\tau_p)^2}$$

9.5
$$E''(y) = \frac{E(\tau_p y)}{y^2 + \tau_p{}^2}$$

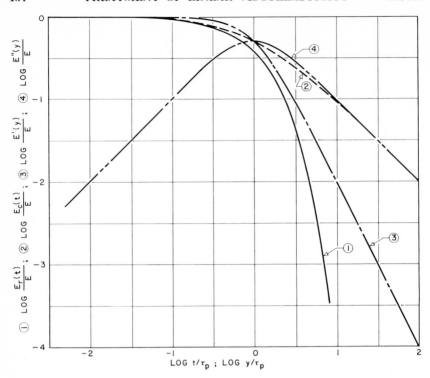

Figure III.13. $E_r(t)$, $E_c(t)$, $E'(y)$ and $E''(y)$ for a Maxwell body ($y = 1/w$).

In equations 9.4 and 9.5, $y = 1/w$. Plots of $\log E_r(t)$, $\log E_c(t)$, $\log E'(y)$ and $\log E''(y)$ vs. $\log t$ or $\log y$ are shown in Figure III.13. From equation 6.7, the first approximation to $H(\tau)$ is given by

9.6 $$H_1(\tau) = -\left[\frac{dE_r(t)}{d \ln t}\right]_{t=\tau} = \frac{\tau}{\tau_p} E \exp (-t/\tau)$$

It is interesting to compare $H_1(\tau)$ with the exact value of $H(\tau)$ given by equation 9.1. It is also worth noting that, at $\tau = \tau_p$,

9.7 $$H_1(\tau_p) = 0.368E$$

9.8 $$\overline{H}_1(\tau_p) = 2.303 H_1(\tau_p) = 0.847E$$

9.9 $$\log \overline{H}_1(\tau_p) = \log H_{2b}(\tau_p) = \log E - 0.072$$

Application of the first-approximation $\bar{H}_1(\tau)$ and the second-approximation $\bar{H}_{2b}(\tau)$ to $E_r(t)$ for the Maxwell body and a comparison with E is shown in Figure III.14.

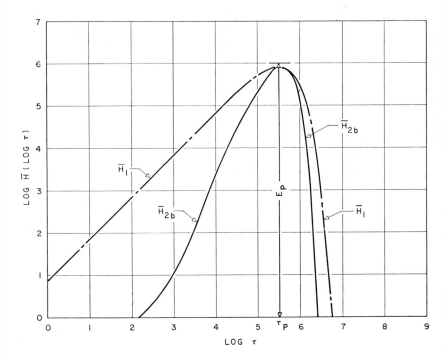

Figure III.14. $\bar{H}_1(\tau)$ and $\bar{H}_{2b}(\tau)$ for a Maxwell body as compared with E_p.

CHAPTER IV

Viscoelastic Behavior of Polymers

1. STRESS RELAXATION OF AMORPHOUS POLYMERS

Stress-relaxation measurements are generally made in a time interval somewhere between 1 and 10^6 sec. The upper limit is determined by the patience of the investigator. The lower limit is due to the fact that very rapid stretching introduces inertial and thermal effects. If the stress is measured without automatic recording, the lower limit is more likely to be 10 sec.

Stress-relaxation data at different temperatures for two different amorphous polymers, polyisobutylene and polymethylacrylate, are shown in Figures IV.1 through IV.6. These figures are reproduced from the original literature and show the general features of relaxation of stress common to all amorphous polymers. They also show how in actual fact the concept of distinct regions of viscoelastic behavior evolved from the experimental results.[1] There are five regions of viscoelastic behavior, a glassy region, a transition region, a rubbery-plateau region, a rubbery-

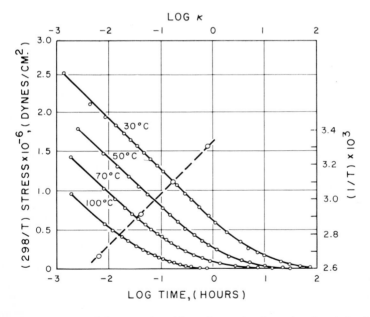

Figure IV.1. Decay of the stress in rubbery-flow region for unfractionated polyiso-butylene ($\overline{M}_v = 1{,}340{,}000$) maintained at 50 per cent elongation. Dotted line represents a plot of $\log \kappa$ vs. $1/T$, with $\kappa = 1$ at 32°C. [After R. D. Andrews, N. Hof-man-Bang and A. V. Tobolsky, *J. Polymer Sci.*, **3**, 669 (1948).]

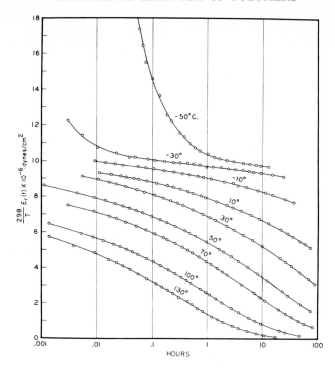

Figure IV.2. $(298/T)E_r(t)$ vs. log t for unfractionated polyisobutylene ($\bar{M}_v =$ 6,600,000) in rubbery-flow region.   The rubbery-plateau region is very clearly seen here and also the lower-modulus portion of the transition region. [After R. D. Andrews and A. V. Tobolsky, *J. Polymer Sci.*, **7**, 224 (1951).]

flow region and a liquid-flow region.   The modulus values which roughly define these intervals were discussed in Chapter II; they are apparent from Figures IV.5 and IV.6.

For amorphous polymers of sufficiently long chain length, the viscoelastic behavior in the glassy and in the transition regions are essentially independent of chain length.   For "infinite" chain length the quasistatic rubbery region would be extended to very high temperatures (until chemical changes such as bond rupture began to affect the polymer).   For cross-linked polymers one achieves a true rubbery state whose modulus depends on the degree of cross linking.   Here too the rubbery state is maintained up to very high temperatures, until chemical changes affect the rubber network.   The regions of rubbery flow and of liquid flow are entirely suppressed in the absence of chemical change.

For linear polymers of finite chain length the regions of rubbery flow and liquid flow depend very markedly on chain length (and chain-length distribution) as can be seen in Figure IV.3, and as will be further discussed in section 7.

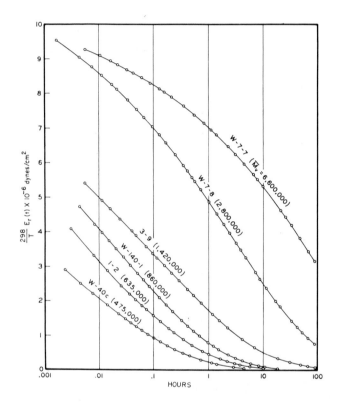

Figure IV.3. $(298/T)E_r(t)$ vs. log t for unfractionated polyisobutylenes of different average molecular weights at 30°C. [After R. D. Andrews, N. Hofman-Bang and A. V. Tobolsky, *J. Polymer Sci.*, **3**, 669 (1948); *ibid.*, **7**, 224 (1951).]

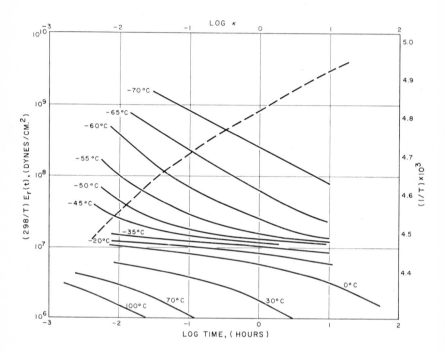

Figure IV.4. Log $(298/T)E_r(t)$ vs. log t for unfractionated polyisobutylene ($\overline{M}_v =$ 1,240,000) in the temperature range between -70 and $100°$, which covers the transition region, rubbery-plateau, rubbery-flow and liquid-flow regions. The results in transition region [$E_r(t)$ 10^7 dynes/cm²] were found to be independent of molecular weight or of the presence of a small amount of cross linking. Dotted line represents a plot of log κ vs. $1/T$, with $\kappa = 1$ at $-66°C$. [After G. M. Brown and A. V. Tobolsky, *J. Polymer Sci.*, **6**, 165 (1951). Also Ph.D. thesis by G. M. Brown, Princeton University (1948).]

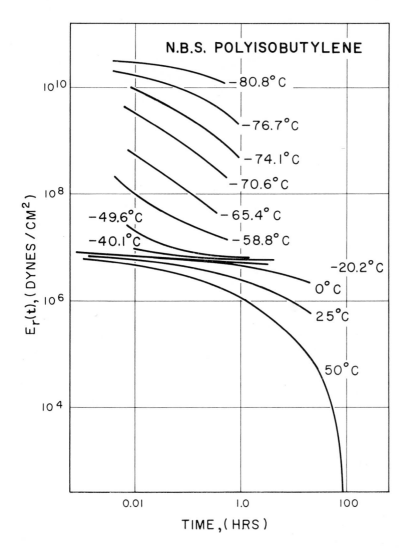

Figure IV.5. Log $E_r(t)$ vs. log t for unfractionated NBS polyisobutylene ($\overline{M}_v$ = 1,350,000) between -83 and $25\,°C$. [After E. Catsiff and A. V. Tobolsky, *J. Coiloid Sci.*, **10**, 375 (1955).]

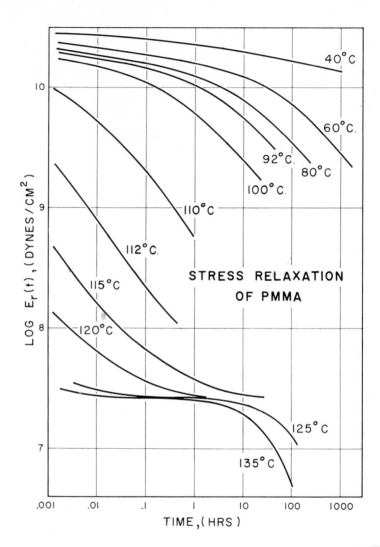

Figure IV.6. Log $E_r(t)$ vs. log t for unfractionated polymethyl methacrylate ($\overline{M}_v$ = 3,600,000) between 40 and 135°C. [After J. R. McLoughlin and A. V. Tobolsky, *J. Colloid Sci.*, **7**, 555 (1952).]

Plate IV.1. Relaxation balance.

A photograph of one of our stress-relaxation balances of recent design is shown in Plate IV.1.

Reference IV.1

1. A. V. Tobolsky and J. R. McLoughlin, *J. Polymer Sci.*, **8**, 543 (1952).

2. TIME-TEMPERATURE SUPERPOSITION PRINCIPLE AND MASTER CURVES

As has already been pointed out, the practical range of time scale for stress-relaxation measurements is 10^1 to 10^5 or 10^6 sec. At a given temperature, the complete range in viscoelastic properties is certainly not covered by this interval of four or five decades of log time. To obtain a satisfactory method of extrapolation is obviously a matter of the utmost importance.

Such a method was first suggested by H. Leaderman,[1, 2] who observed that creep recovery data obtained at different temperatures [3] could be superposed by horizontal translation along the logarithmic time axis. This is equivalent to the assertion that the effect of temperature on viscoelastic properties is to multiply (or divide) the time scale by a constant factor at each temperature. For example,

2.1 $$E_{c,T}(\kappa(T) \cdot t) = E_{c,T_0}(t)$$

2.2 $$E_{c,T_0}\left(\frac{t}{\kappa(T)}\right) = E_{c,T}(t)$$

In equations 2.1 and 2.2, $E_{c,T}(t)$ is the creep modulus at temperature T, $E_{c,T_0}(t)$ is the creep modulus at an arbitrarily chosen reference temperature T_0. The quantity κ is obtained directly from the experimental creep curves plotted against log time by measuring the amount of shift along the log time scale necessary to make the curves identical. The quantity κ, called the time factor, is a function of temperature alone, and is chosen as unity at the reference temperature T_0. κ is a function which decreases as the temperature increases. According to equation 2.2, the function $E_c(t/\kappa)$ is independent of temperature when plotted against t/κ or against log (t/κ).

If the laws of linear viscoelasticity apply, equations analogous to 2.1 and 2.2 are valid for any viscoelastic measurements. For example, some equations analogous to 2.2 are

2.3 $$E_{r,T_0}\left(\frac{t}{\kappa(T)}\right) = E_{r,T}(t)$$

2.4 $$E'_{T_0}\left(\frac{1}{w\kappa(T)}\right) = E'_T\left(\frac{1}{w}\right)$$

2.5 $$E_{T_0}\left(\frac{\tau}{\kappa(T)}\right) = E_T(\tau)$$

2.6 $$\eta_T/\eta_{T_0} = \kappa(T)$$

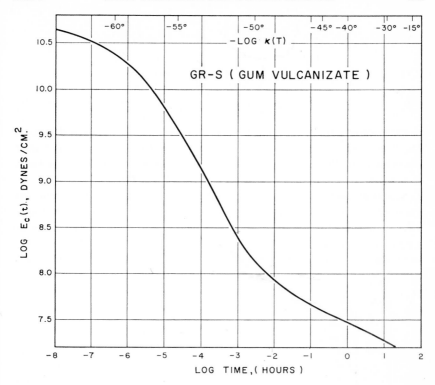

Figure IV.7. Master curve $\log E_c(t)$ vs. $\log t$ for GR-S at $-40°C$. [After A. V. Tobolsky and R. D. Andrews, *J. Chem. Phys.*, **13**, 3 (1945).]

The time-temperature superposition principle was first applied to experimental data in an explicit numerical fashion by Tobolsky and coworkers (Andrews and others).[4-8] They also explicitly introduced and tabulated the time factors $\kappa(T)$ and modified the superposition principle to account for proportionality of modulus to absolute temperature in the following manner:

2.7
$$\frac{T_0}{T} E_{r,T}(\kappa t) = E_{r,T_0}(t)$$

2.8
$$E_{r,T_0}\left(\frac{t}{\kappa(T)}\right) = \frac{T_0}{T} E_{r,T}(t)$$

2.9
$$E_{c,T_0}\left(\frac{t}{\kappa(T)}\right) = \frac{T_0}{T} E_{c,T}(t)$$

2.10
$$E'_{T_0}\left(\frac{1}{w\kappa(T)}\right) = \frac{T_0}{T}\,E'_T\left(\frac{1}{w}\right)$$

2.11
$$E_{T_0}\left(\frac{\tau}{\kappa(T)}\right) = \frac{T_0}{T}\,E_T(\tau)$$

2.12
$$T_0\eta_T/T\eta_{T_0} = \kappa(T)$$

By sliding curves for $(T_0/T)E_{r,T}(t)$ [or $\log (T_0/T)E_{r,T}(t)$] along the log time axis to superpose with $E_{r,T_0}(t)$ [or $\log E_{r,T_0}(t)$], a *master curve* covering a much wider range of log time can be constructed. The same, of course, holds for $(T_0/T)E_c(t)$, $(T_0/T)E'(1/w)$, etc.

The first essentially complete master curve constructed was for vulcanized GR-S (in 1945).[4] The original graph is reproduced in Figure IV.7, using the units dynes per square centimeter instead of pounds per square inch, and the notation $(298/T)E_c(T)$ instead of reduced creep modulus, in order to conform to the usage of this book. This graph

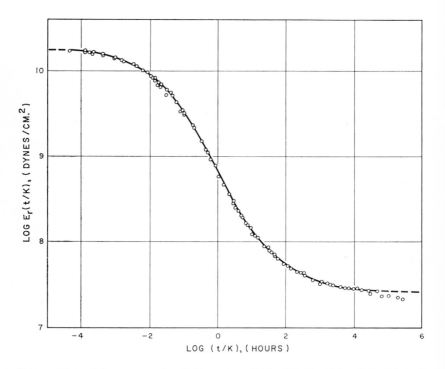

Figure IV.8. Master curve $\log E_r(t)$ vs. $\log t/K$ for GR-S. [After J. R. Bischoff, E. Catsiff and A. V. Tobolsky, *J. Am. Chem. Soc.*, **74**, 3378 (1952).]

Table IV.1

κ VALUES FOR GR-S FROM CREEP AND RELAXATION

T, °C	Relaxation [a] (1952), $\log \kappa(T)$	Relaxation [b] (1945), $\log \kappa(T)$	Creep [b] (1945), $\log \kappa(T)$
−64.0	7.7		
−60.0			6.37
−61.0	6.9		
−58.8	6.3		
−57.6	5.7		
−55.0	4.68	4.60	4.60
−52.5	3.84		
−50		2.48	2.55
−49.5	2.72		
−47.5	2.18		
−45.0			0.70
−44.0	0.80		
−40.0	0.00	0.00	0.00
−32.8	−0.6		
−30.0			−1.05
−21.0		−2.0	
−20.0			−1.37
−15.0			−1.75
−8.5		−3.15	

[a] J. Bischoff, E. Catsiff and A. V. Tobolsky, *J. Am. Chem. Soc.*, **74**, 3378 (1952).
[b] A. V. Tobolsky and R. D. Andrews, *J. Chem. Phys.*, **13**, 3 (1945).

shows $\log (298/T)E_c(T)$ and $- \log \kappa(T)$ plotted against $\log t$. In order to obtain the master curve at any temperature, it is merely necessary to slide the log time scale along the horizontal axis until the value $\log t = 0$ falls directly below the indicated temperature on the $- \log \kappa(T)$ scale. The original publication also showed that the experimental κ values for creep and for stress relaxation were approximately equal. More complete stress-relaxation data were obtained on a similar sample of vulcanized GR-S in 1952.[9] This master curve $E_r(t)$ vs. $\log t$ is reproduced in Figure IV.8. The κ values obtained from relaxation and creep data (1945) are compared to the κ values obtained from the newer relaxation data in Table IV.1. The agreement must be considered excellent in view of the history of this research.

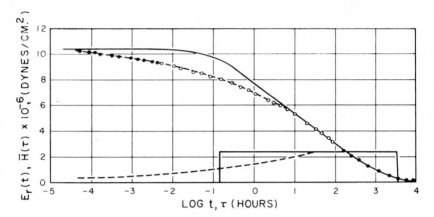

Figure IV.9. Master curve log $E_r(t)$ vs. log t for rubbery region of polyisobutylene Data obtained for sample of viscosity-average molecular weight of 6,600,000. Open circles indicate experimental values obtained at 30°C; solid circles represent extrapolated values obtained at other temperatures and reduced to 30°C by the time-temperature superposition principle. Solid curves represent an idealized fit to the box distribution. Dotted curves represent the actual master curve and the corresponding curve for $\bar{H}(\tau)$. [After R. D. Andrews and A. V. Tobolsky, *J. Polymer Sci.*, **7**, 221 (1951); *ibid.*, **3**, 669 (1948).]

The first master curves in the rubbery-flow and liquid-flow regions were obtained for linear polyisobutylene in 1948 (Figure IV.9), and it was proved that elasticity and viscosity shift with temperature in the same way.[5, 6, 10] The existence of a quasi-static rubbery modulus was also established.[5, 6, 10] The first complete master curve for a linear amorphous polymer was obtained with polymethyl methacrylate (Figure IV.10).

The *shape* of the stress-relaxation curves of amorphous polymers is independent of the extension of the sample as discussed in section 2 of Chapter III. For this reason the time-temperature superposition principle can be applied directly to stress-relaxation data obtained at different temperatures and at a fixed high extension. Many of the early stress-relaxation master curves were constructed for stress at 50% extension rather than for modulus. Those which have been reproduced in this book have been converted to relaxation modulus (using the kinetic theory equation for the stress-strain law) in order to preserve a uniform notation.

An idealized master curve (corresponding to the wedge-box distribution) for polyisobutylene of three different chain lengths and for very lightly cross-linked polyisobutylene (of high original chain length) is shown in Figure IV.11.   An accurate stress-relaxation master curve for a polyisobutylene sample distributed by the National Bureau of Standards is shown in Figure IV.12.[12]

The time-temperature superposition principle was further modified by Ferry to account for density changes in the polymer at different temperatures.[13]   According to this procedure equations 2.7 and 2.12 become

2.13 $$(d_0 T_0/dT)E_{r,T}[\kappa(T)\cdot t] = E_{r,T_0}(t)$$

2.14 $$d_0 T_0 \eta_T / dT \eta_{T_0} = \kappa(T) = a_T$$

with similar changes in equations 2.8 through 2.11.   In equations 2.13 and 2.14, d_0 is the density at T_0, and d is the density at T.   This correction is quite small for pure (undiluted) polymers, but it was also suggested as a means of correlating viscoelastic data on concentrated polymer solutions with data on undiluted polymers.[13]   In this case the density is understood to mean the weight of polymer per unit volume of solution.   The notation a_T, equivalent to $\kappa(T)$, will be discussed shortly.

Since the kinetic theory of elasticity does not apply to polymers in the glassy state, equation 2.13 was further modified to account for this

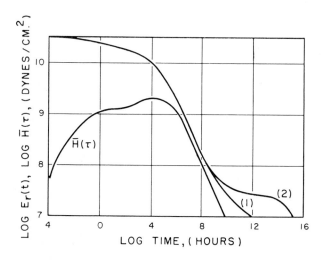

Figure IV.10.   Log $E_r(t)$ vs. log t and log $\bar{H}(\tau)$ vs. log τ for unfractionated poly-methyl methacrylate of two different average molecular weights reduced to 40°C. $\bar{H}(\tau)$ is shown for transition region only.   Sample (1) has $\bar{M}_v = 150{,}000$, sample (2) has $\bar{M}_v = 3{,}600{,}000$.   [After J. R. McLoughlin and A. V. Tobolsky, *J. Colloid Sci.*, **7**, 555 (1952).]

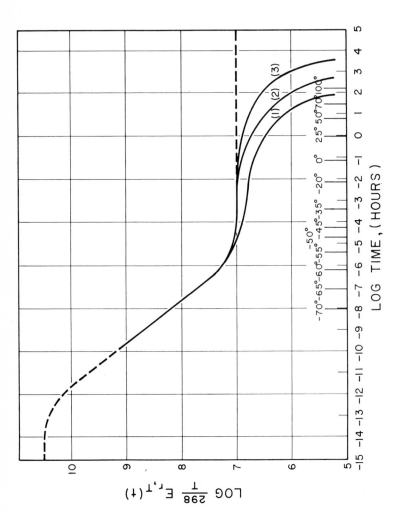

Figure IV.11. Idealized master relaxation curve log $E_r(t)$ vs. log t at 25 °C for polyisobutylene of three different average molecular weights (1) $\overline{M}_v = 1.36 \times 10^6$, (2) $\overline{M}_v = 2.80 \times 10^6$, (3) $\overline{M}_v = 6.60 \times 10^6$ and for Butyl rubber. [After A. V. Tobolsky and J. R. McLoughlin, *J. Polymer Sci.*, **8**, 543 (1952).]

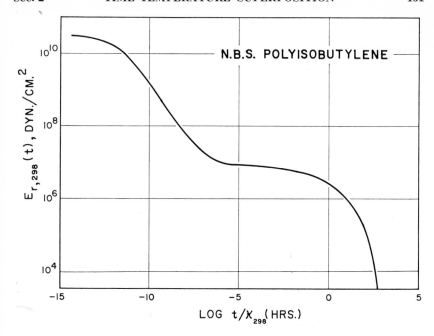

Figure IV.12. Actual master curve log $E_r(t)$ vs. log t for NBS polyisobutylene at 25°C. [After E. Catsiff and A. V. Tobolsky, *J. Polymer Sci.*, **19**, 111 (1956).]

fact. This small correction is best expressed in terms of compliance rather than in terms of modulus.[14]

$$2.15 \qquad J_{T_0}\left(\frac{t}{\kappa(T)}\right) - J_1 = \left(\frac{dT}{d_0 T_0}\right) J_T(t) - J_1$$

where J_1 represents the glassy-state compliance.

Ferry and coworkers have used experimentally measured viscosities as a means of obtaining the time factors $\kappa(T)$ through equation 2.14. This procedure can be used only for non-cross-linked polymers that have a measurable viscosity. They have also used the notation [9] a_T instead of the notation $\kappa(T)$, which was previously introduced for stress-relaxation master curves.[5]

It was proposed [8] that κ be used to denote the time factors obtained from experimental relaxation or other viscoelastic data and that a_T be reserved for the quantity obtained from flow viscosity data and defined by equation 2.14.

References IV.2

1. H. Leaderman, *Textile Research J.*, **11**, 171 (1941).
2. H. Leaderman, *Elastic and Creep of Filamentous Materials*, pp. 16, 30, 76 and 100, The Textile Foundation, Washington, D.C., 1943.
3. P. Kobeko, E. Kuvshinskij and G. Gurevitch, *Tech. Phys. USSR*, **4**, 622 (1937).
4. A. V. Tobolsky and R. D. Andrews, *J. Chem. Phys.*, **13**, 3 (1945).
5. R. D. Andrews, N. Hofman-Bang and A. V. Tobolsky, *J. Polymer Sci.*, **3**, 669 (1948); G. M. Brown, Ph.D. thesis, Princeton University, 1948; K. W. Scott, Ph.D. thesis, Princeton University, 1950.
6. R. D. Andrews and A. V. Tobolsky, *J. Polymer Sci.*, **7**, 221 (1951).
7. J. R. McLoughlin and A. V. Tobolsky, *J. Colloid Sci.*, **7**, 555 (1952).
8. A. V. Tobolsky and J. R. McLoughlin, *J. Polymer Sci.*, **8**, 543 (1952).
9. J. Bischoff, E. Catsiff and A. V. Tobolsky, *J. Am. Chem. Soc.*, **74**, 3378 (1952).
10. H. Mark and A. V. Tobolsky, *Physical Chemistry of High Polymeric Systems*, pp. 333–348, Interscience Publishers, New York, 1950.
11. R. S. Marvin, paper in *Proceeding of the Second International Congress on Rheology*, pp. 156–164, Academic Press, New York, 1954.
12. A. V. Tobolsky and E. Catsiff, *J. Polymer Sci.*, **19**, 111 (1956).
13. J. D. Ferry, *J. Am. Chem. Soc.*, **72**, 3746 (1950).
14. J. D. Ferry and E. R. Fitzgerald, *J. Colloid Sci.*, **8**, 224 (1953).

3. VERIFICATION OF TIME-TEMPERATURE SUPERPOSITION PRINCIPLE

The time-temperature principle which is so important to the experimental development of viscoelastic phenomena is still essentially an empirical principle. No completely cogent theoretical conception has yet been put forward to explain the validity of this principle. It is therefore of the utmost importance to verify this principle by experimental means to see how far it may be considered valid.

The experimental procedure first used for checking the validity of this principle [1] was to construct a master curve $\frac{1}{3}E(t)$ vs. log t at a given reference temperature (30°C) from data obtained with polyisobutylene at several temperatures in the time interval 10^{-2} to 10^1 hr. This master curve covered the region of rubbery flow and liquid flow. This was compared with dynamic data $G'(1/w)$ vs. log $(1/w)$ obtained at 30°C in the time interval $1/w$ between $10^{-7.5}$ and 10^{-5} hr. The theory of linear viscoelasticity predicts that $\frac{1}{3}E(t) \approx G'(1/w)$ for the broad distribution of relaxation times encountered in the region of rubbery flow. This was found to be the case, as shown in Figure IV.13. Actually, for a given value of $t = 1/w$, $G'(1/w)$ should be slightly *larger* than $\frac{1}{3}E(t)$, but the

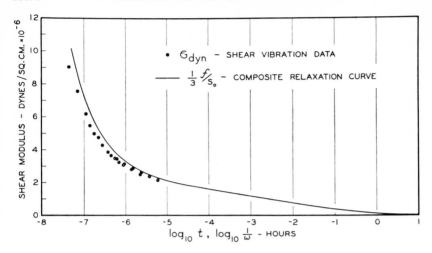

Figure IV.13. $(\frac{1}{3})E_r(t)$ vs. $G'(1/w)$ for polyisobutylene in rubbery-flow region at 30°C. [After A. V. Tobolsky, B. A. Dunell and R. D. Andrews, *Textile Research J.*, **21**, 404 (1951).]

over-all check of the validity of time-temperature superposition in the rubbery region must be considered good, considering experimental difficulties.

A standard sample of polyisobutylene was subsequently distributed by the National Bureau of Standards, which has been here denoted as polyisobutylene NBS. Viscoelastic measurements including stress relaxation, forced vibrations, free vibrations and creep contributed by a number of cooperating laboratories were correlated, and it was found that a continuous master curve could be constructed from these data.[2]

A very comprehensive check on the validity of the time-temperature superposition principle for polyisobutylene in the transition region and the rubbery-plateau region was provided by exceptionally thorough forced-vibration studies by Ferry, Grandine and Fitzgerald,[3] free-vibration studies by Philipoff[4] and stress-relaxation studies by Catsiff and Tobolsky.[5] The procedure used was to construct a master curve $E_r(t)$ from stress-relaxation data obtained at different temperatures in the time interval 10^{-2} to 10^1 hr.[5] This master curve at $-44°C$, together with actual experimental relaxation data at $-44°C$, is shown in Figure IV.14. Dynamic modulus data $3G'(1/w)$ obtained at $-44°C$ in the time interval $10^{-8.2}$ hr $< 1/w < 10^7$ hr are also shown. The fact that $3G'(1/w)$ values lie so close to $E_r(t)$ is a verification of the time-temperature superposition principle.[6]

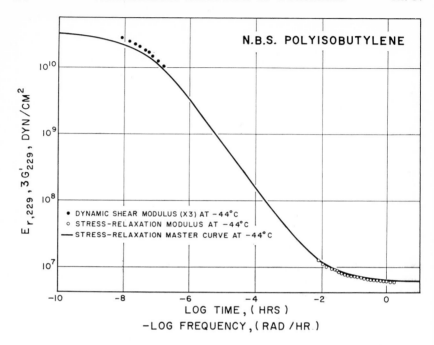

Figure IV.14. $E_r(t)$ and 3 $G'(1/w)$ for NBS polyisobutylene at $-44°C$. Solid curve represents the stress-relaxation master curve. [After A. V. Tobolsky, *J. Appl. Phys.*, **27**, 673 (1956).]

An even more detailed check was made by Catsiff and Tobolsky,[5] using the master curve $E_r(t)$ at 298°K to predict $G'(w)$ and $G''(w)$, using the second approximation methods described in Chapter III. These predictions are compared with experimental values in Figures IV.15 and IV.16 and in Table IV.2. The κ values and K values (discussed in section 4) are given in Table IV.3.

Although such comprehensive checks of the time-temperature superposition principle are not available for other polymers, there is every reason to believe that this principle will be found valid in the transition region, the rubbery-plateau region, the rubbery-flow region and the liquid-flow region for other *amorphous* polymers.

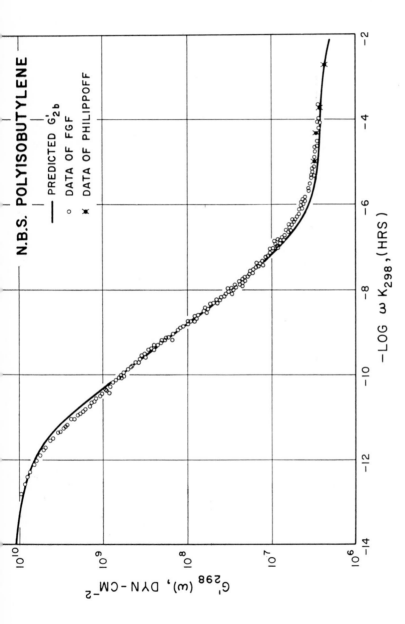

Figure IV.15. $G'(1/w)$ vs. log $(1/w\kappa_{298})$ for NBS polyisobutylene. Comparison of experimental points with solid curve predicted from the stress-relaxation master curve. [After E. Catsiff and A. V. Tobolsky, *J. Colloid Sci.*, **10**, 375 (1955).]

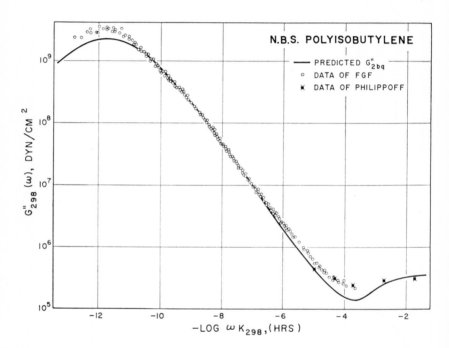

Figure IV.16. $G''(1/w)$ vs. log $(1/w\kappa_{298})$ for NBS polyisobutylene. Comparison of experimental points with solid curves predicted from the stress-relaxation master curve. [After E. Catsiff and A. V. Tobolsky, *J. Colloid Sci.*, **10**, 375 (1955).]

Table IV.2

MECHANICAL PROPERTIES (IN DYNES PER SQUARE CENTIMETER) OF NBS
POLYISOBUTYLENE FROM STRESS-RELAXATION STUDIES [a]

$\log t$ $\log \tau$ $-\log \omega$, hr	$\log$ $E_{r,\,298}(t)^{b}$	$\log \bar{H}$ $(\log \tau)$	$\log 3G'(\omega)$		$\log 3G''(\omega)$	
			Pred.	Obs.[c]	Pred.	Obs.[c]
−14.4	10.48_5					
.2	10.48	8.77				
.0	10.46_5	8.96	10.50			
−13.8	10.45_5	9.12	10.49_5			
.6	10.44_5	9.27	10.49			
.4	10.43	9.41_5	10.48			
.2	10.41	9.55	10.47		9.49	
.0	10.39	9.66_5	10.45_5		9.57_5	
12.8	10.37	9.77	10.43	10.45	9.64_5	9.83
.6	10.34	9.84_5	10.41	10.42	9.70_5	9.88_5
.4	10.30	9.91	10.38	10.38	9.75	9.93
.2	10.25_5	9.96_5	10.34_5	10.32_5	9.78	9.96_5
.0	10.20_5	10.01	10.30	10.27	9.81	9.99
−11.8	10.15	10.03_5	10.24_5	10.20	9.82	10.00
.6	10.07_5	10.05_5	10.17_5	10.12	9.82	9.99_5
.4	9.98	10.04_5	10.09	10.03	9.81	9.96_5
.2	9.88_5	9.99_5	10.00	9.91_5	9.78	9.91
.0	9.77_5	9.93_5	9.90	9.79	9.73_5	9.82
−10.8	9.65_5	9.87	9.78	9.67_5	9.67_5	9.73_5
.6	9.52_5	9.76	9.66	9.55	9.62	9.64
.4	9.39_5	9.64	9.52_5	9.43	9.53_5	9.53
.2	9.26	9.50	9.39	9.33_5	9.45	9.42_5
.0	9.12_5	9.35	9.24_5	9.22	9.35	9.32
−9.8	8.99	9.21_5	9.11_5	9.11	9.24	9.22
.6	8.86_5	9.09	8.99	8.99_5	9.12	9.10_5
.4	8.73_5	8.95	8.86	8.88	9.00	9.00
.2	8.60_5	8.83	8.72_5	8.76_5	8.88	8.88
.0	8.47	8.70	8.59_5	8.62	8.76	8.77_5
−8.8	8.33	8.57_5	8.46_5	8.48_5	8.63	8.66_5
.6	8.19_5	8.43_5	8.33	8.34	8.50	8.53
.4	8.05_5	8.27_5	8.19_5	8.21	8.37_5	8.41
.2	7.92_5	8.11_5	8.04	8.06_5	8.25	8.27_5
.0	7.80_5	7.96	7.92	7.95	8.12	8.14
−7.8	7.69_5	7.83	7.80_5	7.83	7.99	8.00
.6	7.58_5	7.71	7.69	7.72	7.85	7.86
.4	7.48_5	7.58_5	7.57	7.62	7.71_5	7.73
.2	7.38_5	7.46	7.47_5	7.52	7.58_5	7.58_5
.0	7.29_5	7.33	7.38_5	7.42	7.45	7.46_5
−6.8	7.21	7.20	7.29_5	7.34	7.31_5	7.33_5
.6	7.14	7.05_5	7.21_5	7.26	7.18	7.21
.4	7.08_5	6.88	7.13_5	7.20	7.05	7.08
.2	7.04	6.72	7.07_5	7.14_5	6.91	6.96_5
.0	7.00_5	6.60	7.03	7.09_5	6.77	6.85
−5.8	6.98	6.48	7.00	7.05	6.64	6.72
.6	6.96	6.35_5	6.97_5	7.02	6.51	6.60
.4	6.94	6.26	6.95_5	6.99	6.37	6.48

Table IV.2 (Continued)

MECHANICAL PROPERTIES (IN DYNES PER SQUARE CENTIMETER) OF NBS
POLYISOBUTYLENE FROM STRESS-RELAXATION STUDIES [a]

log t log τ $-\log \omega$, hr	log [b] $E_{r,\,298}(t)$ [b]	log $\bar{H}$ (log τ)	log $3G'(\omega)$ Pred.	 Obs.[c]	log $3G''(\omega)$ Pred.	 Obs.[c]
.2	6.92_5	6.16_5	6.94	6.97	6.25	6.36_5
.0	6.91_5	6.07	6.93	6.95_5	6.12_5	6.25
−4.8	6.90_5	5.97	6.91_5	6.94_5	6.01	6.15
.6	6.90	5.87_5	6.91	6.93_5	5.90	6.06
.4	6.89_5	5.78	6.90_5	6.92_5	5.81_5	5.98
.2	6.89	5.68	6.90	6.91_5	5.73_5	5.91
.0	6.88_5	5.58_5	6.89_5	6.91	5.66	5.86
−3.8	6.88	5.49	6.89_5	6.90_5	5.62	5.83_5
.6	6.87_5	5.41_5	6.89	6.89_5	5.63	5.83
.4	6.87	5.45_5	6.88_5	6.88_5	5.66	5.83_5
.2	6.85_5	5.75_5	6.88	6.88	5.72_5	5.85
.0	6.84	5.96	6.86_5	6.87	5.80_5	5.86_5
−2.8	6.82_5	6.07	6.85	6.86	5.86_5	5.88_5
.6	6.81	6.14	6.83_5	6.84	5.91	5.90
.4	6.79_5	6.18	6.81_5	6.82_5	5.95	5.92_5
.2	6.78	6.20	6.79_5	6.81	5.98	5.95
.0	6.75_5	6.20_5	6.77_5	6.79	6.00	5.97_5
−1.8	6.73_5	6.21	6.75_5	6.77	6.01	6.00
.6	6.71	6.21_5	6.73_5	6.75	6.02	6.02_5
.4	6.68_5	6.21_5	6.71_5	6.73	6.03	6.05
.2	6.65_5	6.21_5	6.69	6.71	6.03_5	6.07
.0	6.62_5	6.22	6.66	6.68	6.04	6.09
−0.8	6.59	6.22	6.63	6.65_5	6.04_5	6.11
.6	6.55	6.22	6.59_5	6.62	6.04_5	6.12_5
.4	6.50_5	6.22	6.56	6.58_5	6.04	6.13_5
.2	6.45_5	6.22	6.52	6.53_5	6.03_5	6.14
.0	6.39_5	6.22	6.47_5	6.48	6.03	6.14_5
0.2	6.33	6.22	6.41	6.41_5	6.02	6.14_5
.4	6.26	6.22	6.34_5		6.00_5	
.6	6.17_5	6.22	6.27		5.99	
.8	6.08	6.19	6.19		5.96	
1.0	5.97	6.14	6.09_5		5.92_5	
.2	5.85	6.08	5.98		5.87_5	
.4	5.70	6.00_5	5.85		5.81	
.6	5.54	5.89_5	5.71		5.73_5	
.8	5.34	5.74	5.54		5.64	
2.0	5.18	5.57_5	5.35		5.53_5	
.2	4.9	5.38	5.13		5.41	
.4	4.5	5.18	4.86		5.28	
.6	4.0	4.98	4.5		5.12_5	
.8	$-\infty$	$-\infty$	$-\infty$		4.96	
3.0					4.78_5	

[a] A. V. Tobolsky and E. Catsiff, *J. Polymer Sci.*, **19,** 111 (1956).
[b] E. Catsiff and A. V. Tobolsky, *J. Colloid Sci.*, **10,** 375 (1955).
[c] J. D. Ferry, L. D. Grandine, Jr. and E. R. Fitzgerald, *J. Appl. Phys.*, **24,** 911 (1953).

Table IV.3

VALUES OF LOG K_{298} AND OF LOG K FOR NBS POLYISOBUTYLENE [a]

T, °C	log K_{298}	log K	T, °C	log K_{298}	log K
−82.6	12.05	2.73	−34.7	3.69	−5.63
−81.7	11.89	2.57	−33.4	3.44	−5.88
−80.8	11.53	2.21	−29.8	3.22	−6.10
−79.8	11.95	2.63	−28.5	3.06	−6.26
−79.3	11.51	2.19	−25.0	2.84	−6.48
−77.3	10.89	1.57	−23.0	2.68	−6.64
−76.7	10.70	1.38	−20.2	2.34	−6.98
−76.5	10.47	1.15	−19.9	2.45	−6.87
−74.1	9.70	0.38	−14.8	2.08	−7.24
−71.7	9.13	−0.19	−9.9	1.78	−7.54
−70.6	8.85	−0.47	−5.0	1.51	−7.81
−69.15	8.46	−0.86	−0.1	1.22	−8.10
−66.5	7.93	−1.39	4.9	0.98	−8.34
−65.4	7.62	−1.70	9.8	0.72	−8.60
−62.0	7.06	−2.26	14.8	0.51	−8.81
−60.9	6.79	−2.53	19.9	0.27	−9.05
−58.8	6.55	−2.77	25.0	0.00	−9.32
−56.2	6.04	−3.28	30.2	−0.21	−9.53
−54.0	5.77	−3.55	34.9	−0.42	−9.74
−51.4	5.47	−3.85	40.0	−0.62	−9.94
−49.6	5.31	−4.01	50.0	−0.99	−10.31
−44.6	4.75	−4.57	59.8	−1.31	−10.63
−44.3	4.72	−4.60	80.0	−1.90	−11.22
−40.4	4.23	−5.09	99.9	−2.29	−11.61
−40.1	4.20	−5.12			

[a] A. V. Tobolsky and E. Catsiff, *J. Polymer Sci.*, **19**, 111 (1956).

References IV.3

1. A. V. Tobolsky, B. A. Dunell and R. D. Andrews, *Textile Research J.*, **31**, 404 (1951).
2. R. S. Marvin, paper in *Proceedings of the Second International Congress on Rheology*, pp. 156–164, Academic Press, New York, 1954.
3. J. D. Ferry, L. D. Grandine Jr. and E. R. Fitzgerald, *J. Appl. Phys.*, **24**, 911 (1953).
4. W. Philippoff, data quoted in reference 2 above.
5. E. Catsiff and A. V. Tobolsky, *J. Colloid Sci.*, **10**, 375 (1955).
6. A. V. Tobolsky, *J. Appl. Phys.*, **27**, 673 (1956).

4. CHARACTERISTIC PARAMETERS
FOR AMORPHOUS POLYMERS

From the master curves as exemplified in Figures IV.5 through IV.9, some parameters which characterize the viscoelastic properties of amorphous polymers can be obtained. At sufficiently short times the modulus approaches its glassy-state value, which we shall call E_1. For polymers of sufficiently high chain length we have a quasi-static rubbery modulus E_2; for cross-linked polymers we have a static rubbery modulus which depends on the concentration of cross links but which we shall also denote as E_2.

For any temperature we can define the *characteristic relaxation time* $K(T)$ as the time required to relax to a value of $\log E_r(t) = (\log E_1 + \log E_2)/2$. The function $K(T)$ is linearly proportional to $\kappa(T)$, but, whereas the absolute magnitude of $\kappa(T)$ depends on the value chosen for the reference temperature T_0, the function $K(T)$ is uniquely defined for each polymer by experimental measurements of stress relaxation, with the aid of the time-temperature superposition principle where necessary.

Another defining parameter is the negative slope of the master curve $\log E_r(t)$ vs. $\log t$ at the inflection point of the transition region. We shall call this quantity *n*. Experimental results indicate that *n* ranges from 0.5 to 1.1 for amorphous polymers.

The most important parameter is the characteristic temperature of each amorphous polymer. A number of different choices are here available. The glass transition temperature T_g is a very suitable choice. However, T_g is obtained from vT data rather than from viscoelastic data. Furthermore T_g depends to some extent on the rate of heating or cooling the specimen.

Another choice for the characteristic temperature would be T_i, the inflection temperature, at which $K(T) = 10$ sec. This has already been discussed in Chapter II. This has the advantage of being simply and uniquely defined in terms of viscoelastic measurements. However, this definition does depend on the arbitrary choice of a time value of 10 sec.

A definition that appears to give a unique and nonarbitrary value is the following: [1] A plot of $d \ln K(T)/d(1/T)$ versus temperature is constructed. In general, this plot has a clearly defined maximum, which is denoted as T_d. The quantity $d \ln K(T)/d(1/T)$ is equal to $\Delta H_{act}/R$ where ΔH_{act} is the apparent heat of activation for the characteristic relaxation time. This apparent heat of activation is not a constant quantity but goes through a maximum at T_d. At T_d the characteristic relaxation time $K(T)$ is denoted as K_d or $K(T_d)$.

Another definition of a characteristic temperature has been discussed in Chapter II, section 8. The value $T_s = 298°\text{K}$ was chosen arbitrarily for polyisobutylene. For other polymers T_s is chosen so that $K(T)/K(T_s)$ [or $a(T)/a(T_s)$] is the same function of $T - T_s$ for all amorphous polymers.

The three quantities T_g, T_i and T_d for a given polymer seem to be very close ($\pm 5°$) to each other. The quantity T_s is approximately $50°\text{C}$ larger than T_g.

In terms of the important concept of a reduced equation of state for viscoelastic behavior the quantities T_g, T_i, T_d and T_s can all be utilized.

Values for characteristic parameters of several polymers are shown in Table IV.4. The value of E_1, the glassy-state modulus, seems more or less constant for most polymers, and its magnitude has been discussed in Chapter II, section 6. The value of E_2 depends on the concentration of cross links for cross-linked polymers, and in linear polymers depends on the concentration of "entanglements," which is a simplified description of a complex phenomenon. The quantity n appears to be close to 0.5 for rather stiff polymers such as methyl methacrylate, and has its largest value, near unity, for natural rubber, which has very flexible chains. Another characteristic parameter h closely related to n is also tabulated. It will be defined in section 6.

The dependence of $K(T)$ on temperature is of the utmost importance. Inasmuch as $K(T)/K(T_g)$ and $\eta(T)/\eta(T_g)$ have the same temperature

Table IV.4

PARAMETERS CHARACTERIZING STRESS RELAXATION OF
AMORPHOUS POLYMERS [a]

Polymer	T_d, °K	log E_1	log E_2	n	h	log K_d
Polymethyl methacrylate	384	10.35	7.35	0.52_5	0.31	−1.5
Paracril 26 (buta/acrylo)	241.0	10.10	7.40	0.63	0.41_5	−1.54
GR-S (75/25 buta/sty)	220	10.24	7.44	0.71	0.45	−1.50
60/40 buta/sty	237.1	10.27	8.03	0.50_5	0.40	−1.94
50/50 buta/sty	250.8	10.212	7.558	0.545	0.364	−1.12
30/70 buta/sty	285.1	9.955	7.255	0.55	0.36	−1.13
Polyisobutylene	197.0	10.48	6.88	0.745	0.367	+1.04
Natural rubber (unvulcanized)	205.3	10.42	7.20	1.07	0.495	−1.90
Natural rubber (vulcanized)	206.3	10.39	7.26	1.10	0.555	−1.095

[a] A. V. Tobolsky and E. Catsiff, *J. Polymer Sci.*, **19**, 111 (1956).

dependence, we might expect the various forms of the Williams-Landel-Ferry equation [3] to be applicable (see Chapter II, section 8).

$$4.1 \qquad \log \frac{K(T)}{K(T_g)} = -(1/2.303) \frac{T - T_g}{f_g/a_2 + T - T_g}$$

$$4.2 \qquad \log \frac{K(T)}{K(T_g)} = -17.44 \frac{T - T_g}{51.6 + T - T_g}$$

$$4.3 \qquad \log \frac{K(T)}{K(T_s)} = -8.86 \frac{T - T_s}{101.6 + T - T_s}$$

Experimental results on stress relaxation, using T_d as a reference temperature, gave an equation very similar [2] to equation 4.2 (see Figure IV.17).

$$4.4 \qquad \log \frac{K(T)}{K(T_d)} = -16.14 \frac{T - T_d}{56 + T - T_d}$$

Within a few degrees of T_g, T_d or T_i one might expect that (by the Taylor expansion),

$$4.5 \qquad \log \frac{K(T)}{K(T_c)} = -p(T - T_c) = -(pT_c) \left(\frac{T}{T_c} - 1 \right)$$

where T_c can be taken as T_g, T_d or T_i without appreciably changing the value of p, since these three temperatures are so close to one another.

When equations 4.1, 4.2 and 4.4 are expanded in the vicinity of T_g or T_d, one obtains equations of exactly the same form as 4.5 with the following values for p:

4.6 $\qquad p = a_2/2.303f_g^2 \qquad$ from equation 4.1

4.7 $\qquad p = 0.338 \qquad$ from equation 4.2

4.8 $\qquad p = 0.288 \qquad$ from equation 4.4

In Figure IV.18 a plot of the experimental results of $n \log [K(T)/K(T_c)]$ vs. T/T_c is shown for several polymers for which stress-relaxation data were available. It is seen that, for $0.95 < T/T_c < 1.05$,

$$4.9 \qquad n \log \frac{K(T)}{K(T_c)} = -45 \left(\frac{T}{T_c} - 1 \right) = -\frac{45}{T_c} (T - T_c)$$

For the actual data plotted in Figure IV.18, T_c was taken equal to T_i (and therefore $K(T_i) = 10$ sec), although T_d or T_g could have been used with nearly identical results. An earlier relation very similar to equa-

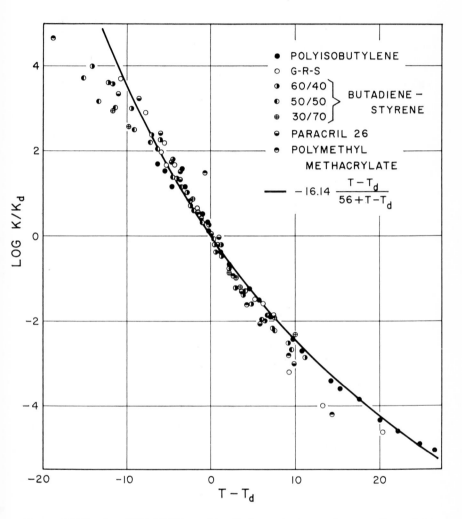

Figure IV.17. Log $K(T)/K(T_d)$ vs. $T - T_d$ for amorphous polymers. Paracril 26 is a vulcanized 74/26 butadiene-acrylonitrile copolymer. [After A. V. Tobolsky and E. Catsiff, *J. Polymer Sci.*, **19**, 111 (1956).]

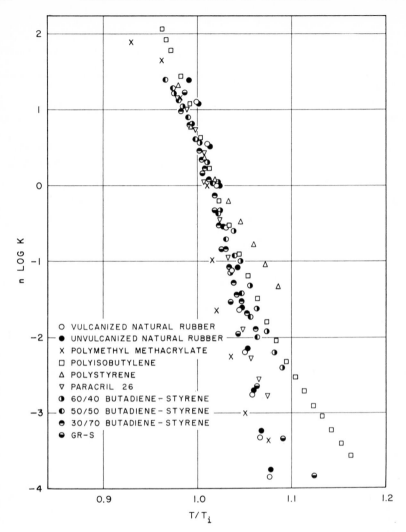

Figure IV.18. $n \log K(T)$ vs. T/T_i for several amorphous polymers.

tion 4.9 was couched in terms of the characteristic parameters h and T_d.[1] (See Figure IV.19.)

4.10 $$ h \log \frac{K(T)}{K(T_c)} = 36 \left(\frac{T_c}{T} - 1 \right) \approx -\frac{36}{T_c} (T - T_c) $$

where in this case T_c was taken as T_d.

By comparing equations 4.9 and 4.10 with equation 4.5 one gets two more empirical equations for p.

4.11 $$p = 45/nT_c$$

4.12 $$p = 36/hT_c$$

Equations 4.11 and 4.12 which are derived from the same data are not inconsistent because h and n are numerically related in such a way that $n \approx \frac{4}{3}h$, as can be seen from Table IV.4. Equations 4.11 and 4.8 are consistent if $nT_c \sim 156$.

Inasmuch as equation 4.5 is most accurate in the vicinity of T_c, whereas equation 4.2 is fairly good over the range between T_c and $T_c + 100°C$ but not necessarily very accurate near T_c, it is desirable to write equation 4.2 in the following manner:

4.13 $$\log \frac{K(T)}{K(T_c)} = - \frac{p(T - T_c)}{1 + p'(T - T_c)}$$

If equation 4.2 is accurate, $p = 0.338$ and $p' = 0.0194$. The experi-

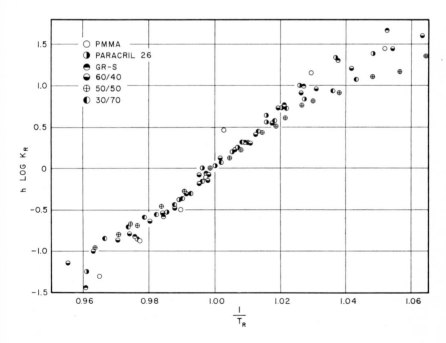

Figure IV.19. $h \log [K(T)/K_d]$ vs. T_d/T. [After E. Catsiff and A. V. Tobolsky, *J. Appl. Phys.*, **25**, 1092 (1954).]

mental results on stress relaxation suggest that it may be useful to retain equation 4.13 as a general form until the experimental facts concerning p are definitely established. The importance of establishing an exact value of p will be emphasized by the results of section 7.

It should be added that Ferry and coworkers [4] have also established in a series of studies on ethyl, butyl, hexyl and octyl methacrylate that a flexible side chain contributes an Arhennius-type term $A \exp (E/RT)$ to $K(T)$ superposed on the "backbone motion" temperature dependence given by equations 4.1 through 4.3.

References IV.4

1. J. Bischoff, E. Catsiff and A. V. Tobolsky, *J. Am. Chem. Soc.*, **74**, 3378 (1952).
2. E. Catsiff and A. V. Tobolsky, *J. Colloid Sci.*, **10**, 375 (1955).
3. M. L. Williams, R. F. Landel and J. D. Ferry, *J. Am. Chem. Soc.*, **77**, 3701 (1955).
4. J. D. Ferry, W. C. Child Jr., R. Zand, D. M. Stern, M. L. Williams and R. F. Landel, *J. Colloid Sci.*, **12**, 53 (1957).

5. MOLECULAR THEORY FOR VISCOELASTICITY

A very significant advance has been made in developing a fundamental molecular theory of viscoelasticity of polymers by the pioneering theoretical researches of P. Rouse [1] and F. Bueche.[2] This work has been extended by B. Zimm,[3] R. Cerf [4] and others.[5-8]

These authors have treated the hydrodynamic problem of polymer molecules in dilute solution acted on by externally applied oscillatory (dynamic) forces. The polymer molecule is idealized as a necklace of spherical beads connected by elastic springs. Each bead and associated spring represent a gaussian segment of the polymer. The spring has an elastic constant $\mathbf{k}T$ (in shear) arising from the kinetic theory of rubber elasticity as applied to the segment. The bead moving through the solvent obeys Stokes' law and represents the damping forces retarding the segment motion. This is the classical problem of the loaded string.[2]

Rouse's results can be couched in terms of the Maxwell-Wiechert model. Consider a unit volume (one cubic centimeter) of solution containing N molecules, each containing z equivalent freely rotating segments. Each segment is composed of sufficient links so that its end-to-end distribution of length obeys the gaussian distribution. The Maxwell-Wiechert model (in shear) for the viscoelastic contribution of the polymer molecules to the over-all properties of the system is shown in Figure IV.20. There are altogether z Maxwell elements in parallel.

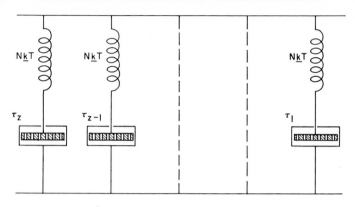

Figure IV.20. The Rouse model.

The spring constant of each Maxwell element is $N\mathbf{k}T$. The relaxation times $\tau_1, \tau_2, \ldots, \tau_p, \ldots, \tau_z$ are given by the formula

5.1
$$\tau_p = \frac{f\sigma^2 z^2}{6\pi^2 \mathbf{k} T p^2} = \frac{\tau_{\max}}{p^2}$$

$$p = 1, 2, 3, \ldots, z$$

It should be noticed that in this notation $\tau_1, \tau_2, \tau_3, \ldots, \tau_z$ are in an inverse order with τ_1 a maximum relaxation time and τ_z a minimum relaxation time.

5.2
$$\tau_1 = \tau_{\max} = \frac{f\sigma^2 z^2}{6\pi^2 \mathbf{k} T}$$

5.3
$$\tau_z = \tau_{\min} = \frac{f\sigma^2}{6\pi^2 \mathbf{k} T} = \frac{\tau_{\max}}{z^2}$$

The quantity f appearing in equations 5.1 through 5.3 is a friction constant. When multiplied by the relative viscosity between solvent and polymer segment it gives the force acting on a particular segment. For a spherical ball of radius r_0 the friction constant is given by Stokes' law.

5.4
$$f = 6\pi r_0 \eta_s$$

σ^2 is the mean-square length of the undeformed freely rotating segments.

The total flow viscosity η of the system is the sum of the solvent viscosity η_s and the contribution of each of the dashpots in Figure IV.17.

5.5
$$\eta = \eta_s + \sum_{p=1}^{z} NkT\tau_p$$

5.6
$$\eta = \eta_s + \frac{Nf\sigma^2z^2}{6\pi^2} \sum_{p=1}^{z} \frac{1}{p^2}$$

Since z is large,

5.7
$$\sum_{p=1}^{z} \frac{1}{p^2} = \frac{\pi^2}{6}$$

Hence

5.8
$$\eta - \eta_s = \frac{fN\sigma^2z^2}{36}$$

Equation 5.8 for the additional viscosity imparted by the polymer molecules to the solvent is identical with the formula developed for this quantity by the "free-draining" model of Huggins,[9] Debye [10] and others. It predicts a viscosity due to the N polymer molecules per cubic centimeter as proportional to the square of the chain length. The intrinsic viscosity of a dilute solution of the polymer comes out proportional to the chain length, in agreement with the free-draining model. It might be stated at this point that the modification introduced by Zimm [3] into the Rouse theory is essentially to treat the molecules as "non-free-draining"; i.e., the lines of flow of the solvent are presumed to be deeply perturbed in the interior of the polymer coil.

From the Rouse formulation shown in Figure IV.17 and equation 5.1 the other viscoelastic properties contributed by the macromolecules can be obtained by the methods of Chapter III, section 5. For example,

5.9
$$G'(w) = NkT \sum_{p=1}^{z} \frac{w^2\tau_p^2}{1 + w^2\tau_p^2}$$

5.10
$$G''(w) = NkT \sum_{p=1}^{z} \frac{w\tau_p}{1 + w^2\tau_p^2}$$

If we assume that the Poisson ratio is $1/2$, then

5.11
$$E_r(t) = 3NkT \sum_{p=1}^{z} \exp\left(-\frac{t}{\tau_{max}} p^2\right)$$

At $t = 0$, the maximum modulus $E_1^{(R)}$ is

5.12
$$E_1^{(R)} = 3zNkT$$

In equation 5.12, zN is clearly the number of freely rotating segments per cubic centimeter.

For values of t larger than $\tau_{\min}$ but smaller than $\tau_{\max}$, the sum in equation 5.11 can be replaced by an integral

5.13
$$\sum_{p=1}^{z} \exp\left(-\frac{t}{\tau_{\max}} p^2\right) \approx \int_0^\infty \exp\left(-\frac{t}{\tau_{\max}} p^2\right) dp$$

$$= \frac{\pi^{1/2} \tau_{\max}^{1/2}}{2t^{1/2}} = \frac{z\pi^{1/2} \tau_{\min}^{1/2}}{2t^{1/2}}$$

$$\tau_{\min} \ll t \ll \tau_{\max}$$

Substituting equation 5.13 into equation 5.11 and also inserting the definition of $\tau_{\min}$ from equation 5.3, one obtains

5.14
$$E_r(t) \approx 3zN\mathbf{k}T \frac{[(\pi/4)\tau_{\min}]^{1/2}}{t^{1/2}}$$

$$= E_1^{(R)} [K^{(R)}(T)]^{1/2} / t^{1/2}$$

where

5.15
$$K^{(R)}(T) = \left(\frac{\pi}{4}\right)\tau_{\min} = \frac{f\sigma^2}{24\pi \mathbf{k}T}$$

The quantity $K^{(R)}(T)$ may be regarded as a characteristic relaxation time obtained from the Rouse theory. It depends on temperature because, aside from the factor $1/T$ in equation 5.15, the friction constant also depends on temperature. This is best seen in equation 5.4, where f is shown proportional to η_s, which in turn is clearly temperature-dependent.

The Rouse theory for the viscoelasticity of dilute polymer solutions can also be applied to undiluted amorphous polymers. The polymer segments may be considered as immersed in a liquid composed of the other polymer segments. Except for changing the total concentration of segments zN, the only important way that the solvent viscosity enters the mathematical formulation is through an equation such as equation 5.4 for the friction factor. In the absence of solvent, the friction factor f, or even more conveniently $\tau_{\min}$ or $K^{(R)}(T)$, may be taken as a fundamental property of the system to be determined by experiment.

It is seen that the theory predicts the slope of $-\frac{1}{2}$ when $\log E_r(t)$ is plotted versus $\log t$ (i.e., the characteristic parameter n is equal to $\frac{1}{2}$). This is the same result as was previously empirically proposed in the "wedge" spectrum of relaxation times for the transition region (section 7 of Chapter III). It has been very tempting to regard the Rouse-

Bueche theory as applicable to the low-modulus portion of the transition region. Here the assumptions of the molecular model are probably applicable. However, neither the upper (high-modulus) portion of the transition region, nor the rubbery-plateau region nor the rubbery-flow and liquid-flow regions for linear polymers of high molecular weight are satisfactorily accounted for by the unmodified Rouse theory.

A first modification is for the case of cross-linked three-dimensional networks.[2, 5, 6] Here one considers that N network chains per cubic centimeter play exactly the same role as N molecules per cubic centimeter. The results embodied in Figure IV.17 and equation 5.1 are the same, except that we replace the maximum relaxation time by an infinite relaxation time. It is, of course, an approximation to consider that only the maximum relaxation time is changed, and that the others are unaffected. However, it is experimentally verified that the smaller relaxation times corresponding to the transition region are unaffected by the presence of cross links as was shown in Figure IV.9 by comparing polyisobutylene with Butyl rubber.[11]

In Chapter III, section 8, it was shown that in linear amorphous polymers of high molecular weight the longer relaxation times are all dependent on molecular weight to the 3.3 ($\approx$ 3.4) power; this was the portion of the relaxation spectrum approximately described as a "box." The rubbery plateau was described in terms of a molecular weight between entanglements.[12]

In order to modify the Rouse theory so as to make it apply to the rubbery-plateau, rubbery-flow and liquid-flow regions for high-molecular-weight linear polymers, Bueche has suggested [13] that the friction factor in equation 5.1 should be made to vary with molecular weight to the 3.4 power for values of p larger than p_{ent}, where p_{ent} is the number of segments corresponding to the rubbery-plateau modulus E_2. The author regards this treatment [13, 14] as being so far no more satisfactory than the wedge-box treatment of Chapter III, section 8. Both treatments are essentially mathematical statements of the experimental behavior, but are not derived in a truly a priori fashion. A much more cogent theory of the effect of entanglement on diffusion is needed to explain the rubbery-plateau, rubbery-flow and liquid-flow regions.

(It is possible to regard the relaxation spectrum in the rubbery-plateau and rubbery-flow regions as due to the breaking and remaking of unusually strong secondary valences and/or entanglements. This approach was used by Green and Tobolsky [15] as a mathematical model for viscoelastic behavior, and is very successful in explaining the viscoelasticity of chemically interchanging networks where a *single* relaxation time is involved. This will be discussed in sections 12 through 14. However, no cogent a priori derivation of a *distribution* of relaxation times corresponding to the slippage and re-forming of nonspecific entanglements has yet been achieved.)

The Rouse-Bueche theory also fails in the high-modulus portion of the transition region. If the experimental value for E_1 (the glassy modulus) is taken as 3×10^{10} dynes/cm^2 and is equated to $E_1^{(R)}$ in equation 5.12, the total number of freely rotating segments zN per cubic centimeter of polymer is calculated as 2.4×10^{23}. This is an impossibly high figure amounting to a molecular weight of the freely rotating segment of 2.5 for a polymer of density unity. Birefringence measurements to be discussed in section 15 of this chapter indicate a change in the basic molecular origin of stress as T_g is approached, no doubt a change from entropy elasticity to internal energy elasticity. No molecular theory which is based on configurational entropy alone will adequately describe the entire spectrum of viscoelastic behavior in the near-glassy region.

References IV.5

1. P. E. Rouse, *J. Chem. Phys.*, **21**, 1272 (1953).
2. F. Bueche, *J. Chem. Phys.*, **22**, 603 (1954).
3. B. H. Zimm, *J. Chem. Phys.*, **24**, 269 (1956).
4. R. Cerf, *J. Polymer Sci.*, **23**, 125 (1957).
5. O. Nakada, *J. Phys. Soc. Japan*, **10**, 804 (1955).
6. A. Miyake, *J. Polymer Sci.*, **22**, 560 (1956).
7. Y. H. Pao, *J. Chem. Phys.*, **25**, 1294 (1956).
8. M. Copic, *J. chim. phys.*, **53**, 440 (1956).
9. M. L. Huggins, *J. Phys. Chem.*, **42**, 911 (1938); **43**, 439 (1939).
10. P. Debye, *J. Chem. Phys.*, **14**, 636 (1946).
11. G. M. Brown and A. V. Tobolsky, *J. Polymer Sci.*, **6**, 165 (1951).
12. H. Mark and A. V. Tobolsky, *Physical Chemistry of High Polymeric Systems*, p. 344, Interscience Publishers, New York, 1950.
13. F. Bueche, *J. Appl. Phys.*, **26**, 738 (1955); *J. Chem. Phys.*, **25**, 599 (1956).
14. J. D. Ferry, R. F. Landel and M. L. Williams, *J. Appl. Phys.*, **26**, 359 (1955).
15. M. S. Green and A. V. Tobolsky, *J. Chem. Phys.*, **14**, 80 (1946); M. Yamamoto, *J. Phys. Soc. Japan*, **11**, 413 (1956).

6. STRESS RELAXATION IN THE GLASSY STATE

Stress-relaxation studies of amorphous polymers below T_g give some insight into the nature of the glassy state. It was found, for example, that the stress-relaxation curves below T_g depend very much on the manner of annealing the polymer sample. If polymethyl methacrylate

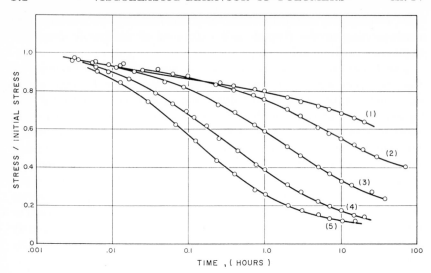

Figure IV.21. Effect of cooling rate on stress relaxation of polymethyl methacrylate at 80°C. Sample cooled from 130°C as follows: (1) 5°C per hr.; (2) 30°C per hr.; (3) convection in 25°C air; (4) plunged in 25°C oil; (5) plunged in Dry Ice–naphtha bath. [After J. R. McLoughlin and A. V. Tobolsky, *J. Polymer Sci.*, **7**, 658 (1951).]

or polystyrene maintained at a temperature above T_g is rapidly quenched to room temperature, its density will be lower than if it is very slowly cooled to room temperature. The rapidly quenched structure apparently freezes in some empty space in the form of "holes" of atomic dimensions. Stress relaxation is very much more rapid in these quick-frozen samples than in slowly annealed samples as shown in Figure IV.21.

If stress-relaxation studies in the glassy state are carried out at any but the smallest extensions, relaxation will occur by means of internal crazing, i.e., formation of small but macroscopic ruptures.

At temperatures below T_g there is the possibility of libration of small atomic groups, particularly side groups such as the methyl group in polypropylene. These motions in the glassy state have not yet been definitively observed by the stress-relaxation technique. However such short-range motions are reportedly observed by free-vibration studies.[2–6] These are generally made at an almost constant frequency over a wide range of temperature. Both torsional modulus and amplitude decrement (damping) are measured, the latter being the more sensitive measurement. There is always a peak in the decrement-temperature curve, which occurs in the neighborhood of the glass transition temperature. However, other smaller damping peaks have been reported at temperatures far below the glass transition temperature. These are believed to be due to vibrations and torsional motions of relatively small groups of atoms.

A new tool for investigating the motions of small atomic groupings in polymers in the solid state (including glassy state, crystalline state and rubbery state) is nuclear magnetic resonance.[7-19] A detailed discussion of this technique (and other techniques involving electromagnetic theory) is beyond the scope of this book. However, the measurement that is used is the proton resonance line width as a function of temperature. (Sometimes the resonance line width of other atoms such as fluorine is measured as a function of temperature.) A pronounced narrowing of the resonance line width indicates the onset of motion, generally presumed to consist of chain torsion and rotation. The frequencies of molecular motion adequate to cause narrowing of the resonance curve are of the order of 10^4 sec^{-1}. The temperature region at which narrowing occurs corresponds to the onset of molecular motions of this approximate frequency.

Nuclear magnetic resonance has also been used to calculate the degree of crystallinity of crystalline polymers. This determination is based on the assumption that there exists a temperature at which the average correlation time for molecular motion in the crystalline regions is much greater than 10^{-4} sec, whereas the corresponding correlation time for the amorphous regions is much less than 10^{-4} sec. If these conditions are met, the nuclear magnetic resonance absorption (plotted as absorption versus magnetic field strength) appears as a superposition of a narrow resonance and a broad resonance. The degree of crystallinity can be estimated by measuring the areas under each curve.

Dielectric constant and dielectric loss as a function of frequency also are useful in studying molecular motions. Dispersion regions occur at electrical frequencies which correspond to the frequencies of molecular motion. However, only those motions which involve a change of dipole moment are reflected in the electrical measurements. Interesting correlations have been made between dielectric measurements and viscoelastic measurements on the same polymers. In particular, it has been shown that the time-temperature superposition factors $[\kappa(T)$ or $a_T]$ are the same for both types of measurement.[20]

References IV.6

1. J. R. McLoughlin and A. V. Tobolsky, *J. Polymer Sci.*, **7**, 658 (1951).
2. K. Wolf and K. Schmieder, *Ricerca sci. Suppl.*, **25**, 732 (1955).

3. J. Hiejboer, *Kolloid-Z.*, **148**, 36 (1956); *Chem. Weekblad*, **52**, 481 (1956).
4. J. A. Sauer and D. E. Kline, *J. Polymer Sci.*, **18**, 491 (1955).
5. D. E. Kline, J. A. Sauer and A. E. Woodward, *J. Polymer Sci.*, **22**, 455 (1956).
6. E. Butta, *J. Polymer Sci.*, **25**, 239 (1957); N. G. McCrum, *J. Polymer Sci.*, **34**, 355 (1959).
7. E. R. Andrew, *Nuclear Magnetic Resonance*, Cambridge University Press, Cambridge, England, 1955.
8. R. Newman, *J. Chem. Phys.*, **18**, 1303 (1950).
9. L. V. Holroyd, B. A. Mrowca and E. Guth, *Phys. Rev.*, **79**, 1026 (1950).
10. L. V. Holroyd, R. S. Codrington, B. A. Mrowca and E. Guth, *J. Appl. Phys.*, **22**, 696 (1951).
11. H. S. Gutowsky and L. H. Meyer, *J. Chem. Phys.*, **21**, 2122 (1953).
12. V. R. Honnold, F. McCaffrey and B. A. Mrowca, *J. Appl. Phys.*, **25**, 1219 (1954).
13. W. P. Slichter, *J. Appl. Phys.*, **25**, 1219 (1954).
14. J. A. S. Smith, *Disc. Faraday Soc.*, **19**, 207 (1955).
15. I. J. Lowe, L. O. Brown and R. E. Norberg, *Bull. Am. Phys. Soc.*, **30**, 16 (1955).
16. J. G. Powles, *Proc. Phys. Soc. London*, **69**, 281 (1956).
17. W. P. Slichter, *J. Polymer Sci.*, **24**, 173 (1957); *ibid.*, **26**, 171 (1957).
18. C. W. Wilson and G. E. Pake, *J. Polymer Sci.*, **10**, 503 (1953).
19. W. P. Slichter, *J. Polymer Sci.*, **25**, 230 (1957).
20. J. D. Ferry and S. Strella, *J. Colloid Sci.*, **13**, 459 (1958).

7. THE TRANSITION REGION AND MODULUS-TEMPERATURE CURVES

A simple empirical function that approximately fits the observed relaxation modulus in the transition region is the modified wedge.[1]

$$7.1 \qquad E_{r,T}(t) - E_2 = \frac{(E_1 E_2)^{\frac{1}{2}}}{[t/K + (E_2/E_1)^{1/2n}]^n}$$

All the parameters appearing in equation 7.1, namely, E_1, E_2, $K(T)$ and n are the characteristic parameters already discussed in section 4.

The distribution of relaxation times that corresponds to $E_{r,T}(t) - E_2$ in equation 7.1 is

$$7.2 \qquad H\left(\frac{\tau}{K}\right) = \frac{(E_1/E_2)^{\frac{1}{2}}}{\Gamma(n)} \left(\frac{\tau}{K}\right)^{-n} \exp\left(-\frac{(E_2/E_1)^{1/2n}}{\tau/K}\right)$$

By taking the logarithm of both sides of equation 7.1 one obtains

$$7.3 \quad \log [E_{r,T}(t) - E_2] = \tfrac{1}{2}(\log E_1 + \log E_2) - n \log \left[\frac{t}{K} + \left(\frac{E_2}{E_1}\right)^{1/2n}\right]$$

In the transition region itself $E_2 < E_{r,T}(t) < E_1$, so that equation 7.3 has the following approximate form:

7.4 $\log E_{r,T}(t) = \frac{1}{2}(\log E_1 + \log E_2) - n \log t$

$$+ n \log K(T) \qquad E_2 < E_{r,T}(t) < E_1$$

Equation 7.4 is of most interest in the neighborhood of T_c (where T_c is T_g, T_i or T_d). In this connection it is interesting to recall equation 4.5 in the following form:

7.5 $$\log K(T) = \log K(T_c) - p(T - T_c)$$

If 7.5 is substituted in equation 7.4, there results

7.6 $\log E_{r,T}(t) = \frac{1}{2}(\log E_1 + \log E_2) - n \log t$

$$+ n \log K(T_c) - np(T - T_c)$$

We can use equation 7.6 to interpret modulus-temperature curves in the neighborhood of T_c. It is particularly convenient to choose T_c as equal to T_i where T_i is the temperature at which $K(T_i)$ is 10 sec.

If in equation 7.6 we hold t constant at 10 sec, we obtain a predicted modulus-temperature curve.

7.7 $\log E_{r,T}(10 \text{ sec}) = \frac{1}{2}(\log E_1 + \log E_2) - np(T - T_i)$

Equation 7.7 predicts a log modulus-temperature curve that is linear in the neighborhood of T_i. Empirically this is found to be the case for amorphous polymers, and we may consider the negative slope s of the $\log E_{r,T}(10)$ vs. T plot in the neighborhood of T_i as another characteristic parameter.

According to equation 7.7,

7.8 $$s = np$$

In section 4 numerous empirical equations for p were given (4.6, 4.7, 4.8, 4.11 and 4.12).

If equation 4.11 is valid, and this was the equation we found from our own relaxation studies, then

7.9 $$s = \frac{45}{T_i} \approx \frac{45}{T_g}$$

For the time being it is better to consider equation 7.8 as more valid than equation 7.9, because not enough information is at hand concerning the exact value of p. In fact it may be desirable to evaluate p from experimental values of s and n, using equation 7.8.

It is interesting to note that the tensile flow viscosity arising from distribution 7.2 is

7.10 $\eta^{(t)} = K(T)E_1[\Gamma(n - 1)/\Gamma(n)](E_1E_2)^{1/2n}$

The viscosity arising from the relaxation times of the modified wedge alone is enormous. In fact $\eta^{(t)}(T_i) \gg 10^{13}$ poises, and this of course neglects completely the much more important contribution of the "box" relaxation times. This is worth mentioning since T_g (which is close to T_i in value) is frequently defined as the temperature at which the viscosity is 10^{13} poises.

Reference IV.7

1. A. V. Tobolsky and J. R. McLoughlin, *J. Polymer Sci.*, **8**, 543 (1952).

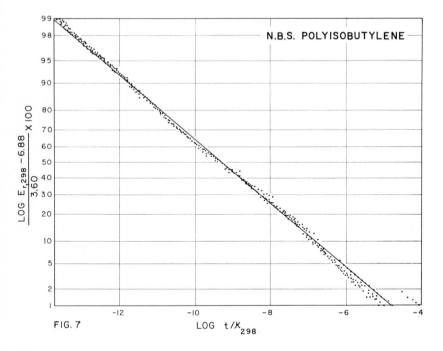

Figure IV.22. Probability paper plot of $E_r(t)$ vs. log t for NBS polyisobutylene in the transition region. [After E. Catsiff and A. V. Tobolsky, *J. Appl. Phys.*, **25**, 1092 (1954).]

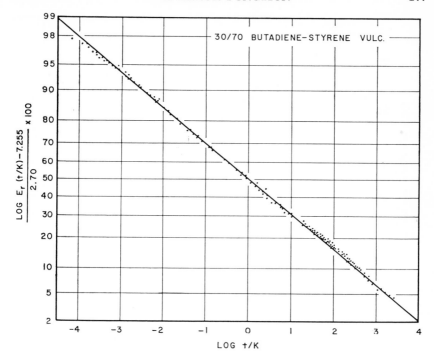

Figure IV.23. Probability paper plot of $E_r(t/K)$ vs. $\log t/K$ for a 30/70 butadiene-styrene vulcanizate. [After E. Catsiff and A. V. Tobolsky, *J. Appl. Phys.*, **25**, 1092 (1954).]

8. THE TRANSITION REGION AND THE ERROR FUNCTION

Another empirical function which gives a very good fit to viscoelastic data in the transition region is the following: [1]

8.1 $\quad \log E_{r,T}(t) = \frac{1}{2}(\log E_1 + \log E_2)$

$$- \frac{1}{2}(\log E_1 - \log E_2) \, \mathrm{erf} \, (h \log t/K)$$

In equation 6.5 the notation erf corresponds to the tabulated Gauss error function. The quantity h appearing in equation 8.1 has already been discussed as one possible characteristic parameter for $E_r(t)$. When the experimental data of $E_r(t)$ vs. t is properly plotted on probability paper (e.g., Codex 32,451), a straight line should be obtained if equation 8.1 is valid (see Figures IV.22 and IV.23). From the slope of this straight line h is readily determined. As mentioned before, $h \approx \frac{3}{4}n$.

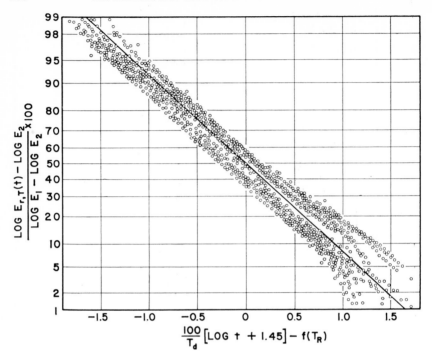

Figure IV.24. Reduced equation for viscoelastic behavior of butadiene-styrene copolymers in the transition region. Combined data for the following copolymers: 75/25, 60/40, 50/50, 30/70. Also included are data for a butadiene-acrylonitrile 74/26 copolymer. All copolymers slightly cross-linked. [After A. V. Tobolsky and E. Catsiff, *J. Am. Chem. Soc.*, **76**, 4204 (1954).]

In section 4, equation 4.10, it was stated that, for values of T close to T_d,

8.2
$$h \log \frac{K(T)}{K(T_d)} = 36 \left(\frac{T_d}{T} - 1 \right)$$

For the butadiene-styrene copolymer series it was further found that

8.3
$$h T_d \approx 100$$

$$\log K(T_d) = -1.45 \quad \text{in hours}$$

If equations 8.1, 8.2 and 8.3 are combined, a universal equation for $E_r(t)$ as a function of T/T_d (or $T - T_d$) and T_d is obtained which is valid for all radical-produced amorphous butadiene-styrene copolymers

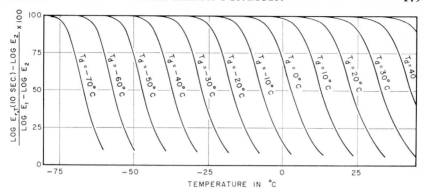

Figure IV.25. Ten-second modulus versus temperature according to reduced equation for viscoelastic behavior of butadiene-styrene copolymers. [After A. V. Tobolsky and E. Catsiff, *J. Am. Chem. Soc.*, **76,** 4204 (1954).]

in the transition region:

$$8.4 \quad \frac{\log E_{r,T}(t) - \frac{1}{2}\log E_1 E_2}{\frac{1}{2}\log (E_1/E_2)}$$

$$= -\operatorname{erf}\left[\frac{100}{T_d}(\log t + 1.45) + 36\left(\frac{T}{T_d} - 1\right)\right]$$

Equation 8.4 can be plotted on probability paper as shown in Figure IV.24. All the stress-relaxation data on four different butadiene-styrene

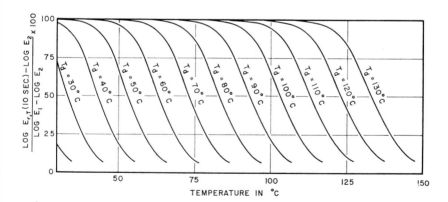

Figure IV.26. Ten-second modulus versus temperature according to reduced equation for viscoelastic behavior of butadiene-styrene copolymers. [After A. V. Tobolsky and E. Catsiff, *J. Am. Chem. Soc.*, **76,** 4204 (1954).]

compositions are shown plotted on this graph, and they do indeed show that 8.4 is a satisfactory representation of very diverse data.

By placing $t = 10$ sec in equation 8.4, one can obtain modulus-temperature curves which are a function of T and T_d. Such curves for a range of values of T_d are shown in Figures IV.25 and IV.26.

References IV.8

1. J. Bischoff, E. Catsiff and A. V. Tobolsky, *J. Am. Chem. Soc.*, **74**, 3378 (1952).
2. A. V. Tobolsky and E. Catsiff, *J. Am. Chem. Soc.*, **76**, 4204 (1954).

9. THE RUBBERY-FLOW AND LIQUID-FLOW REGION: DISCRETE RELAXATION TIMES

The distribution of relaxation times $H(\tau)$ in the rubbery-flow region has already been approximately described as a "box" in Chapter III. For times of measurement exceeding the maximum relaxation time, the behavior of amorphous polymers may be properly described as liquid flow.

It was also shown that the width of the "box" depends on the narrowness of the distribution of molecular weights.

In order to obtain a more detailed knowledge concerning the behavior of the rubbery-flow and liquid-flow regions, two samples of atactic polystyrene designated A and B were subjected to extensive study.[1] Sample A was made in a fashion designed to produce "monodisperse" polymer. The weight-average molecular weight was $\overline{M}_w = 164,000$. The quantity $\overline{M}_w/\overline{M}_n$ was estimated as 1.17. Sample B was prepared in a fashion such that the distribution of sizes was given by $X(\mathfrak{N}) = \mathfrak{N}p^{\mathfrak{N}-1}(1 - p)^2$, where $X(\mathfrak{N})$ is the mole fraction of polymer of $\mathfrak{N}$ links, and p is a parametric constant. For this distribution $\overline{M}_w/\overline{M}_n$ is 1.5. The value of $\overline{M}_w$ for sample B was 171,000. One might regard sample A as reasonably monodisperse, whereas sample B is polydisperse but with a fairly narrow distribution of molecular sizes.

Stress-relaxation data for samples A and B are shown in Figures IV.27 and IV.28. Master stress-relaxation curves in the rubbery region are shown for polystyrene samples A and B in Figures IV.29 and IV.30.

Hitherto all experimental analyses of viscoelastic data have been made in terms of an assumed continuous distribution of relaxation times $H(\tau)$. First- and second-approximation methods for obtaining $H(\tau)$ were discussed in Chapter III. If the second-approximation method

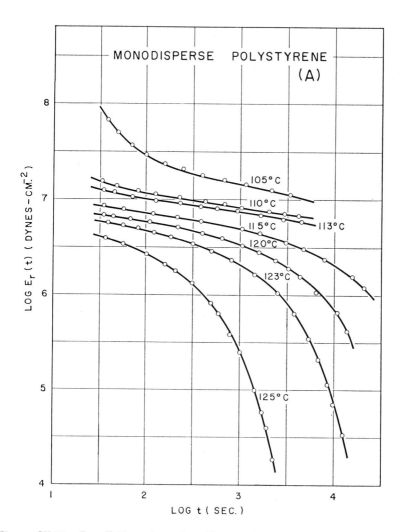

Figure IV.27. Log $E_r(t)$ vs. log t in rubbery region for polystyrene sample A.

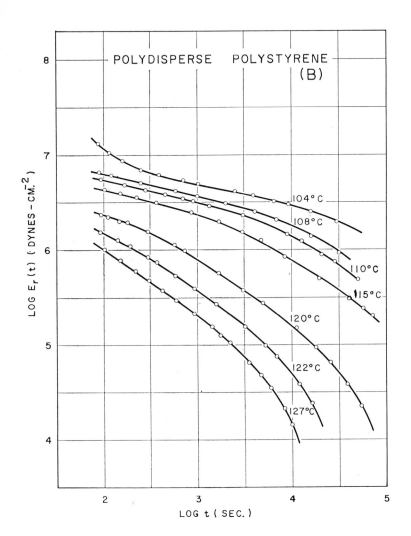

Figure IV.28. Log $E_r(t)$ vs. log t in rubbery region for polystyrene sample B.

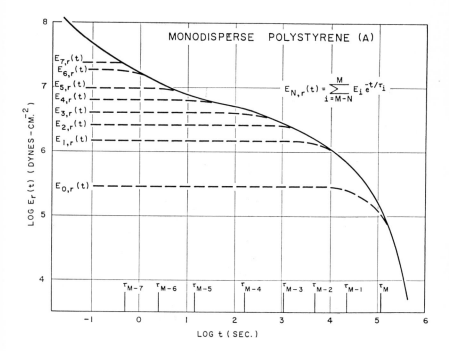

Figure IV.29. Master relaxation curve $E_r(t)$ in rubbery region for polystyrene sample A reduced to 115°C. Also shown are the contributions from the individual relaxation times obtained from procedure X whose sum is identical with the experimental master curve shown as the solid black line. [After A. V. Tobolsky and K. Murakami, *J. Polymer Sci.*, **40**, 443 (1959).]

$\overline{H}_{2b}(\tau)$ [where $\overline{H}_{2b} = 2.303H_{2b}(\tau)$] is applied to samples A and B, one obtains the results shown in Figure IV.31 and IV.32.

The approximation methods for $H(\tau)$ are very adequate where $H(\tau)$ varies slowly with τ. Where $H(\tau)$ changes rapidly, $H_1(\tau)$ and $H_{2b}(\tau)$ are no longer very satisfactory approximations. This has already been shown by applying these approximations to $E_r(t)$ obtained from the box

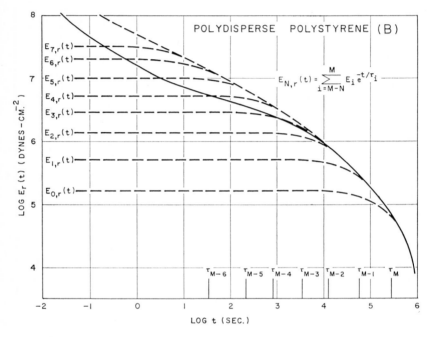

Figure IV.30. Master relaxation curve in rubbery region for polystyrene sample B reduced to 115°C. Also shown are the contributions from the individual relaxation times obtained from procedure X. The resultant master curve from procedure X is shown as a dotted line. The experimental master curve is the solid black line. [A. V. Tobolsky and K. Murakami, *J. Polymer Sci.*, **40**, 443 (1959).]

function for $H(\tau)$. (See Figures III.10 and IV.36.) The same result was shown even more strikingly when the first and second approximations were applied to a single Maxwell element (Figure III.14). It was also shown (equation 9.9 of Chapter III) that

9.1 $\log \overline{H}_1(\tau_p) = \log \overline{H}_{2b}(\tau_p) = \log E_p - 0.072$

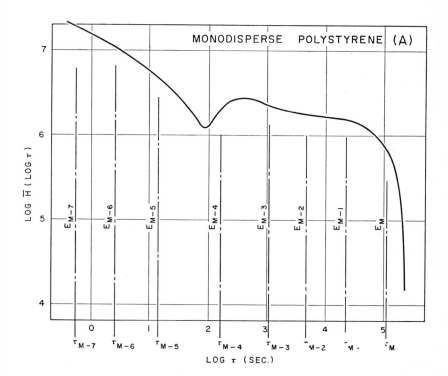

Figure IV.31. $\bar{H}_{2b}(\tau)$ vs. log τ (at 115°C) for polystyrene sample A shown as solid curve. The E_i and τ_i values obtained from procedure X are also shown. [A. V. Tobolsky and K. Murakami, *J. Polymer Sci.*, **40**, 443 (1959).]

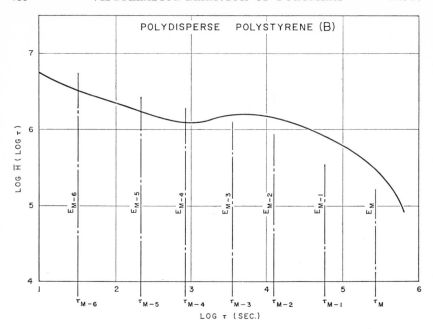

Figure IV.32. $\bar{H}_{2b}(\tau)$ vs. log τ (at 115°C) for polystyrene sample B shown as solid curve. The E_i and τ_i values obtained from procedure X are also shown. [A. V. Tobolsky and K. Murakami, *J. Polymer Sci.*, **40**, 443 (1959).]

If the distribution of relaxation times in the rubbery-flow region is expressed as a discrete distribution, we have

$$9.2 \quad E_r(t) = E_a \exp\left(-\frac{t}{\tau_a}\right)$$

$$+ \cdots + E_{m-1} \exp\left(-\frac{t}{\tau_{m-1}}\right) + E_m \exp\left(-\frac{t}{\tau_m}\right)$$

A plot of log $E_r(t)$ vs. t should approach a straight line for $t > \tau_m$ if a maximum relaxation time truly exists. The slope of the line is $-1/2.303\tau_m$; the intercept of the line is log E_m.

A straight line is indeed approached when log $E_r(t)$ is plotted against t for polystyrene samples A and B. This is shown in Figures IV.33 and IV.34. The values of τ_m and E_m for these polymers can thus be calculated.

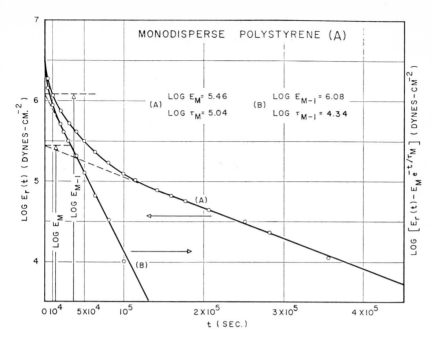

Figure IV.33. Log $E_r(t)$ vs. t for polystyrene sample A. [A. V. Tobolsky and K. Murakami, *J. Polymer Sci.*, **40**, 443 (1959).]

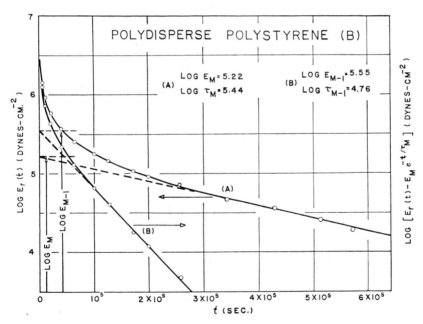

Figure IV.34. Log $E_r(t)$ vs. t for polystyrene sample B. [A. V. Tobolsky and K. Murakami, *J. Polymer Sci.*, **40**, 443 (1959).]

Equation 9.2 can now be cast in the form

$$9.3 \quad E_r(t) - E_m \exp\left(-\frac{t}{\tau_m}\right)$$

$$= E_a \exp\left(-\frac{t}{\tau_a}\right) + \cdots + E_{m-1} \exp\left(-\frac{t}{\tau_{m-1}}\right)$$

A plot of $\log[E_r(t) - E_m \exp(-t/\tau_m)]$ vs. t should approach a straight line for $t > \tau_{m-1}$ if a discrete relaxation time τ_{m-1} truly exists that is reasonably separated in time value from τ_m and τ_{m-2}. After determining τ_{m-1} and E_{m-1} from the slope and intercept, the process can be repeated to find τ_{m-2}, E_{m-2}, etc. This is called procedure X. The value of the E_i and τ_i obtained for sample A and B by procedure X are given in Table IV.5. The successive stages of procedure X for sample A are shown in Figure IV.35.

Table IV.5

DISCRETE RELAXATION-TIME SPECTRA FOR POLYSTYRENE SAMPLES A AND B [a]

	Monodisperse Polystyrene A		Polydisperse Polystyrene B	
	$\log E_i$	$\log \tau_i$	$\log E_i$	$\log \tau_i$
m	5.46	5.04	5.22	5.44
$m-1$	6.08	4.34	5.55	4.76
$m-2$	5.92	3.67	5.95	4.09
$m-3$	6.20	3.01	6.19	3.54
$m-4$	6.34	2.20	6.39	2.91
$m-5$	6.50	1.14	6.68	2.33
$m-6$	6.95	0.40	7.03	1.51
$m-7$	7.03	−0.30		

[a] A. V. Tobolsky and K. Murakami, *J. Polymer Sci.*, **40**, 443 (1959).

The validity of this procedure for obtaining a maximum relaxation time τ_m and the associated E_m is mostly a matter of accuracy of experimental measurements of stress for low-stress values. There is little reason to doubt that monodisperse polymer will have a well-defined maximum relaxation time.

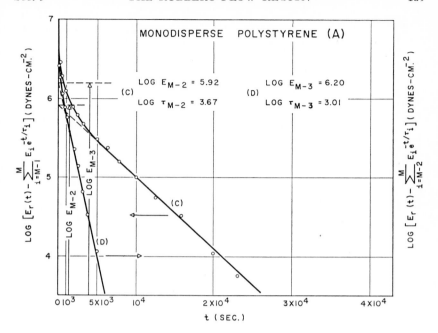

Figure IV.35. Successive steps of procedure X for polystyrene sample A. [A. V. Tobolsky and K. Murakami, *J. Polymer Sci.*, **40**, 443 (1959).]

The validity of procedure X for the other values of E_i and τ_i is much more difficult to ascertain. Procedure X has been tested by what may best be described as a program of experimental mathematics, listed below in items 1 through 6.

1. Do the plots of $\log [E_r(t) - E_m \exp (-t/\tau_m) - E_{m-1} \exp (-t/\tau_{m-1})$ $- \cdots]$ vs. t approach reasonably straight lines over a long-time interval? Is the difference between $\log E_r(t)$ and the asymptotic line $\log E_m - t/2.303\tau_m$ small at $t = \tau_m$, and similarly for the other τ_i? That this appears to be so is shown in Figure IV.35.

2. Are the relaxation times obtained fairly widely separated? The answer given by Table IV.5 is that the spacings are on the border line of what might be expected to be resolvable.

3. If the values of E_i and τ_i obtained by procedure X are inserted back in equation 9.2, do they reproduce the experimental $E_r(t)$ from which they were derived? The answer is that, for sample A, the mathematical curve from procedure X could not be distinguished from the experimental curve; for sample B (the polydisperse sample), agreement is excellent at the long-time values corresponding to $t > \tau_{m-2}$. For shorter

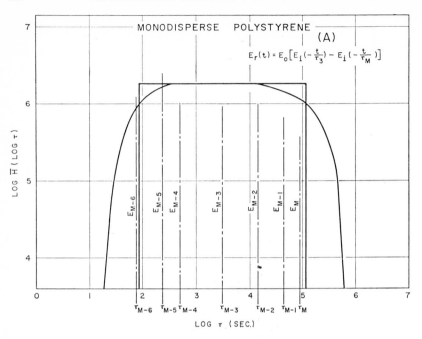

Figure IV.36. E_i and τ_i values obtained by applying procedure X to the $E_r(t)$ obtained from the box distribution. Solid curve shows $\overline{H}_{2b}(\tau)$ obtained from the same $E_r(t)$. Parameters of the box distribution used are $E_0 = 1.86 \times 10^6 \, \text{dynes/cm}^2$; $\tau_3 = 91.2 \, \text{sec}$; $\tau_m = 1.10 \times 10^5 \, \text{sec}$. [A. V. Tobolsky and K. Murakami, *J. Polymer Sci.*, **40**, 443 (1959).]

time values the agreement is only approximate (see Figures IV.29 and IV.30).

4. If $E_r(t)$ was truly given by equation 9.2 with the τ_i values widely separated, procedure X would be expected to work. If the approximation $\overline{H}_{2b}(\tau)$ were applied in this case, one would obtain a continuous curve, which would have maxima at the τ_i values if the τ_i values were very widely spaced. However, at the τ_i values, $\log \overline{H}(\tau_i) \approx \log E_i$, according to equation 9.1. We might therefore expect that, where $\overline{H}_{2b}(\tau_i) \approx E_i$, procedure X is valid. This is followed pretty well for samples A and B.

5. If procedure X were applied to a function $E_r(t)$ which arose from a continuous distribution of relaxation times, would criteria 1 through 4 above show that the discrete spectrum produced by procedure X was an artifact? To check this, procedure X was applied to $E_r(t)$ arising from the "box" distribution, and the discrete spectrum shown in Figure IV.36

and tabulated in reference 1 was obtained. All four criteria 1 through 4 above showed procedure X to be less valid than when it was applied to the experimental $E_r(t)$ curves of samples A and B. The "straight lines" of criterion 1 showed much scatter; the relaxation times that were obtained were quite closely spaced especially near the cutoffs τ_3 and τ_m; contrary to criterion 4, $\log E_i \ll \log \overline{H}(\tau_i)$; the exact $E_r(t)$ curve from the "box" was only moderately well reproduced when the τ_i and E_i values from procedure X were inserted in equation 9.2. The last result is shown in Figure IV.37. All criteria showed that the τ_i and E_i values that we were obtaining through procedure X were artifacts, although they provide a moderately adequate representation, in a mathematical sense, of the true $H(\tau)$ given by the "box."

6. Does procedure X when used by different people give rise to the same τ_i and E_i values? In an independent calculation, very good agreement was obtained with the τ_m, τ_{m-1}, E_m and E_{m-1} values of samples A and B shown in Table IV.5.

7. Procedure X can be applied to a known discrete distribution to see how well it will reproduce the known values. It was applied to the last

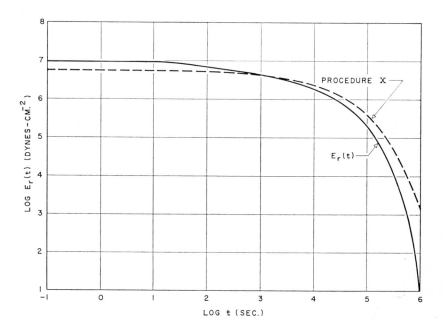

Figure IV.37. $E_r(t)$ arising from box distribution versus result obtained by procedure X. (A. V. Tobolsky and K. Murakami, *J. Polymer Sci.*, **40**, 443 (1959).]

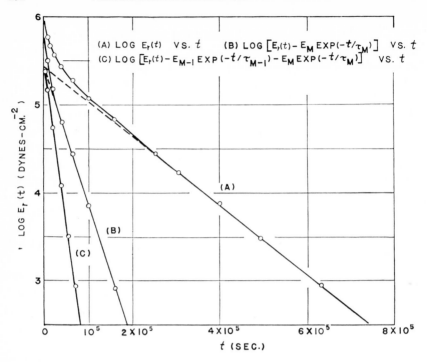

Figure IV.38. Procedure X applied to Rouse equation 9.4. [A. V. Tobolsky, and K. Murakami, *J. Polymer Sci.*, **40**, 443 (1959).]

three terms of the Rouse distribution (equations 5.1 and 5.11):

9.4
$$E_r(t) = E_{m-2} \exp\left(-t/\tau_{m-2}\right)$$
$$+ E_{m-1} \exp\left(-t/\tau_{m-1}\right) + E_m \exp\left(-t/\tau_m\right)$$
$$E_{m-2} = E_{m-1} = E_m$$
$$\tau_{m-2} = \tau_m/3^2 \qquad \tau_{m-1} = \tau_m/2^2$$

For definiteness E_m was taken as 2.88×10^5 dynes/cm^2, and τ_m was taken as 1.10×10^5 sec. Procedure X applied to equation 9.4 gave very good results as shown in reference 1 and in Figure IV.38. When the τ_i and E_i obtained by procedure X were substituted in equation 9.4, they reproduced the given $E_r(t)$ curve exactly as shown in Figure IV.39. In Figure IV.40 are shown $\overline{H}_1(\tau)$ and $\overline{H}_{2b}(\tau)$ obtained from equation 9.4 compared with the E_i and τ_i obtained from equation 9.4 by procedure X. The conclusions from this program of experimental mathematics are

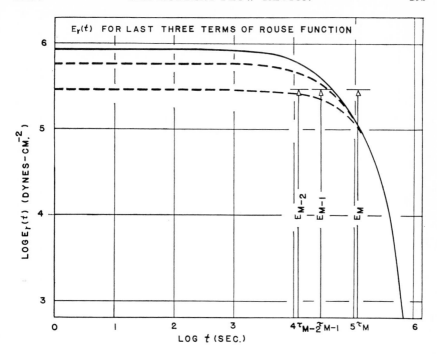

Figure IV.39. $E_r(t)$ for Rouse relaxation function compared to result obtained by procedure X. [A. V. Tobolsky and K. Murakami, *J. Polymer Sci.*, **40**, 443 (1959).]

that procedure X when applied to monodisperse polymer very probably gives rise to significant discrete relaxation times τ_m and τ_{m-1}, and it may *possibly* isolate even more relaxation times that are meaningful. For the polydisperse sample B, procedure X gives rise to τ_m and τ_{m-1} values that are probably meaningful, but the other relaxation times are probably artifacts.

Reference IV.9

1. A. V. Tobolsky and K. Murakami, *J. Polymer Sci.*, **40**, 443 (1959).

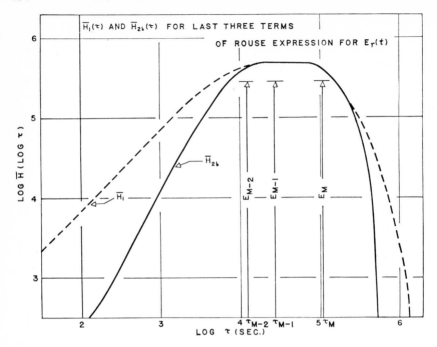

Figure IV.40. $\overline{H}_1(\tau)$, $\overline{H}_{2b}(\tau)$, E_i and τ_i for the Rouse function. [A. V. Tobolsky and K. Murakami, *J. Polymer Sci.*, **40**, 443 (1959).]

10. HEAT GENERATION IN RUBBERS

A historically very important and interesting problem in viscoelasticity was brought to the fore dramatically by World War II. The synthetic rubber GR-S (butadiene-styrene 75/25) was found to generate more heat during flexing than natural rubber. For this reason it was found not entirely satisfactory for heavy-duty truck and airplane tires. This deficiency is still not entirely overcome.

In equation 1.10 of Chapter III it was shown that the heat generated per cycle per unit volume for forced vibrations of amplitude $s_0 e^{iwt}$ was

10.1 $$W = \pi w \eta_{\text{dyn}} s_0^2 = \pi G'' s_0^2$$

The heat loss h per unit volume per unit time is

10.2 $$h = \frac{W}{2\pi/w} = (w/2)G'' s_0^2$$

We therefore expect that for tires of the same geometrical construction and operating under the same conditions, but made of different types of rubber, the heat generated would be proportional to G'' (or E''), a property of the rubber.

Stress-relaxation data on a natural-rubber gum vulcanizate and a GR-S gum vulcanizate were obtained, κ values were obtained, master curves constructed, and $E'(w)$ and $E''(w)$ both reduced to 25°C computed therefrom.[1] The results are shown graphically in Figures IV.41 and IV.42 and tabulated in Tables IV.6 and IV.7. The master stress-relaxation curve for natural rubber is much steeper than for GR-S, having a maximum negative slope of 1.10, compared with 0.74 for the latter. The dynamic loss E'' shows a much sharper peak value for natural rubber than for GR-S. The peak is also displaced to shorter time values for natural rubber, since natural rubber has a lower value of T_g (see Table II.4).

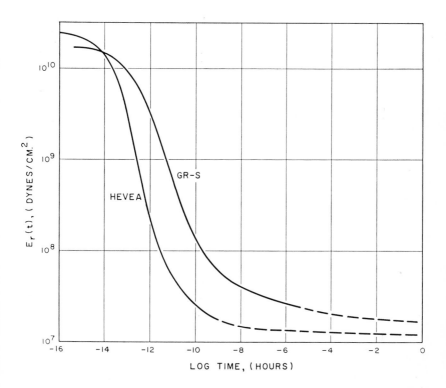

Figure IV.41. $E_r(t)$ for GR-S and natural-rubber gum vulcanizates at 25°C. (After E. Catsiff and A. V. Tobolsky, *Tech. Rept. RLT-21* to the ONR, Dec. 18, 1956.)

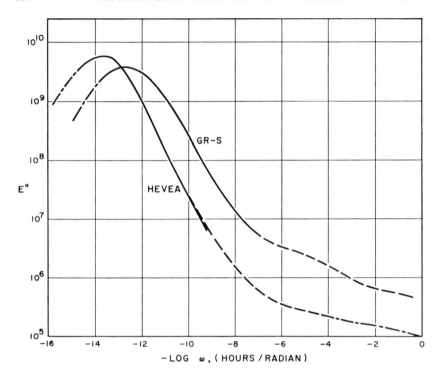

Figure IV.42. $E''(1/w)$ for GR-S and natural-rubber gum vulcanizates at 25°C obtained by computation from the $E_r(t)$ curves. (After E. Catsiff and A. V. Tobolsky, *Tech. Rept. RLT-21* to the ONR, Dec. 18, 1956.)

A tire having a circumference of 10 ft on a vehicle traveling at slightly less than 60 mph undergoes 30,000 complete flexures/hr. Hence $w \sim$ 200,000 radians/hr, and $\log w = 5.3$. While this frequency lies somewhat to the right of the available frequency range, it appears probable that the curves could be extrapolated smoothly, indicating at least a ten times higher loss modulus for GR-S than for natural rubber.

The higher loss modulus of GR-S at frequencies encountered in tires appears to arise from a higher transition temperature and a broader relaxation spectrum. It is also possible that relaxation of chain entanglements [2] and "dangling" network chains contribute to E'' in the tire frequency range. It is certain that, in actual tires which always are reinforced with large quantities of carbon black, the filler particle-particle interactions and slippage and also the particle-rubber interactions and slippages contribute to heat build-up.

Table IV.6

TIME-TEMPERATURE SHIFT FACTORS FOR GR-S AND NATURAL RUBBER,
REFERRED TO 25°C

GR-S		Natural Rubber	
T, °C	$\log \kappa_{298}$	T, °C	$\log \kappa_{298}$
−64.0	13.20	−75.3	13.67_5
−61.0	12.60	−74.9	13.31
−58.8	11.89_5	−72.6	13.04_5
−57.6	11.40	−69.9	12.32
−55.0	10.38	−66.6	11.23_5
−52.5	9.55_5	−64.6	10.37_5
		−61.1	9.57_5
−49.5	8.44_5	−59.6	9.20
−47.7	7.99	−55.3	8.35_5
−44.0	6.52	−50.9	7.51
−40.0	5.95		
−32.8	4.05		

Table IV.7

MASTER STRESS-RELAXATION AND DYNAMIC MODULUS CURVES REDUCED
TO 25°C

log Time, hours	$\log E_r(t)$		$\log \overline{H}(\tau)$		$\log E'(1/w)$		$\log E''(1/w)$	
	GR-S	Hevea	GR-S	Hevea	GR-S	Hevea	GR-S	Hevea
−16.5		10.40						
−16.0		10.38		8.83		10.39		
−15.5		10.35		9.32		10.37		
−15.0	10.22	10.30		9.67		10.33		9.53
−14.5	10.21	10.19	8.89	9.91	10.23	10.26		9.70
−14.0	10.17	10.01	9.32	10.04	10.20	10.12		9.78
−13.5	10.10	9.66	9.62	10.05	10.15	9.85	9.45	9.73
−13.0	9.96	9.10	9.82	9.50	10.04	9.38	9.45	9.52
−12.5	9.77	8.54	9.83	8.85	9.87	8.78	9.57	9.15
−12.0	9.50	8.10	9.68	8.33	9.61	8.27	9.48	8.77
−11.5	9.16	7.81	9.42	7.89	9.30	7.90	9.32	8.36
−11.0	8.78	7.61	9.05	7.55	8.93	7.68	9.06	7.94
−10.5	8.41	7.45	8.59	7.28	8.55	7.50	8.75	7.55
−10.0	8.13	7.34	8.18	6.93	8.23	7.38	8.41	7.31
−9.5	7.92	7.28	7.85	6.53	7.99	7.30	8.07	
−9.0	7.78	7.26	7.58		7.83	7.27	7.73	
−8.5	7.68	7.25	7.34		7.72	7.25	7.40	
−8.0	7.60		7.12		7.63		7.14	
−7.5	7.55		6.92		7.57		6.92	
−7.0	7.51		6.79		7.53		6.73	
−6.5	7.47		6.71		7.49			
−6.0	7.43		6.62		7.45			
−5.5	7.39				7.41			

References IV.10

1. E. Catsiff and A. V. Tobolsky, *Tech. Rept.* RLT-21 to the Office of Naval Research, Contract Nonr-1858(07), Project NR 356–377, Dec. 18, 1956.
2. L. J. Zapas, S. L. Shuler and T. W. DeWitt, *J. Polymer Sci.*, **18**, 245 (1955).

11. STRESS RELAXATION IN CRYSTALLINE POLYMERS

The viscoelastic properties of crystalline polymers are much more complex than those of amorphous polymers. In the first place the Boltzmann superposition principle and the general concepts of *linear* viscoelastic behavior do not apply universally. This is particularly true if the crystalline character of the polymer is changing during the viscoelastic experiment, e.g., by a growth of new crystalline material.

It is necessary to classify crystalline polymers into at least four categories to make an orderly discussion of viscoelastic properties.

1. Very slightly crystalline: ~5 to 10% crystalline, with very small crystalline regions. Examples are highly plasticized polyvinyl chloride, gelatin gels, elastic polyamides. The last-named are made by partial methyl substitution of the amide hydrogen and by breaking up the orderly arrangement of the amide groups by using mixtures of adipic and sebacic acid with hexamethylenediamine.

2. Intermediate crystallinity: ~50%. A very important example is low-density polyethylene.

3. High crystallinity: ~90%. A good example are the new linear polyethylenes.

4. Very high crystallinity: >90%. It is possible that some of the new isotactic polymers such as isotactic poly-(3-methyl-1-butene) may be in this category.

Polymers in category 1 behave like lightly cross-linked amorphous polymers, the crystallites acting as cross links. The "cross links" are rather time-stable (except in the region of maximum rate of crystalline growth) but are not temperature-stable. As the melting point is approached, the equilibrium amount of crystallinity changes and completely disappears at T_m. The polymers thereupon enter a liquid or rubbery state depending on molecular weight.

The transition region of polymers in category 1 is very much broadened on the temperature scale.

Polymers in categories 2 and 3 are similar to those in category 1 except that they have a higher modulus throughout the region between

T_g and T_m. Category 1 is "rubbery" over much of this range; category 2 is "leathery"; category 3 is "hard." All have good impact resistance in this range, although category 3 may have brittle failure on occasion when the crystallites or spherulites get very large and become oriented under stress in the temperature range of crystal growth. An example of this latter phenomenon is the stress cracking of plastic pipes made from polyethylene.

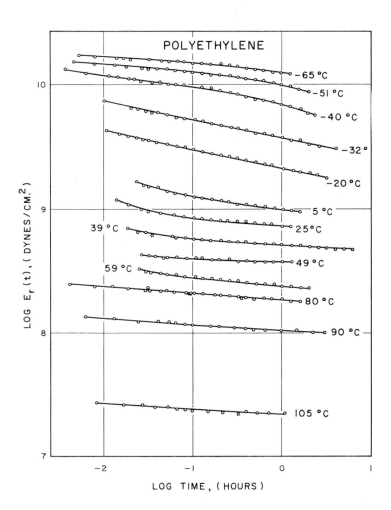

Figure IV.43. Stress-relaxation curves for low-density polyethylene. [After E. Catsiff, J. Offenbach and A. V. Tobolsky, *J. Colloid Sci.*, **11**, 48 (1956).]

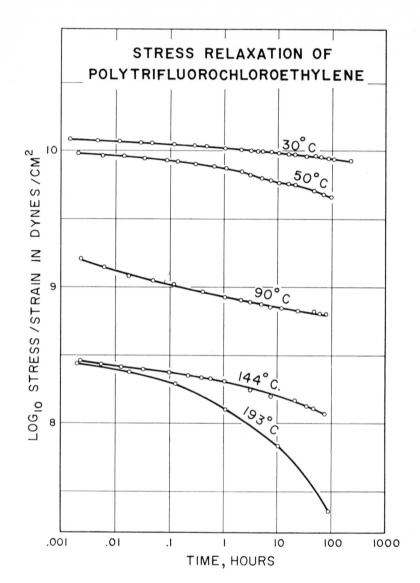

Figure IV.44. Stress-relaxation curves log $E_r(t)$ vs. log t for polytrifluorochloroethylene. [After A. V. Tobolsky and J. R. McLoughlin, *J. Phys. Chem.*, **59**, 989 (1955).]

Category 4 may exhibit some of the viscoelastic features of metals, such as are associated with dislocations and grain boundaries.

Stress-relaxation studies on crystalline low-density polyethylene and polytrifluorochloroethylene are shown in Figures IV.43 and IV.44.[1,2] These show definite contrast to the typical stress-relaxation curves for amorphous polymers, as represented for example by polyisobutylene (Figure IV.4).

For polyisobutylene the behavior in the transition region has been thoroughly discussed. In the time scale of the relaxation experiments (0.01 to 10 hr) the transition region occurs in the temperature interval between -80 and $-40°C$. In this interval the modulus changes very rapidly with temperature and time as can be seen in Figure IV.4. The values of $E_r(t)$ range between the "glassy-modulus" value of $10^{10.5}$ dynes/cm^2, to the rubbery-modulus value of $10^{6.88}$ dynes/cm^2. Stress-relaxation curves at different temperatures can be superposed by a horizontal translation along the log time axis, and this principle of superposition permits the construction of a master curve that covers the complete time scale.

Polytrifluorochloroethylene is a polycrystalline polymer of category 3 for which $T_g = 39°C$ and $T_m = 221°C$. In the interval between T_g and $\frac{8}{9}T_m$ (the temperature of maximum rate of crystallization), the stress-relaxation curves for polytrifluorochloroethylene are relatively flat; i.e., the modulus change with time in the "transition region" is much less marked for the crystalline polymer than for the amorphous polymer. Also for polytrifluorochloroethylene the modulus value at $t = 0.01$ hr changes from a value of $10^{10.1}$ dynes/cm^2 at $30°$ to a value of $10^{8.35}$ dynes/cm^2 at $144°$, a very gradual change. The "transition region" blends into a high-modulus "rubbery region," the crystallites playing the same role that entanglements or cross links do in amorphous polymers.

The relatively rapid decay of stress at $193°$ is no doubt associated with a change of microcrystalline structure or texture, i.e., an orientation of crystalline material. It is interesting to note that this polymer shows "heat embrittlement" (or lowered impact strength) if kept for long periods of time in the temperature range 170 to 195°. This is also due to continued growth and/or orientation of crystalline material. If maintained under stress for long periods of time in this temperature range, the material will manifest "stress cracking."

The stress-relaxation data for (low-density) polyethylene (Figure IV.43) shows much the same characteristics. The relatively rapid decrease in the 0.01-hr modulus values as the melting point of $110°C$ is approached is due to the rapidly changing degree of crystallinity in this temperature interval.   Empirical relations between modulus and per cent crystallinity have in fact been proposed for polyethylene.

Because there are changes in temperature in the microcrystalline structure and in the stress-bearing mechanisms, it is the author's opinion that the simple time-temperature superposition that is valid for amorphous polymers is not valid without severe restrictions for crystalline polymers.   "There is not only a horizontal displacement along the log time axis due to changing rates of molecular motions with temperature, but also an even more important vertical shift along the $E_r(t)$ axis (especially near the melting point) due to the changing structure and other factors." [1]

Some authors have proposed that the time-temperature superposition principle is in fact applicable to relaxation of stress curves for crystalline

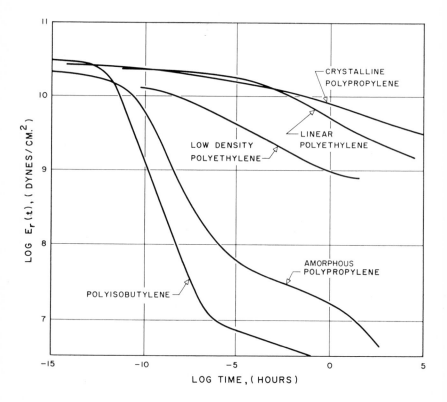

Figure IV.45.   Log $E_r(t)$ vs. log t master curves at 25°C for crystalline polypropylene, amorphous polypropylene, high-density (linear) polyethylene, low-density (branched) polyethylene and polyisobutylene (NBS).   [After J. A. Faucher, *Trans. Soc. Rheol.* (in press).]

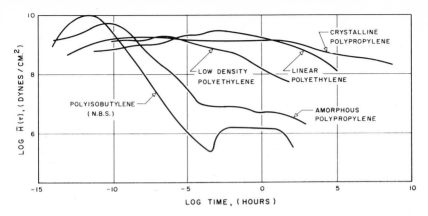

Figure IV.46. Log $\overline{H}_1(t)$ vs. log t at 25 °C for crystalline polypropylene, amorphous polypropylene, high-density polyethylene, low-density polyethylene and polyisobutylene (NBS). [After J. A. Faucher, *Trans. Soc. Rheol.* (in press).]

polymers at very low extensions, at temperatures sufficiently below the melting temperature and for times that are not too long.[3, 4] This can be completely authenticated only by an extensive comparison of stress-relaxation and dynamic modulus data as was done for polyisobutylene (see section 3). The distributions of relaxation times for polycrystalline polymers obtained by the unmodified time-temperature superposition procedure are exceptionally broad (see Figures IV.45 and IV.46).

More recently Takemura, Nagamatsu and coworkers [5] have proposed a quantitative equation for a *vertical* shift along the $E_r(t)$ axis for crystalline polymers. In order to construct a master curve at a reference temperature T_0, the $E_r(t)$ curves at other temperatures must first be reduced to temperature T_0 by the following formula:

$$11.1 \quad \log E_r(t, \text{reduced}) = \log E_r(t) + \log \frac{T_0}{T} - \log \frac{1 - \lambda}{\lambda} + \log \frac{1 - \lambda_0}{\lambda_0}$$

In equation 11.1, $1 - \lambda_0$ is the degree of crystallinity at temperature T_0, and $1 - \lambda$ is the degree of crystallinity at temperature T.

Once this shift along the log $E_r(t)$ axis has been accomplished, the data reduced in this fashion are then subjected to horizontal shifts along the log time axis in the usual manner, in order to construct the master curve. This procedure has been successfully applied to high-density polyethylene. [5]

An illustration of the difficulties associated with a complete interpretation of stress relaxation of crystalline polymer is demonstrated by stress-

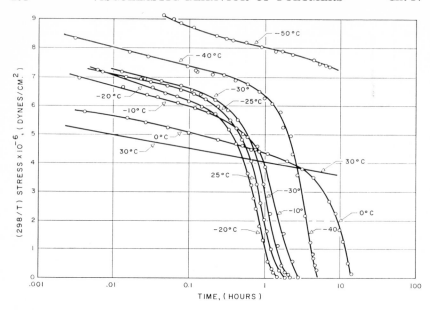

Figure IV.47. Stress-decay curves for unvulcanized natural rubber at 50% elongation in the temperature range of crystallization. [After A. V. Tobolsky and G. M. Brown, *J. Polymer Sci.*, **17**, 547 (1958); G. M. Brown, Ph.D. thesis, Princeton University (1948).]

relaxation studies on unvulcanized natural rubber in the temperature interval −50 to 30° shown in Figures IV.47 and IV.48. Natural rubber shows a maximum rate of crystallization at −20°. When maintained at constant length in the temperature interval between −40 and 0°, the stress decays to zero because of the growth of oriented crystalline material.[6,7] The samples actually eventually increase in length beyond the original stretched length. This phenomenon is known as "spontaneous elongation." It is as though a bowl of cooked spaghetti, when subjected to slight tension, suddenly remembered that it was originally packed in a long narrow box!

Stress relaxation arising from growth of oriented crystalline material can be diagnosed by birefringence studies as discussed in section 15.

In order for a crystalline polymer to display its full strength and impact resistance it is necessary that the average polymer chain should traverse at least two crystallites. Otherwise the crystalline polymer has the physical attributes of a wax; chain ends tend to migrate to establish planes of cleavage. This means that for optimum properties crystalline polymers require at least a minimum value of chain length. Further-more, it is desirable that the crystallites be small in order to accomplish the same objective of having one polymer chain traverse several crystal-lites. Small crystallites can be achieved by proper annealing procedures, or, more satisfactorily, by breaking up the regularity of the chain by the introduction of a very small amount of comonomer; e.g., less than 5% of vinylidene fluoride markedly enhances the impact strength of polytri-fluorochloroethylene polymers and especially their resistance to "em-brittlement" when maintained at temperatures of about 180°C.

It is noteworthy (though unexplained) that many crystalline polymers have a fair measure of impact resistance even below their glass transi-tion temperatures. Examples are polytrifluorochloroethylene, poly-vinyl chloride, nylon 6, nylon 66, polytetrafluoroethylene, all with T_g values in excess of room temperature. In this connection it is well to recall that the proper determination of T_g for crystalline polymers

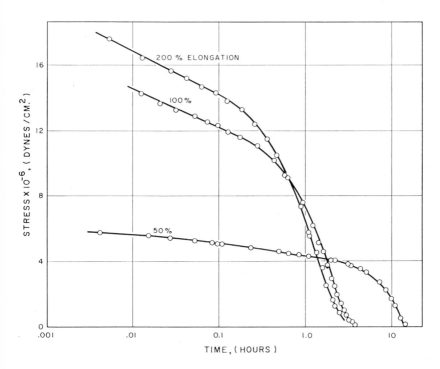

Figure IV.48. Stress-decay curves at $-20°C$ for unvulcanized natural rubber: effect of elongation. [After A. V. Tobolsky and G. M. Brown, *J. Polymer Sci.*, **17**, 547 (1958).]

generally requires that these polymers be obtained in an amorphous condition by quick-chilling procedures or by copolymerization, and various statements in the literature that the T_g values for these polymers are below room temperature are in error.

A further discussion of crystalline polyethylene and crystalline polypropylene is given in Appendix K.

References IV.11

1. A. V. Tobolsky and J. R. McLoughlin, *J. Phys. Chem.*, **59**, 989 (1955).
2. E. Catsiff, J. Offenbach and A. V. Tobolsky, *J. Colloid Sci.*, **11**, 48 (1956).
3. T. Yoshitomi, K. Nagamatsu and K. Kosiyama, *J. Polymer Sci.*, **27**, 335 (1958).
4. K. Nagamatsu, T. Yoshitomi and T. Takemoto, *J. Colloid Sci.*, **13**, 257 (1958).
5. K. Nagamatsu, T. Takemura, T. Yoshitomi and T. Takemoto, *J. Polymer Sci.*, **33**, 515 (1958); T. Takemura, *J. Polymer Sci.*, **38**, 471 (1959).
6. G. M. Brown and A. V. Tobolsky, *J. Polymer Sci.*, **17**, 547 (1955); G. M. Brown, Ph.D thesis, Princeton University, 1948.
7. A. N. Gent, *Trans. Faraday Soc.*, **50**, 521 (1954).

12. STRESS RELAXATION IN INTERCHANGING NETWORKS

A class of substances which appear to be nearly ideal Maxwell bodies are the polysulfide rubbers.[1,2] These are rubber networks composed of polysulfide chains of the following structural types:

$$—\!\wedge\!\wedge\!\wedge\!—CH_2CH_2SSCH_2CH_2SS—\!\wedge\!\wedge\!\wedge\!—$$
ethyl disulfide polymer

$$—\!\wedge\!\wedge\!\wedge\!—CH_2CH_2OCH_2CH_2SSCH_2CH_2OCH_2CH_2SS—\!\wedge\!\wedge\!\wedge\!—$$
diethylether disulfide polymer

$$—\!\wedge\!\wedge\!\wedge\!—CH_2CH_2OCH_2OCH_2CH_2SSCH_2CH_2OCH_2OCH_2CH_2SS—\!\wedge\!\wedge\!\wedge\!—$$
diethylformal disulfide polymer

Although the disulfide linkages are predominant, there are also monosulfide linkages —S—, trisulfide linkages —SSS—, and tetrasulfide linkages —SSSS— along the main polymer chains. The network junctures are generally trifunctional covalent linkages. The ends of terminal network chains are SH linkages.

In addition to these major features of the network structure, there are minor amounts of linkages of the type $—S^-\ldots{}^+Pb^+\ldots{}^-S—$ along the chains or $—S^-\ldots Na^+$ at the ends of the terminal network chains.

For rapid stresses and strains these rubbers obey the kinetic theory of rubber elasticity developed in Chapter II. However chemical interchanges are occurring in the network, which become manifest if the rubber is maintained at a fixed strain for an appreciable length of time.[1] The chemical interchanges are of the following kinds:

12.1
$$
\begin{array}{c}
\text{R—S—S—R} \\
+ \\
\text{R}'\text{—S—S—R}'
\end{array}
\xrightarrow{\text{cat}}
\begin{array}{c}
\text{R—S} \quad \text{S—R} \\
| + | \\
\text{R}'\text{—S} \quad \text{S—R}'
\end{array}
$$

12.2
$$
\begin{array}{c}
\text{R—S—H} \\
+ \\
\text{R}'\text{—S—S—R}'
\end{array}
\xrightarrow{\text{cat}}
\begin{array}{c}
\text{R—S} \quad \text{H} \\
| + | \\
\text{R}'\text{—S} \quad \text{S—R}'
\end{array}
$$

12.3
$$
\begin{array}{c}
\text{R—S—Na} \\
+ \\
\text{R}'\text{—S—S—R}'
\end{array}
\longrightarrow
\begin{array}{c}
\text{R—S} \quad \text{Na} \\
| + | \\
\text{R}'\text{—S} \quad \text{S—R}'
\end{array}
$$

12.4
$$
\begin{array}{c}
\text{R—S—Pb—S—R} \\
+ \\
\text{R}'\text{—S—S—R}'
\end{array}
\longrightarrow
\begin{array}{c}
\text{R—S—Pb} \quad \text{S—R} \\
| + | \\
\text{R}'\text{—S} \quad \text{S—R}'
\end{array}
$$

where R and R' represent polymer chains.

Trisulfide and tetrasulfide linkages are also involved in these bond interchanges. The catalysts indicated in formulas 12.1 or 12.2 are ionic substances (acids, bases or salts) left over from the polymerization or vulcanization process.

If the rubber were always maintained in an unstrained or unstressed condition, there would be no simple physical means of inferring that these exchanges were occurring. However, if the rubber is stretched to a fixed length and maintained at that length, these interchanges will allow the network structure to come to equilibrium with its new strained condition, and so there will occur a relaxation of stress, which will eventually go to completion (zero stress). The situation is analogous (on a different scale of time) to what occurs in liquid flow. It is not immediately obvious that the molecules in a beaker of water are continually exchanging places. This becomes quite apparent if the water is poured into a new shape of container. Just as the water poured from one container to another is identical in its properties save for its shape, so too is stretched polysulfide rubber, which has been allowed to decay to zero stress, identical with the original material except for its shape. *The rate of bond interchange is independent of strain.*

For simplicity we shall consider that the bond interchanges occurring in a given type of polysulfide rubber are all of the type shown in equation 12.3.   For a stretched rubber sample, the elementary process of stress decay is

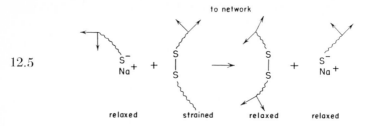

12.5

relaxed   strained   relaxed   relaxed

Immediately after stretching from length L_u to length L, the stress f_0 (based on *attained* cross-sectional area) is given by

$$12.6 \qquad f(0) = N(0)\mathbf{k}T\left[\left(\frac{L}{L_u}\right)^2 - \frac{L_u}{L}\right]$$

where $N(0)$ is the number of effective network chains per cubic centimeter of rubber (*not* including terminal chains) at time zero, and T is the temperature (see equation 7.5).

If the rubber is maintained at constant length L, at the time t only $N(t)$ of the $N(0)$ network chains per cubic centimeter will *not* have been effected by the interchange 12.5.   We shall assume that, if a chain has engaged in bond interchange, it is relaxed with respect to the external length L of the sample, and will no longer contribute to the stress in a sample maintained at that length.   Only the $N(t)$ network chains that have not undergone bond interchange will contribute to the stress, and therefore

$$12.7 \qquad f(t) = N(t)\mathbf{k}T\left[\left(\frac{L}{L_u}\right)^2 - \frac{L_u}{L}\right]$$

The interchange reaction might be expected to obey the following rate law,

$$12.8 \qquad -\frac{dN(t)}{dt} = k'n_1m_2N(t)$$

where n_1 is the average number of linkages along each chain available for interchange (e.g., the total number of disulfide, trisulfide and tetrasulfide linkages), m_2 is the number of S-Na terminals per cubic centimeter of rubber, and k' is a specific rate constant.   The boundary condition is $N(t) = N(0)$ at $t = 0$.

Integrating equation 12.8, one obtains

12.9 $N(t) = N(0) \exp (-kt) = N(0) \exp (-t/\tau)$

where $k = n_1 m_2 k'$ $\tau = 1/k$

Substituting equation 12.9 into equation 12.7 and dividing the result by equation 12.6, there results

12.10 $\dfrac{f(t)}{f(0)} = \exp (-kt) = \exp (-t/\tau)$

Equation 12.10 is the same law for decay of stress at constant extension as is obtained from the Maxwell equations for viscoelasticity for shear and tension:

12.11 $\dfrac{ds}{dt} = \dfrac{1}{G}\dfrac{df}{dt} + \dfrac{1}{\tau G}f$

12.12 $\dfrac{ds}{dt} = \dfrac{1}{E}\dfrac{df}{dt} + \dfrac{1}{\tau E}f$

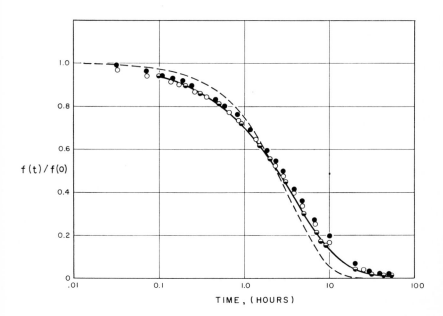

Figure IV.49. Relaxation of stress in polysulfide rubber H-11 at various elongations, and plot of $\exp (-t/\tau)$ at 60°C.: ●, 10% extension; ○, 30% extension; ◖, 50% extension; – – – – $\exp (-t/\tau)$ with $\tau = 3$ hr. [After M. D. Stern and A. V. Tobolsky, *J. Chem. Phys.*, **14**, 93 (1946).]

It will in fact be shown in section 11 that equations 12.11 and 12.12 are theoretically valid for polysulfide rubbers *at smal strains*, provided that G is taken as $N(0)\mathbf{k}T$, and E is taken as $3N(0)\mathbf{k}T$. Experimentally it was found that the relaxation of stress at constant extension does indeed follow equation 12.10 quite closely. Figure IV.49 shows stress relaxation at constant extension for a typical polysulfide rubber compared to the Maxwellian decay law 12.10. It is found that the relative stress decay $f(t)/f(0)$ is completely independent of the extension of the sample up to the highest elongations used (150% extension), which confirms the assumption that the rate of bond interchange is independent of strain. In Chapter V an extended discussion of the chemical stress relaxation of polysulfide rubbers will be given, which will emphasize the chemical aspects of the problem.

The theoretical considerations presented here and in the next section can be applied to rubbers other than polysulfide rubbers, which also undergo interchange reactions. For example, the silicone rubbers whose basic chain structure is

$$
\begin{array}{ccccccccc}
\text{CH}_3 & & \text{CH}_3 & & \text{CH}_3 & & \text{CH}_3 & & \text{CH}_3 \\
| & & | & & | & & | & & | \\
-\!\!\sim\!\!\sim\!\!\sim\!\!-\text{Si}-\text{O}-\text{Si}-\text{O}-\text{Si}-\text{O}-\text{Si}-\text{O}-\text{Si}-\text{O}-\!\!\sim\!\!\sim\!\!\sim\!\!- \\
| & & | & & | & & | & & | \\
\text{CH}_3 & & \text{CH}_3 & & \text{CH}_3 & & \text{CH}_3 & & \text{CH}_3
\end{array}
$$

also can undergo interchange reactions of the type

12.13
$$
\begin{array}{c}
\diagdown\diagup \\
\text{R}-\text{O}-\text{Si}-\text{R} \\
+ \qquad\qquad\qquad \xrightarrow{\text{cat}} \\
\text{R}'-\text{Si}-\text{O}-\text{R}' \\
\diagup\diagdown
\end{array}
\qquad
\begin{array}{c}
\diagdown\diagup \\
\text{R}-\text{O} \quad\ \text{Si}-\text{R} \\
| \ + \ | \\
\text{R}'-\text{Si} \quad \text{O}-\text{R}' \\
\diagup\diagdown
\end{array}
$$

where the catalyst is an acid, base or salt left over from polymerization or vulcanization.[3, 4]

The interchanges considered need not be along the chain but may occur at the cross links. Certain chemical cross links such as salt linkages

$$
\begin{array}{ccc}
| & & | \\
\text{O} & & \text{O} \\
\| & & \| \\
-\text{C}-\text{O}^-\ \cdots\cdots\ \text{M}^{++}\ \cdots\cdots\ {}^-\text{O}-\text{C}- \\
& & \\
& & \\
| & & |
\end{array}
$$

are very labile and may be involved in interchange reactions.[5, 6] (Salt linkages may, of course, also occur within the network chains.) The interchanges in this case may, of course, be regarded as a two-stage process, the breaking and remaking of cross links, where the breaking and re-forming of bonds occur at equal rates. When the rubber network is maintained in a stretched condition, the breaking of a cross link causes the disappearance of the strained network chains associated with the cross link. The re-forming of the cross links produces an equal number of network chains, but these are in a molecularly unstrained configuration, even though the rubber network as a whole is under strain. This type of cross-link interchange leads to the same viscoelastic equations as does chain-chain interchange (equation 12.13), or terminal-chain interchange (equation 12.5). This will be shown in the following section.

Furthermore, temporary "physical" cross links that break and remake may be formed between polymer chains, and play the same role as labile chemical cross links. Such a situation may possibly occur in a polymer containing a few functional groups that could give rise to strong points of interaction with neighboring chains, e.g., a hydrogen bond or a salt linkage.[6] These types of linkages may actually be encountered in swollen wool fibers in addition to the covalent —S—S— cross linkages,[7] and they may well be encountered in carboxyl containing polymers.[6]

In general, however, the long-range physical interactions between high-molecular-weight linear polymers is best described as a complex "entanglement." The "entanglements" act as temporary cross links that break and remake, but the viscoelastic behavior is far more complex than can be comprehended by a single relaxation time. An *a priori* derivation of the actual distribution of relaxation times for this situation remains to be accomplished.

References IV.12

1. M. D. Stern and A. V. Tobolsky, *J. Chem. Phys.*, **14**, 93 (1946).
2. M. Mochulsky and A. V. Tobolsky, *Ind. Eng. Chem.*, **40**, 2155 (1948).
3. D. H. Johnson, J. R. McLoughlin and A. V. Tobolsky, *J. Phys. Chem.*, **58**, 1073 (1954).
4. R. C. Osthoff, A. M. Bueche and W. I. Grubb, *J. Am. Chem. Soc.*, **76**, 4659 (1954).
5. M. S. Green and A. V. Tobolsky, *J. Chem. Phys.*, **14**, 80 (1946).
6. W. Cooper, *J. Polymer Sci.*, **28**, 628 (1958).
7. S. M. Katz and A. V. Tobolsky, *Textile Research J.*, **20**, 87 (1950).

13. VISCOELASTICITY OF INTERCHANGING NETWORKS [1]

Consider a network that exhibits chain-chain interchange, terminal-chain interchange, or cross-link interchange (including the two-stage processes of breaking and re-forming of bonds).[1]   We shall at first consider only one type of bond to be involved in these interchanges so that, at constant extension or shear, the law of stress decay is (see equation 12.10)

13.1 $f(t)/f(0) = \exp(-kt)$

The explanation for the decay of stress at constant extension or at constant shear strain, which occurs in spite of the fact that bond breaking and bond re-forming are proceeding at equal rates, is that the breaking of bonds relaxes the stress in network chains that are in a strained condition, but the re-forming of bonds occurs in such a way that does not contribute to the stress at constant extension.   It is conceptually reasonable to suppose that formation of bonds produces relaxed chains, no matter what the external dimensions of the sample or what stresses are acting on the sample.

Consider what happens when the sample undergoes a strain history. Mathematically speaking, we can classify the chains of the polymeric network into classes N' (per cubic centimeter) which were formed at time t' when the rubber sample was maintained at length $L(t')$ or shear strain $\gamma(t')$.   According to the kinetic theory of rubber elasticity and the assumption that chains formed at length $L(t')$ or shear strain $\gamma(t')$ are formed in a relaxed state, the relation between current stress $f(t)$ on attained section and current length $L(t)$ or shear $\gamma(t)$ is

13.2 $$f(t) = \mathbf{k}T \sum_{t'} N' \left\{ \left[\frac{L(t)}{L(t')} \right]^2 - \frac{L(t')}{L(t)} \right\} \exp[-k(t - t')]$$

13.3 $$f(t) = \mathbf{k}T \sum_{t'} N'[\gamma(t) - \gamma(t')] \exp[-k(t - t')]$$

The N' are governed by the following equations,

13.4 $$\Sigma N' = N$$

13.5 $$dN'/dt' = kN$$

where N is the number of network chains of all types N' per cubic centimeter.   The quantity N is a constant according to the assumptions of our model.   In equation 13.5 dN' is the number of network chains *forming* in the time interval $t' \rightarrow t' + dt'$ when the length of the sample is $L(t')$ or the shear of the sample is $\gamma(t')$.   The number per cubic centimeter of network chains $-dN'$ that are *breaking* in the time interval $t \rightarrow t + dt$ is given by

13.6 $$-dN'/dt = kN'$$

also

13.7 $$-dN/dt = kN$$

If we assume that a sample of unstretched length L_u is subjected to a suddenly imposed length $L(0)$ at time zero, and thereafter is subjected to a *continuous* strain history $L(t')$, equation 13.2 becomes

13.8 $$f(t) = NkT \left\{ \left[\frac{L(0)}{L_u} \right]^2 - \frac{L_u}{L(0)} \right\} \exp (-kt)$$

$$+ NkT \int_0^t \left\{ \left[\frac{L(t)}{L(t')} \right]^2 - \frac{L(t')}{L(t)} \right\} \exp [-k(t - t')]k \, dt'$$

Equation 13.8 is an integral equation, which can be converted to a second-order differential equation and solved under certain boundary conditions.[1] The solution for creep under constant load is given in section 14.

If a sample of initial shear zero is subjected to a *continuous* shear-strain history $\gamma(t')$, equation 13.3 becomes

13.9 $$f(t) = NkT \int_0^t [\gamma(t) - \gamma(t')] \exp [-k(t - t')]k \, dt'$$

An integration by parts gives

13.10 $$f(t) = NkT \int_0^t \frac{d\gamma(t')}{dt'} \exp [-k(t - t')] \, dt'$$

Equation 13.10 can be transformed into the following differential equation,

13.11 $$\frac{d\gamma}{dt} = \frac{1}{G} \frac{df}{dt} + \frac{f}{\tau G}$$

with $G = NkT$ and $\tau = 1/k$. Equation 13.11 is the Maxwell equation discussed in section 9 of Chapter I.

Suppose that we consider a network which undergoes interchanges at the cross links, but that the cross links were of different types j characterized by rate constants k_j. Furthermore, N_j network chains per cubic centimeter are associated with cross links of type j, with the restricting condition $\Sigma N_j = N$. Equation 13.10 becomes

13.12 $$f(t) = \int_0^t \frac{d\gamma(t')}{dt'} [G_r(t - t')] \, dt'$$

where

13.13 $$G_r(t - t') = \sum_{j=1}^{n} N_j \mathbf{k} T \exp\left[-k_j(t - t')\right]$$

Equation 13.12 can be transformed to the following set of differential equations,

13.14 $$\frac{d(\gamma)}{dt} = \frac{(1/G_j)\, df_j(t)}{dt} + \frac{f_j(t)}{\tau_j G_j}$$

$$j = 1, 2, 3, \ldots, n$$

where

13.15 $$G_j = N_j \mathbf{k} T$$

$$\tau_j = 1/k_j$$

$$f_j(t) = G_j \int_0^t \frac{d\gamma(t')}{dt'} \{\exp\left[-k_j(t - t')\right]\}\, dt'$$

$$\Sigma N_j = N$$

Equation 13.12 is a form of the Boltzmann superposition principle for linear viscoelastic behavior, whereas equation 13.14 is the Wiechert formulation for linear viscoelastic behavior, both discussed in Chapter III. The Boltzmann formulation is introduced as a *fundamental postulate* in Chapter III, equation 2.3. The Wiechert formulation, Chapter III, section 3, is deducible from the Boltzmann formulation (and vice versa). It is interesting to note that both these formulations can be derived from the physical model introduced in this section.

The same derivations apply to tension if we restrict ourselves to very small tensile strains. The shear moduli G_j are replaced by tensile moduli $E_j = 3N_j \mathbf{k} T$.

Reference IV.13

1. M. S. Green and A. V. Tobolsky, *J. Chem. Phys.*, **14**, 80 (1946).

14. CREEP UNDER CONSTANT LOAD FOR INTERCHANGING NETWORKS

If a constant load X is attached to a strip of rubber of initial cross section A_u, there is an immediate elastic extension at time $t = 0$ from the unstretched length L_u to a stretched length $L(0)$. This is governed by the equation of state

14.1
$$F = \frac{X}{A_u} = NkT \left\{ \frac{L(0)}{L_u} - \left[\frac{L_u}{L(0)} \right]^2 \right\}$$

If the rubber manifests viscoelastic behavior, it will continue to extend with time, a phenomenon known as creep. The quantity $F = X/A_u$ remains constant during this process, but the force per *attained* cross-sectional area $f(t)$ will be given at time t by

14.2
$$f(t) = [L(t)/L_u]F$$

where $L(t)$ is the length at time t.

In section 13 we showed that the equation relating $f(t)$ and $L(t)$ for an interchanging network is

14.3
$$\frac{f(t)}{NkT} = \exp(-kt) \left\{ \left[\frac{L(t)}{L_u} \right]^2 - \frac{L_u}{L(t)} \right\}$$

$$+ \int_0^t k \left\{ \left[\frac{L(t)}{L(t')} \right]^2 - \frac{L(t')}{L(t)} \right\} \exp[-k(t - t')] \, dt'$$

For creep under constant load in an interchanging network we have merely to substitute equation 14.2 into equation 14.3. The resulting equation may be transformed into a differential equation.[1] For simplicity, the following changes in notation are made:

14.4
$$y = \frac{L(t)}{L_u} \qquad y_0 = \frac{L(0)}{L_u} \qquad x = kt$$

The differential equation is

14.5
$$\frac{y''}{y} = 1 + \frac{2y'}{y} - 2 \left(\frac{y'}{y} \right)^2 - R \frac{y'}{y^2}$$

where

14.6
$$R = \frac{3}{y_0 - 1/y_0{}^2}$$

and y' and y'' are first and second derivatives, respectively, with respect to x.

The solution of this equation was obtained by Laplace transformations giving [1]

14.7

$$\exp{(kt)} = P\left[\frac{2L(t)}{RL_u} - 1\right] + Q\left[\frac{2L(t)}{RL_u} + 1\right]\exp\left\{-R\left[\frac{L_u}{L(0)} - \frac{L_u}{L(t)}\right]\right\}$$

$$P = -\frac{y_0^2 - 2y_0 + 3}{Ry_0}$$

$$Q = \frac{R}{2y_0 + R} + \frac{(2y_0 - R)(y_0^2 - 2y_0 + 3)}{(2y_0 + R)Ry_0}$$

Graphs of this function in the form $\ln L(t)/L_u$ plotted against kt are given in Figure IV.50 for several values of $\lambda_0 \equiv L(0)/L_u$. It is particularly to be noted that the creep rate shows a very marked dependence on the load (as measured by the initial extension), even though the molecular relaxation is assumed independent of the stress. It should be

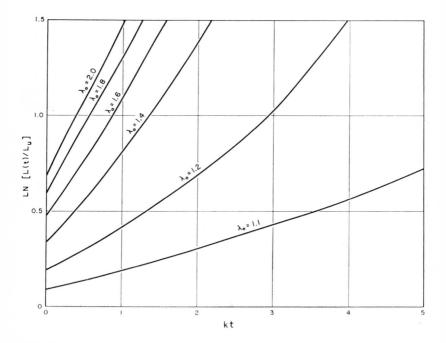

Figure IV.50. $\ln{[L(t)/L_u]}$ vs. kt for various values of L_0/L_u according to equation 12.7. [After P. J. Blatz and A. V. Tobolsky, *J. Chem. Phys.*, **14**, 113 (1946).]

remembered that these creep curves apply only to interchanging networks exhibiting a single relaxation time.

Reference IV.14

1. P. J. Blatz and A. V. Tobolsky, *J. Chem. Phys.*, **14**, 113 (1946).

15. BIREFRINGENCE STUDIES

When a rubber network is stretched it becomes optically anisotropic and hence birefringent. The theory of this phenomenon was worked out by W. Kuhn [1] and by L. R. G. Treloar.[2] The following expression for the birefringence Δ of a sample stretched from length L_u to length L_0 ($\alpha = L_0/L_u$) was obtained:

15.1
$$\Delta = \frac{(r^2 + 2)^2}{r} \frac{2\pi}{45} N(b_\parallel - b_\perp) \left(\alpha^2 - \frac{1}{\alpha} \right)$$

$$\Delta = r_x - r_y$$

In equation 15.1 r_x is the refractive index in the direction of stretch, r_y is the refractive index perpendicular to that direction and r is the average refractive index of the rubber, i.e., the refractive index of the rubber in the unstretched condition which is an easily measured quantity. N is the number of network chains per unit volume, and $b_\parallel$ and $b_\perp$ are the principal polarizabilities of the "statistical segment" along and perpendicular to the contour of the polymer chain. The "statistical segment" is defined as a hypothetical unit of a polymer chain which itself is internally rigid but which can orient freely at any angle with respect to other statistical segments. The calculations underlying equation 15.1 are based on the very same physical and geometrical considerations by which the decrease in entropy of a stretched rubber network was computed in section 9 of Chapter II.

The equation for the stress (per attained cross section) of this same ideal rubber sample is

15.2
$$f = NkT[\alpha^2 - (1/\alpha)]$$

By dividing equation 15.2 by equation 15.1, one obtains

15.3
$$\frac{f}{T\Delta} = \frac{45kr}{2\pi(r^2 + 2)(b_\parallel - b_\perp)}$$

The quantity $f/T\Delta$ is a constant which is characteristic of a polymer and which is dependent only upon the local structure of the polymer chain. Its determination enables one to obtain the quantity $b_{\parallel} - b_{\perp}$ for a given polymer.

Treloar showed how for natural rubber one may compare $b_{\parallel} - b_{\perp}$ obtained from equation 15.3 with a computed value of $(b_{\parallel} - b_{\perp})_0$ of the repeating unit of the chain.[3] The latter quantity is calculated from the principal polarizabilities of the constituent bonds. The value for $(b_{\parallel} - b_{\perp})_0$ which is calculated depends upon the assumptions which are made concerning the configuration of the monomer unit. Treloar assumes that the isoprene unit in natural rubber is constrained to a planar rigid configuration. An alternative assumption would be to permit free rotation about all single bonds within the monomer unit. The actual configuration is somewhere between these two assumptions.[4] For an isoprene segment in natural rubber $(b_{\parallel} - b_{\perp})_0$ is 30.8×10^{-22} cm^3 if the planar configuration is assumed; if free rotation around single bonds is assumed, the value is 17.8×10^{-22} cm^3.

In general, one finds that the actual value of $b_{\parallel} - b_{\perp}$ obtained from equation 15.3 is larger than the computed value of $(b_{\parallel} - b_{\perp})_0$ for the repeating unit. This is a consequence of the stiffness of the polymer chain and results from factors such as asymmetrical restricted rotation and steric hindrance discussed in section 1, Chapter II. For example Treloar finds that $(b_{\parallel} - b_{\perp})/(b_{\parallel} - b_{\perp})_0$ is 1.52.[3] He interprets this as indicating that "one random link is the optical equivalent of 1.52 isoprene units." The value of the quantity $z = (b_{\parallel} - b_{\perp})/(b_{\parallel} - b_{\perp})_0$ will, of course, depend somewhat on the method for calculating $(b_{\parallel} - b_{\perp})_0$.

Table IV.8

OPTICAL ANISOTROPY OF THE STATISTICAL SEGMENT FOR NATURAL RUBBER

$f/T\Delta \times 10^{-7}$ dynes/cm^2	T, °C	$(b_{\parallel} - b_{\perp}) \times 10^{25}$ cm^3	z
1.1 [a]	30	73	3.0
2.0 [b]	20	40	1.7
1.7 [c]	25	46.7	2.0
1.4 [d]	50	50	2.1

[a] W. Kuhn and H. Grun, *Kolloid Z.*, **101**, 248 (1942); W. Kuhn, *J. Polymer Sci.*, **1**, 380 (1946).

[b] J. J. Hermans, *Kolloid Z.*, **103**, 210 (1943).

[c] L. R. G. Treloar, *The Physics of Rubber Elasticity*, p. 148, Oxford Press, 1949.

[d] R. S. Stein and A. V. Tobolsky, *Textile Research J.*, **18**, 201, 302 (1948).

Table IV.8 gives some results for $b_\parallel - b_\perp$ obtained for natural rubber (Hevea rubber) and the range of calculated values of z. The value of $(b_\parallel - b_\perp)_0$ for the isoprene segment was taken as 24×10^{-22} cm^3, which is the average of the planar configuration value and the free-rotation value.

Equations 15.1 to 15.3 were used by Tobolsky and Stein [5] as a diagnostic test for identifying the molecular origin of stress in strained polymer samples as well as the molecular mechanism for stress relaxation (see Figure IV.51).

Polyisobutylene samples were maintained at constant extension (and constant temperature) in the range 50 to $-40°$C, and measurements were made of both stress and birefringence. It was found that birefringence decayed in exactly the same manner as stress, and in fact the quantity $f/T\Delta$ was a constant, independent of time, temperature and elongation.[6]

For polyisobutylene the temperature range of 50 to $-40°$ covers the region of rubbery flow, the rubbery plateau, and the low-modulus portion of the transition region. In these regions the stress in a strained sample arises from the decrease of conformational entropy during stretching. The relaxation of stress at constant strain arises from a diffusion of polymer chains back to the isotropic macrostates of highest thermodynamic probability. Equations 15.1 through 15.3 are valid in these regions because stress and birefringence are computed from the same geometrical considerations. For $f/T\Delta$ to be independent of temperature in this interval as observed for polyisobutylene it is necessary that the size and the optical properties of the "statistical segment" should not change with temperature.

The quantity $f/T\Delta$ also remained constant as expected during stress-relaxation experiments in polysulfide rubbers (interchanging networks) and in vulcanized natural rubber during chemical stress relaxation (see Chapter V).[4,5]

In the case of Lactoprene rubber, which is essentially a cross-linked polyethyl acrylate, it was observed that the ratio of stress to birefringence remained constant during relaxation of stress experiments at constant temperature at all temperatures above $-17.5°$C (the T_g value of polyethyl acrylate is $-22°$C). However for Lactoprene rubber the birefringence at a given value of $\alpha = L_0/L_u$ is a function of temperature in the temperature range -20 to $+30°$C, and according to equation 15.1 this can only mean a change in the optical properties of the "statistical segment." The quantity $f/T\Delta$ also varies with temperature, showing a marked and almost discontinuous change near T_g. In fact, in the

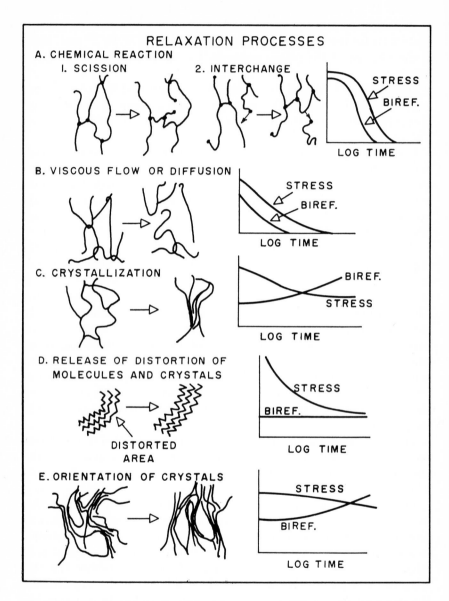

Figure IV.51. Types of relaxation unit processes which a polymer sample may undergo. The accompanying curves illustrate the type of variation of stress and birefringence expected for each of these unit processes. [After R. S. Stein and A. V. Tobolsky, *Textile Research J.*, **18**, 201 (1948).]

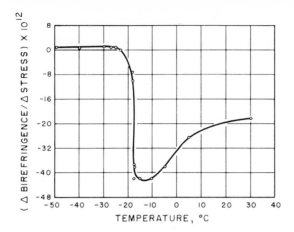

Figure IV.52. The variation of the ratio Δ birefringence/Δ stress with temperature for a Lactoprene vulcanizate. Sample stretched to 30% elongation at 30°C and maintained at fixed length while sample was cooled. [After R. S. Stein, S. Krimm and A. V. Tobolsky, *Textile Research J.*, **19**, 8 (1949).]

neighborhood of T_g the birefringence changes sign, and so does $f/T\Delta$, as shown in Figure IV.52.

In the high-modulus portion of the transition region, it is perhaps not surprising that there is a gradual change in $f/T\Delta$ with T. The optical properties of the "statistical segment" can change for two reasons: (1) The "statistical segment" may be changing in size as the temperature is lowered; more chain atoms per "statistical segment" are required in order that this entity may be regarded as a freely rotating unit of the polymer chain; (2) even if the "statistical segment" does not change in size with temperature, its optical properties may change, owing to change in rotation of side groups.

As the glass transition temperature and the glassy region of visco-elastic behavior are approached, the stress cannot be computed from equation 15.2, nor can the birefringence be computed from equation 15.1. The stress in the glassy state no longer arises from an entropy contribution exclusively, nor can the optical anisotropy be described in terms of randomly orienting "statistical segments." It is not surprising that $f/T\Delta$ often undergoes an abrupt change near T_g. In fact, birefringence of polymers in their glassy state is more usually described in terms of a stress optical coefficient Δ/f than in terms of $f/T\Delta$.

The stress optical coefficient in the glassy state depends very much on the local configurational relationships along the main chain.[7] This is interestingly brought out in Table IV.9. Substitution of groups on the

Table IV.9

Stress Optical Coefficient of Polymers in Glassy State [a]

Polymer	$\Delta/f \times 10^{13}$ cm^2/dyne
Atactic polystyrene	$+10$
Atactic poly-(p-tert-butylstyrene)	$+11$
Atactic poly-(α-methylstyrene)	-2
Isotactic polystyrene (quick-quenched to an amorphous condition)	$+12$

[a] R. D. Andrews, private communication.

main chain produces marked change in the stress optical coefficient, whereas a similar substitution remote from the chain backbone has only a slight effect.

In crystalline polymers birefringence may increase (in an absolute sense) during stress decay at constant extension because stress decay may result from orientation of crystalline regions and from oriented growth of nuclei and crystallites. This was applied as a diagnostic procedure to gelatin gels: Since these gels remain birefringent after stress decay at constant strain is complete, it was concluded that stress decay occurs in these "rubbery" gels because of orientation and oriented growth of crystalline regions.[8]

The quantitative interpretation of birefringence in stretched crystalline polymers by Stein treats the contributions from both the crystalline and amorphous regions and is as yet a rather complex computation.[9]

References IV.15

1. W. Kuhn and H. Grun, *Kolloid-Z.*, **101**, 248 (1942); W. Kuhn, *J. Polymer Sci.*, **1**, 380 (1946).
2. L. R. G. Treloar, *Trans. Faraday Soc.*, **43**, 277, 289 (1947).
3. L. R. G. Treloar, *The Physics of Rubber Elasticity*, pp. 147–150, Clarendon Press, Oxford, England, 1949.
4. R. S. Stein and A. V. Tobolsky, *J. Polymer Sci.*, **11**, 285 (1953).
5. R. S. Stein and A. V. Tobolsky, *Textile Research J.*, **18**, 201 (1948); *ibid.*, **18**, 302 (1948); R. S. Stein, S. Krimm and A. V. Tobolsky, *Textile Research J.*, **19**, 8 (1949).
6. R. S. Stein, F. H. Holmes and A. V. Tobolsky, *J. Polymer Sci.*, **14**, 443 (1954). See also R. S. Stein, Ph.D. thesis, Princeton University, 1948.
7. R. D. Andrews, private communication.
8. A. V. Tobolsky, *J. Phys. Chem.*, **59**, 575 (1955).
9. R. S. Stein, *J. Polymer Sci.*, **27**, 567 (1958).

CHAPTER V

Chemical Stress Relaxation

1. CHEMICAL STRESS RELAXATION IN HYDROCARBON RUBBER NETWORKS

The phenomenon of chemical stress relaxation was discovered in an investigation of cross-linked (vulcanized) rubbers of the hydrocarbon type.[1] The rubbers included natural rubber, neoprene, Butyl, butadiene-styrene copolymers, and butadiene-acrylonitrile copolymers.

It was found that in the temperature range 100 to 150°C these vulcanized rubbers showed a fairly rapid decay to zero stress at constant extension. Since in principle a cross-linked rubber network in the rubbery range of behavior should show little stress relaxation, and cer-

223

tainly no decay to zero stress, the phenomenon was attributed to a chemical rupture of the rubber network. This rupture was specifically ascribed to the effect of molecular oxygen since under conditions of *very low* oxygen pressures ($< 10^{-4}$ atm) the stress-relaxation rate was markedly diminished. However at moderately low oxygen pressures the rate of chemical stress relaxation was the same as at atmospheric conditions. This result parallels the very long established fact that in the liquid phase the rate of reaction of hydrocarbons with oxygen is independent of oxygen pressure down to fairly low pressures.

It is essential to ensure that the rubber samples used in these studies are thin enough to permit steady-state conditions of oxygen diffusion; otherwise the rate of chemical stress relaxation may become diffusion-controlled.

At the same time as the discovery of chemical stress relaxation, it was shown that creep of rubber at high temperatures was caused by molecular oxygen.[2]

In the original study of chemical stress relaxation, many other im-

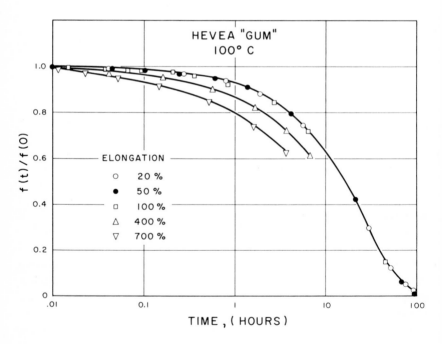

Figure V.1. Effect of elongation on chemical stress relaxation of sulfur-cured natural rubber at 100°C. [After A. V. Tobolsky, I. B. Prettyman and J. H. Dillon, *J. Appl. Phys.*, **15**, 324 (1944).]

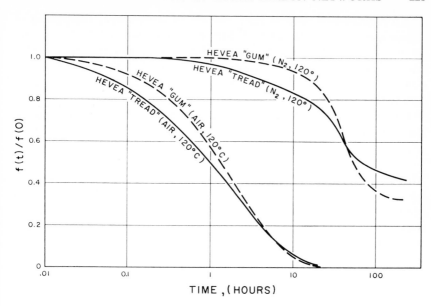

Figure V.2. Chemical stress-decay curves in air for sulfur-cured natural rubber The "gum" contains no filler; the "tread" contains $33\frac{1}{3}\%$ by weight of reinforcing carbon black. Also shown are the stress-decay curves of these same rubbers in highly purified nitrogen. [After A. V. Tobolsky, I. B. Prettyman and J. H. Dillon, *J. Appl. Phys.*, **15**, 324 (1944); W. C. Schneider, Ph.D. thesis, Princeton University (1944).]

portant facts were established.[1] The relative stress-decay curves $f(t)/f(0)$, where $f(t)$ is the stress at time t, and $f(0)$ the initially measured stress, were found to be independent of the elongation at which the rubber was maintained up to values of at least 200% extension (extension ratio $\alpha = 3$). Some data of this type are shown for the natural-rubber vulcanizate in Figure V.1. The relative stress-decay curves $f(t)/f(0)$ were found to be nearly independent of the presence or absence of carbon black or other fillers, as shown in Figure V.2. Also shown in Figure V.2 is an example of the marked reduction in rate of stress relaxation which can be achieved by rigorous exclusion of oxygen. Complete exclusion is impossible, however, and it is of course impossible to remove peroxide groups along the chain simply by evacuation.

For natural rubber the decay curves were found to be Maxwellian, i.e., of the form

1.1 $$f(t)/f(0) = \exp{(-k't)}$$

The characteristic behavior of Maxwellian decay is that, when

$f(t)/f(0)$ is plotted against $\log t$, the decay occurs over two cycles of logarithmic time as shown in Figure I.5. This is very definitely true for natural rubber, as can be seen in Figure V.1. For the other hydrocarbon rubbers (GR-S, neoprene, Butyl, GR-N, etc.) the chemical stress decay, though not exactly Maxwellian, was also found to occur in two to three cycles of logarithmic time, as shown in Figure V.3.

For all these rubbers it was possible to describe the effect of temperature on chemical stress decay as follows,

1.2 $$f(t)/f(0) = \phi(k't)$$

where k' is a function of T alone. This, of course, means that, if $f(t)/f(0)$ for a given rubber is plotted against $\log t$, the decay curves at various temperatures can be superposed by horizontal translation along the logarithmic time axis. The functional dependence of k' on temperature was found to be expressed by the Arhennius equation

1.3 $$k' = A \exp\left(-E_{act}/RT\right)$$

For the rubbers shown in Figure V.3, E_{act} was found to be 30 ± 2 kcal/mole. For the particular natural-rubber vulcanizate used in this

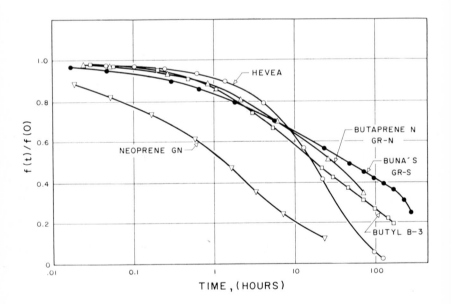

Figure V.3. Chemical stress-decay curves for several synthetic rubber vulcanizates of hydrocarbon-type structure at 100°C. [After A. V. Tobolsky, I. B. Prettyman and J. H. Dillon, *J. Appl. Phys.*, **15**, 324 (1944).]

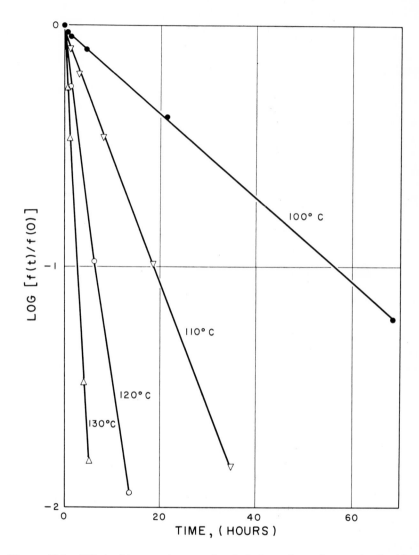

Figure V.4.   Effect of temperature on chemical stress decay for a natural-rubber vulcanizate.   Lines are computed from equations 1.1 and 1.4.   Points are experimental data.   [After A. V. Tobolsky, I. B. Prettyman and J. H. Dillon, *J. Appl. Phys.*, **15**, 324 (1944); R. D. Andrews, R. B. Mesrobian and A. V. Tobolsky, *India Rubber World*, **112**, May (1945).]

first study it was found that

1.4 $\qquad k' = 8.1 \times 10^{12} \exp(-30.4 \, \text{kcal}/RT)$

The predicted stress-decay curves based on equations 1.4 and 1.1 at 100, 110, 120 and 130° are shown compared to the experimental data in Figure V.4, plotted in the form $\log f(t)/f(0)$ vs. t.

Chemical stress relaxation therefore becomes a useful physical method for measuring a chemical-bond cleavage in rubber networks. The rate of this cleavage reaction was considered to be completely independent of the forces acting on the rubber network or of the elongation of the network (up to very high elongations).

References V.1

1. A. V. Tobolsky, I. B. Prettyman and J. H. Dillon, *J. Appl. Phys.*, **15**, 380 (1944).
2. M. Mooney, W. E. Wohlstenholme and D. S. Villars, *J. Appl. Phys.*, **15**, 324 (1944).

2. SCISSION AND CROSS LINKING

It was observed that during the chemical stress-relaxation experiments in the temperature range 100 to 150°C some of the rubber vulcanizates such as Butyl became progressively softer, others such as GR-S showed a continued hardening, and others such as natural rubber first softened and then hardened. It was deduced that at these elevated temperatures *both* cross linking and scission were occurring simultaneously, and the rates of both cross linking and scission were essentially unaffected by the stress or elongation of the sample.[1]

When the rubber is maintained at constant length, the scission reaction clearly causes a decay of stress. It was assumed that, to a first approximation, the cross-linking reaction does not affect the stress of the sample held at constant length, unless the cross linking becomes so very extensive that there is a volume shrinkage. Stated another way, we expect the cross links should form in such a way that the network produced is in a relaxed condition with respect to the momentary geometrical restraints of the sample, no matter whether the sample happens to be in stretched or unstretched condition.

On the other hand, the cross-linking reaction will be readily manifested if the length of the sample is changed after cross linking occurs.

From these considerations there arose the techniques of continuous stress relaxation and intermittent stress measurements as a method for measuring separately the effects of scission and of cross linking.[1,2]   The technique of continuous stress relaxation is the usual method by which a sample is continuously maintained at a fixed elongation, say 50%, and stress is measured as a function of time. According to our assumption, this method measures the effect of scission alone at least to a first approximation. In the intermittent stress measurements the sample is maintained in a relaxed, unstretched condition at a suitable constant temperature. At widely spaced time intervals the rubber is rapidly stretched to a fixed elongation (say 50%), the equilibrium stress is rapidly measured, and the sample is immediately returned to its unstretched length. This, of course, is nothing more than an intermittent measurement of the "modulus" of the network under conditions where the time duration of the stress measurements is very short compared to the time intervals between measurement. Nearly all the scission and cross linking may be considered as occurring while the network is in the unstretched condition. The intermittent stress measurements reflect the combined effect of scission and cross linking.

Sometimes for verbal brevity the measurements of continuous stress relaxation and the intermittent stress measurements have collectively been termed "continuous and intermittent stress-relaxation" measurements.

Suppose that the original network structure is characterized by $c(0)$ moles of effective tetrafunctional cross linkages per cubic centimeter. The number of moles of additional cross links per cubic centimeter that have subsequently formed up to time t will be denoted by $c(t)$, and the number of moles of cleavages per cubic centimeter by $q(t)$. If the unstretched length of the sample is L_u, the length at which stress is measured is L_0, and the intermittent stress measurement at time t is $f_i(t)$, then

$$2.1 \qquad f_i(t) = [2c(0) + 2c(t) - q(t)]RT \left[\left(\frac{L_0}{L_u}\right)^2 - \frac{L_u}{L_0} \right]$$

On the other hand, the stress $f(t)$ measured in a *continuous* relaxation of stress experiment, where the sample is maintained at length L_0 throughout the experiment, is

$$2.2 \qquad f(t) = [2c(0) - q(t)]RT \left[\left(\frac{L_0}{L_u}\right)^2 - \frac{L_u}{L_0} \right]$$

In both cases the initial stress $f(0)$ is

$$2.3 \qquad f(0) = 2c(0)RT \left[\left(\frac{L_0}{L_u}\right)^2 - \frac{L_u}{L_0} \right]$$

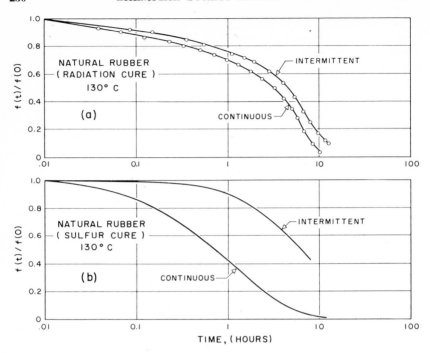

Figure V.5. (a) Continuous stress-relaxation and intermittent stress measurements for radiation-cured natural rubber at 130°C. [After A. V. Tobolsky and A. Mercurio, *J. Appl. Polymer Sci.* (in press).]   (b) Continuous stress relaxation and intermittent stress measurements for sulfur-cured natural rubber at 130°C. [After A. V. Tobolsky and R. D. Andrews, *J. Chem. Phys.*, **11**, 145 (1945).]

If only scission were occurring, the continuous stress-relaxation curves and the intermittent stress curves would be identical. In all the *early* experiments it was found that the stress at any given time in the intermittent experiment was larger than that in the continuous experiment: This difference represents the contribution of the cross-linking reaction.

The presence of cross linking could be attributed to two causes: first a continued cross linking by the vulcanizing reagents not completely used up in the vulcanizing process; second, a cross linking that is part of the same oxidative chain reaction as is the scission reaction.

Recent work has indicated how these two contributions to cross linking can be resolved.[3]   It is possible to obtain cross-linked networks of natural rubber, polybutadiene, etc., by exposure of the linear polymer to high-energy radiation.   This has the great advantage that no impurities are introduced into the network, i.e., no chemicals that may remain active as cross-linking agents after the vulcanization process.

In Figure V.5a are presented the data obtained by continuous and intermittent stress relaxation at 130° on natural rubber cross-linked by a 1-Mev electron beam. The near identity of these two curves indicates that for this substance scission occurs with practically no cross-linking reaction. Under the conditions of the experiment molecular oxygen produces no cross linking in natural rubber.

By contrast, continuous and intermittent stress-relaxation curves at 130° are shown in Figure V.5b for natural rubber, which was cross-linked by sulfur plus chemical accelerators. Here the difference between the intermittent stress measurements and the continuous stress-relaxation curves must be attributed to a continued cross linking by the chemical vulcanization agents.

On the other hand, results of continuous stress relaxation and intermittent stress measurements for emulsion-prepared butadiene and for all-*cis*-1,4-polybutadiene, both cross-linked by a 1-Mev electron beam are shown in Figure V.6. It is clear that in these cases an important cross

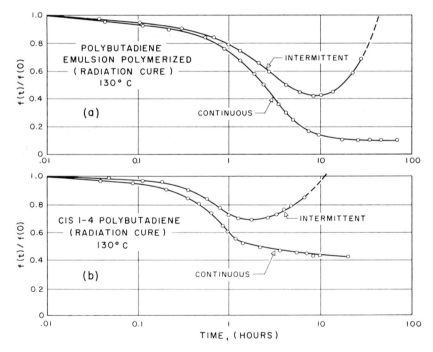

Figure V.6. Continuous stress-relaxation and intermittent stress measurements at 130°C for (a) radiation-cured emulsion polybutadiene and for (b) all *cis*-1,4-poly-butadiene. [After A. V. Tobolsky and A. Mercurio, *J. Appl. Polymer Sci.*, **2**, 186 (1959).]

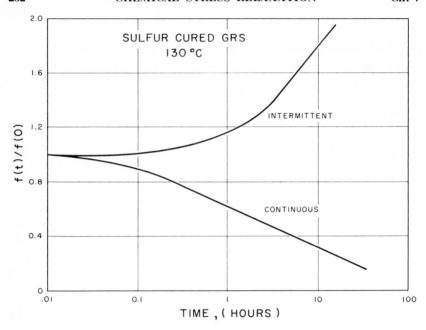

Figure V.7. Continuous stress-relaxation and intermittent stress measurements for sulfur-cured GR-S at 130°C. [After A. V. Tobolsky, I. B. Prettyman and J. H. Dillon, *J. Appl. Phys.*, **15**, 309 (1944).]

linking due to oxidation indubitably exists. The emulsion-prepared polybutadiene contains 20% 1,2 structure, 60% *trans*-1,4 structure and 20% *cis*-1,4 structure.[4] Since both polybutadienes show oxidative cross linking, this reaction cannot be attributed to the 1,2 structure alone.

An example of an intermittent stress curve which shows a steady increase from the very beginning is shown in Figure V.7 for sulfur-cured GR-S at 130°C.

References V.2

1. A. V. Tobolsky, I. B. Prettyman and J. H. Dillon, *J. Appl. Phys.*, **15**, 309 (1944).
2. A. V. Tobolsky and R. D. Andrews, *J. Chem. Phys.*, **11**, 125 (1945).
3. A. V. Tobolsky and A. Mercurio, *J. Appl. Polymer Sci.* (in press).
4. J. L. Binder, *Anal. Chem.*, **26**, 1877 (1954).

3. CLEAVAGE RATES FROM STRESS RELAXATION

In a rubber network with $n(0)$ moles of network chains per cubic centimeter at temperature T the relation between stress (force per unit area of attained cross-sectional area) and the extension ratio $\alpha = L/L_u$ is given by

3.1 $$f = n(0)\mathbf{R}T[\alpha^2 - (1/\alpha)]$$

The quantity $n(0)$ can be determined by measuring f, α and T under appropriate experimental conditions.

Suppose that the rubber network is maintained at fixed extension ratio α. At time t we suppose that $q(t)$ moles per cubic centimeter of cuts have occurred, and that there are $n(q)$ moles of network chains per cubic centimeter of the original network that are still supporting the stress. We have to identify $n(q)$ [it may also be termed $n(t)$] as those network chains which have *never* been cut up through time t. Furthermore, $n(q)$ can be measured directly by continuous stress relaxation by the following relation,

3.2 $$\frac{f(t)}{f(0)} = \frac{n(q)}{n(0)} = \frac{n(t)}{n(0)}$$

where $f(0)$ is the stress at time zero, and $n(0)$ is the concentration of network chains at time zero, i.e., before scission.

It is now necessary to derive the relationship between $n(q)$ and q so that q may be obtained from the experimentally determined values of $f(t)/f(0)$. We shall consider two cases.

Case A.   Random cleavage at the links of the network chains. First we shall assume that chain cleavage occurs randomly throughout the rubber network and that there are a large number of available sites for scisson along each network chain. This means that a network chain once cut can be cut again with equal likelihood.

It has already been established that $n(q)$ are the chains per cubic centimeter that have not been cut up to time t. At time t the probability that a new cut will occur among the $n(q)$ chains is $n(q)/n(0)$. The relationship between $n(q)$ and q is therefore [1]

3.3 $$\frac{-dn(q)}{dq} = \frac{n(q)}{n(0)}$$

Upon integration, and inserting the boundary condition $n(q) = n(0)$ at $q = 0$, one obtains

3.4
$$q = -n(0) \ln [n(q)/n(0)]$$

Inserting equation 3.2,

3.5
$$q(t) = -n(0) \ln [f(t)/f(0)]$$

Hence $q(t)$ can be obtained directly from a stress-relaxation measurement and a measurement of equilibrium stress-strain properties at $t = 0$ to obtain $n(0)$.

For a series of rubbers cross-linked to different degrees but otherwise identical we should expect $q(t)$ to be the same. However, $f(t)/f(0)$ should be different, if equation 3.5 is valid. This is a most powerful criterion for determining in any given case whether random scission of the network is occurring as discussed here or whether scission is occurring at the sites of cross linkage.

If the rate of scission is constant, i.e., if $q = q_0' t$, then substituting into equation 3.5, one obtains

3.6
$$\frac{f(t)}{f(0)} = \exp\left(-\frac{q_0' t}{n(0)}\right)$$

which is, of course, Maxwellian decay.

The kinetics of the cleavage reaction and therefore the functional form of $q(t)$ will depend entirely on the chemistry of the scission reaction. A constant rate of cleavage might be expected in certain cases; however, the kinetics of scission may be much more complex, especially if scission occurs in a chain reaction. Maxwellian decay is therefore neither a necessary nor a sufficient consequence of random scission along the links of the network chains.

Case B. Cleavage at the cross-link sites. Suppose that cleavage took place specifically at or adjacent to the network junctures. For convenience, consider that the cleavage at or near the cross link severed one network chain, and that each network chain had just one site of cleavage. The relationship between $n(q)$ and q is

3.7
$$n(q) = n(0) - q$$

or, upon substituting equation 3.2, one obtains

3.8
$$q(t) = n(0)[1 - f(t)/f(0)]$$

3.9
$$\frac{f(t)}{f(0)} = 1 - \frac{q(t)}{n(0)}$$

In this case we expect the total number of cuts per cubic centimeter that have occurred up to time t, which we have designated $q(t)$, to be proportional to $n(0)$ for a series of rubbers cross-linked to different degrees but otherwise identical. This follows from the fact that sites for scission are here assumed to be restricted to the cross links. We should therefore expect that $q(t)$ should be proportional to $n(0)$ for a series of such rubbers, but that $f(t)/f(0)$ would be independent of $n(0)$, as can be seen from equation 3.9.[2]

The simplest kinetic relationship one might anticipate in case B is

3.10 $\qquad -dn(q)/dt = k'\, n(q)$

3.11 $\qquad n(q) = n(0)\exp(-k't)$

3.12 $\qquad f(t)/f(0) = \exp(-k't)$

Therefore scission at the cross-link sites may lead to Maxwellian decay. However, the scission reaction need not obey equation 3.10; the kinetic law of bond cleavage may not necessarily be a first-order law. Cleavage at the network junctures is neither a necessary nor a sufficient condition for Maxwellian decay.

The shapes of the stress-relaxation curves cannot be used to distinguish between random scission of a rubber network between cross links as opposed to scission specifically at the cross-link sites.

References V.3

1. A. V. Tobolsky, D. J. Metz and R. B. Mesrobian, *J. Am. Chem. Soc.*, **72**, 1942 (1950).
2. A. V. Tobolsky, *J. Appl. Phys.*, **27**, 673 (1956).

4. CLEAVAGE AT CROSS LINKS VERSUS CLEAVAGE ALONG THE NETWORK CHAINS

In the original study of chemical stress relaxation, it was found that natural rubber vulcanized with sulfur and natural rubber vulcanized with dinitrosobenzene had very similar scission rates. On the other hand, a series of rubbers of different chain structure but vulcanized in identical fashion had very different relaxation curves. It was concluded that scission must therefore be occurring along the network chains rather than at the cross links.[1]

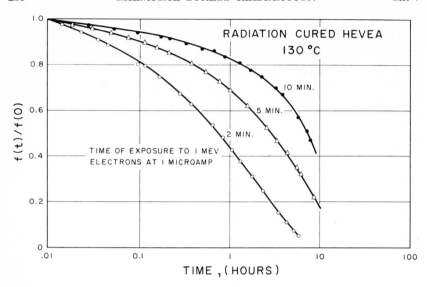

Figure V.8. Stress-decay curves at 130°C of radiation-cured natural rubber of different cross-link densities. [After A. V. Tobolsky, A. Mercurio and H. Yu, *J. Appl. Polymer Sci.* (manuscript in preparation).]

This conclusion was subsequently challenged on the basis of analysis of the shape of the stress-decay curves. It was asserted that, in natural rubber vulcanized by sulfur or peroxides, scission occurs at the cross links.[2]

An exhaustive group of investigations has proved beyond any doubt that the original contention was true.

Part A. Oxidative stress relaxation of radiation cross-linked natural rubber.[3] Natural rubber in the form of a thin sheet cast from the latex was cross-linked by exposing it to a 1-Mev electron beam from a Van de Graaff source. Such samples are eminently suited for chemical stress-relaxation studies because they introduce a minimum of chemicals which may subsequently act as pro-oxidants or antioxidants. The use of chemical cures is greatly complicated for this reason. Various samples were prepared of different cross-link density, i.e., different values of $n(0)$. The $n(0)$ values for the samples were determined by measuring the stress at 100% elongation and using the equation of state for rubber.

$$4.1 \qquad f(0) = n(0)\mathbf{R}T\left[\left(\frac{L_0}{L_u}\right)^2 - \frac{L_u}{L_0}\right]$$

It was found that 1.9 cross links were formed per 100 ev of energy absorbed.

The subsequent stress-relaxation experiments at 130°C are shown in Figure V.8. The same data are shown plotted in the form of $q(t)$ versus time in Figure V.9, where $q(t)$ was obtained from equation 3.5.

The results clearly follow the pattern discussed under case A of section 3, the case of random cleavage of the links of the network chains as opposed to cleavage at the cross links. Explicitly, $q(t)$ is seen to be independent of $n(0)$ but the $f(t)/f(0)$ vs. t curves are seen to depend on $n(0)$, as predicted for random scission of the network chains.[4] This result has also been found for natural rubber cross-linked by azodicarboxylates.[5]

Part B.   Cleavage rate of unvulcanized natural rubber.[3] The scission in unvulcanized natural rubber exposed to air at 130°C was measured by following the change in number-average molecular weight with time. The sample used was in the form of a thin film of rubber, and the molecular weight as a function of time was determined by withdrawing small samples and measuring intrinsic viscosity. The quantity

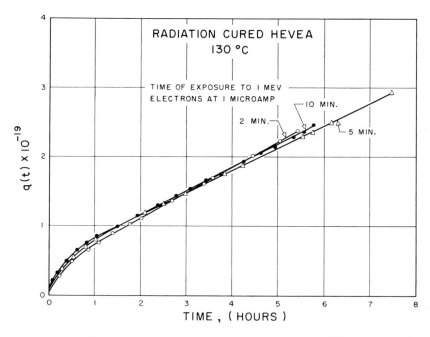

Figure V.9. $q(t)$ vs. t for radiation-cured natural rubber at 130°C. $Q(t)$ vs. t for unvulcanized natural rubber at 130°C is approximately the same. [After A. V. Tobolsky, A. Mercurio and H. Yu (manuscript in preparation).]

Table V.1

CHAIN STRUCTURE OF CERTAIN RUBBERS *

Material	Structure
Natural rubber	$-CH_2-C=CH-CH_2-CH_2-C=CH-CH_2-CH_2-C=CH-CH_2-$ (with CH_3 groups) cis-1,4-polyisoprene
GR-S	$-CH-CH_2-CH_2-CH=CH-CH_2-CH=CH-CH_2-CH=CH-CH_2-CH_2-CH=CH-CH_2-$ ϕ ... ϕ 75% butadiene, 25% styrene, random copolymer
Butyl rubber	$-CH_2-C-CH_2-C=CH-CH_2-CH_2-C-CH_2-C-$ (with CH_3 groups) Polyisobutylene copolymerized with 2% isoprene
Polyester rubber	$-O-(CH_2)_x-O-C-(CH_2)_x-O-C-(CH_2)_x-CH=CH-(CH_2)_x-C-O-(CH_2)_x-O-$ (with O double bonds) Aliphatic polyester containing a few % unsaturated segments
Adduct rubber	$CH_2-CH-CH_2-CH_2-CH-CH_2-CH_2-CH=CH-CH_2-$ (with SCH_3 groups) Polybutadiene in which 97% of the double bonds are saturated with methyl mercaptan

* The vulcanized rubbers used in this study (reference 6) were in fact thoroughly extracted before use to remove antioxidant, contrary to the statement made in J. R. Dunn, J. Scanlan and W. F. Watson, *Trans. Faraday Soc.*, **55**, 667 (1959).

$Q(t)$, the moles of cleavages per cubic centimeter of rubber, was determined by the equation

4.2
$$Q(t) = d \left[\frac{1}{\overline{M}_n(t)} - \frac{1}{\overline{M}_n(0)} \right]$$

In equation 4.2, d is the density of the rubber, $\overline{M}_n(t)$ the number-average molecular weight at time t and $\overline{M}_n(0)$ the number-average molecular weight at time zero.

A comparison of $q(t)$ from stress relaxation of radiation-cured natural rubber at 130°C with $Q(t)$ from scission of unvulcanized natural rubber at the same temperature is shown in Figure V.9. It is seen that there is good agreement between these quantities. This must mean that scission measured by stress relaxation is, in fact, a random cleavage along the polyisoprene chains, *not* specifically at the cross links, at least in the radiation-cured networks.

Part C. Stress decay in sulfur cures versus sulfurless cures for five different chain structures.[6] Five hydrocarbon rubbers of very different chain structure were vulcanized by sulfur cures (elemental sulfur plus sulfur-containing accelerators) and also by non-sulfur-containing cures (high-energy radiation, dicumyl peroxide and p-quinone dioxime plus lead peroxide). In all the chain structures at least one or two mole per cent of carbon-carbon double bonds was present in the unvulcanized polymer so that the sites at which cross linking took place are believed to be somewhat similar. Very different types of cross linkages are undoubtedly produced by these two classes of curing agents: The sulfur cures are thought to produce thioether and other sulfur-containing cross linkages; high-energy radiation and dicumyl peroxide are thought to produce carbon-carbon cross linkages.

The chain structures of the rubbers used (natural rubber, GR-S, Butyl, polyester rubber and Adduct rubber) are shown in Table V.1. The vulcanizates were prepared without antioxidant and were solvent-extracted before the stress-relaxation studies were made. The concentration of cross links as between the sulfur cure and the sulfurless cure of the same rubber were made very similar, as verified by a similar value obtained for $n(0)$.

Stress-relaxation curves were plotted in the form $\log f(t)/f(0)$ versus time, which will give a straight line for Maxwellian decay. The stress-decay curves at 130° plotted in this manner are presented in Figure V.10. Table V.2 gives the chemical relaxation time τ_{ch} for the 10 samples investigated. The chemical relaxation time τ_{ch} is the time required to reach

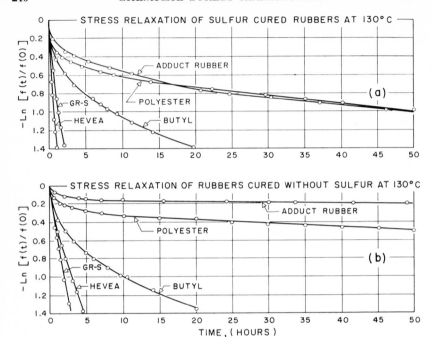

Figure V.10. ln $[f(t)/f(0)]$ vs. t for sulfur and nonsulfur cures of five polymers of different chain structure. [After A. V. Tobolsky and A. Mercurio, *J. Polymer Sci.*, **36**, 467 (1959).]

a value of $f(t)/f(0) = 1/e = 0.368$ in a chemical stress-relaxation experiment.

It is interesting to note that for the purely hydrocarbon rubbers (natural rubber, GR-S and Butyl) the difference in relaxation time between sulfur cures and sulfurless cures is not large, at the very largest a factor of four. Actually a wide spectrum of such cures was tried and the differences in relaxation times shown are extremes. Addition of small amounts of antioxidant to the natural rubber and GR-S did in effect nearly eliminate the difference in τ_{ch} between the sulfur and sulfurless cures of these rubbers.[7]

It is interesting to note that the chemical relaxation time of Butyl rubber was practically unaffected by the nature of the cure.

On the other hand, for both the sulfur cures and the sulfurless cures there is an extremely marked dependence of chemical relaxation time upon chain structure. For the sulfur cures the range in chemical relaxation times is from 0.7 to 50 hr; for the sulfurless cures from 2.8 to much

Table V.2

CHEMICAL RELAXATION TIMES AT 130°C FOR SULFUR-CURED AND
SULFURLESS-CURED RUBBERS

τ_{ch}, hours

Material	Sulfur Cure	Sulfurless Cure
Natural rubber	0.7	2.8
GR-S	1.2	1.9
Butyl rubber	9	10
Polyester rubber	51	300
Adduct rubber	50	>1,000

over 1,000 hr. In the case of the sulfur cures it appears that a limiting chemical relaxation time of 50 hr is reached by the polyester rubber and Adduct rubber.

It is clear that, for natural rubber, GR-S and Butyl rubber, scission must occur along the hydrocarbon chains; otherwise much larger differences would be observed between the sulfur and sulfurless cures. For polyester rubber and for Adduct rubber, whose chains are highly resistant to scission, the cross links may be the sites of cleavage, at least in certain cures such as sulfur cures.

Chemical stress-relaxation studies and oxygen-absorption studies on a wide variety of rubbers have indicated that electron-withdrawing groups in the polymer chain seem to confer stability toward oxidative scission, while electron-donating groups seem to make a polymer more susceptible to oxidation.[8, 9]

Stress-relaxation studies have also proved valuable in the evaluation of chemical antioxidants.[10]

References V.4

1. A. V. Tobolsky, I. B. Prettyman and J. H. Dillon, *J. Appl. Phys.*, **15**, 324 (1944).
2. J. P. Berry and W. F. Watson, *J. Polymer Sci.*, **18**, 201 (1955); *J. Polymer Sci.*, **25**, 493, 494, 497 (1957).
3. A. V. Tobolsky, A. Mercurio and H. Yu, manuscript in preparation.
4. A. V. Tobolsky, D. J. Metz and R. B. Mesrobian, *J. Am. Chem. Soc.*, **72**, 1942 (1950).
5. D. J. Metz and R. B. Mesrobian, *J. Polymer Sci.*, **11**, 83 (1953).

6. A. V. Tobolsky and A. Mercurio, *J. Polymer Sci.*, **36**, 467 (1959).
7. A. Mercurio, Ph.D. thesis, Princeton University, 1959.
8. R. B. Mesrobian and A. V. Tobolsky, *J. Polymer Sci.*, **2**, 463 (1947).
9. A. V. Tobolsky, *Disc. Faraday Soc.*, **2**, 384 (1948).
10. R. B. Mesrobian and A. V. Tobolsky, *Ind. Eng. Chem.*, **41**, 1496 (1949).

5. CHEMICAL PERMANENT SET

If rubber samples are maintained at constant extension at temperatures at which their properties are governed by chemorheological behavior, they will exhibit a "permanent set" or irrecoverable deformation when released from their strained position. There are two reasons for this permanent set: In the first place, the original network structure that is under strain is being gradually destroyed by scission, so that the retractive force that tends to restore the sample to its original length is gradually decreasing; second, new network structure is being formed by cross linking, which is in equilibrium with the strained condition of the sample, and which therefore resists any change from the strained length of the sample. When the sample is released, it will return to a length at which these two opposing forces balance each other.

These two opposing forces can be related to the quantities U and X

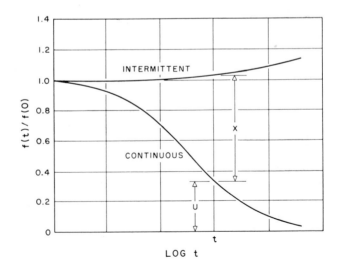

Figure V.11. U and X as defined in the theory of chemical permanent set. [After R. D. Andrews, A. V. Tobolsky and E. E. Hanson, *J. Appl. Phys.*, **17**, 352 (1946).]

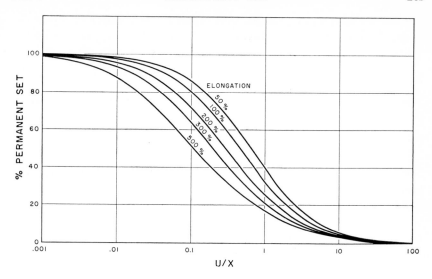

Figure V.12. Permanent set versus U/X for various elongations. [After A. V. Tobolsky, R. D. Andrews and E. E. Hanson, *J. Appl. Phys.*, **17**, 352 (1946).]

obtained from continuous and intermittent relaxation curves as shown in Figure V.11 and discussed below.

Let us denote the unstretched and the extended lengths of the rubber sample by L_u and L_x, respectively, and the "set" length by L_s. The "set" length is the length to which the rubber sample will return (eventually) when released from the stretched length L_x.

When the rubber sample has been released and attains its new length L_s, we may write for the two sets of chains in the rubber network the equations

5.1
$$f_u = n_u RT \left[\left(\frac{L_s}{L_u} \right)^2 - \frac{L_u}{L_s} \right]$$

5.2
$$f_x = n_x RT \left[\left(\frac{L_s}{L_x} \right)^2 - \frac{L_x}{L_u} \right]$$

In these equations f_u is the stress (per unit attained cross-sectional area) on the chains which have their equilibrium position at the unstretched length L_u, and N_u is the number of uncut network chains per cubic centimeter which have their equilibrium position at the unstretched length L_u. Correspondingly, f_x and n_x are defined for the network chains which are at equilibrium (or unstressed) at the extended length L_x. Now the condition for equilibrium in a sample with permanent-set length L_s is that the retractive force exerted by the chains of type u is just balanced by the stretching force exerted by chains of type x.

5.3 $$f_u = -f_x$$

Combining equations 5.1 through 5.3, one obtains after simplification

5.4 $$\frac{n_u L_x{}^2}{n_x L_u{}^2} = \frac{L_x{}^3 - L_s{}^3}{L_s{}^3 - L_u{}^3}$$

Permanent set (which we shall term PS) is generally expressed as the percentage of the deformation retained by the sample; stated mathematically:

5.5 $$PS = \frac{L_s - L_u}{L_x - L_u} \times 100$$

$$= \frac{L_s/L_u - 1}{L_x/L_u - 1} \times 100$$

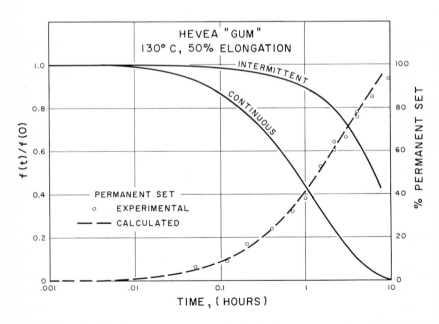

Figure V.13. Theoretical versus experimental permanent-set curve for sulfurcured natural rubber. [After R. D. Andrews, A. V. Tobolsky and E. E. Hanson, *J. Appl. Phys.*, **17**, 352 (1946).]

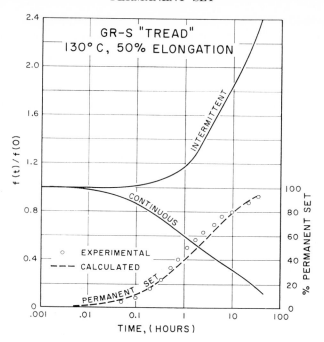

Figure V.14. Theoretical versus experimental permanent set for sulfur-cured GR-S. [After R. D. Andrews, A. V. Tobolsky and E. E. Hanson, *J. Appl. Phys.*, 17, 352 (1946).]

Eliminating between equations 5.4 and 5.5, there results

$$5.6 \qquad \mathrm{PS} = C_3 \left[\left(\frac{C_1}{(n_u/n_x)C_2} + 1 \right)^{1/3} - 1 \right]$$

where C_1, C_2 and C_3 are all simply defined in terms of the experimental quantity L_x/L_u.

$$5.7 \qquad C_1 = (L_x/L_u)^3 - 1$$

$$C_2 = (L_x/L_u)^2$$

$$C_3 = \frac{100}{(L_x/L_u - 1)}$$

The basic idea of the theory of permanent set is that $n_u/n_x = U/X$, where U and X are obtained from continuous and intermittent stress relaxation, as shown in Figure V.11. This follows from the discussion of intermittent and continuous stress relaxation and is inherent in the "two-network theory." The equation for permanent set becomes

5.8
$$PS = C_3 \left[\left(\frac{C_1}{(U/X)C_2 + 1} + 1 \right)^{\!\!1/3} - 1 \right]$$

A graph of the permanent-set function plotted as PS vs. log (U/X) for a number of different per cent elongations is shown in Figure V.12.

It is necessary to add a few remarks concerning the assumption that cross linking takes place in such a manner as to form chains which are relaxed when the sample is at the length at which the cross links were formed. It is not possible to describe satisfactorily in mathematical fashion a *single* cross-linking process; the effect must rather be considered a statistical one, and it is necessary to say that the *average effect* of the cross linking is to form new chains which are relaxed at the length at which they are formed.

The experimental results used to verify the theory of permanent set are shown in Figures V.13 to V.15. Very good agreement between theory and experiment was obtained. The experimental procedure is fully described in reference 1. It is necessary to wait until the equilibrium

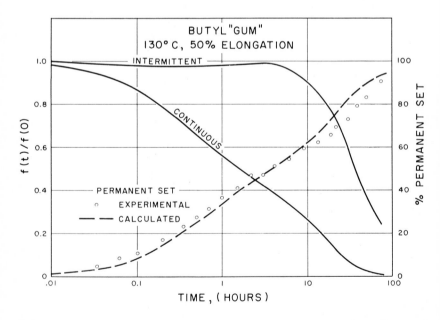

Figure V.15. Theoretical versus experimental permanent set for sulfur-cured Butyl rubber. [After R. D. Andrews, A. V. Tobolsky and E. E. Hanson, *J. Appl. Phys.*, **17**, 352 (1946).]

permanent-set length is obtained after the sample is released. In those rubbers where scission is caused by diffusion of molecular oxygen, sufficiently thin samples must be used so that the reaction is uniform throughout and not confined to a surface skin.

It must be emphasized that the theory developed applies to samples at sufficiently high temperatures so that the chief cause of viscoelastic behavior is chemorheological. Many "compression-set" experiments which are used in industrial practice and are frequently carried out at 70°C do not fall into this category. On the other hand, many of these experiments carried out at 100°C or higher do reflect the effect of cross-linking reactions, such as continued action of the vulcanizing ingredients. The samples used in industrial practice however are usually too thick to give a uniform scission reaction.

Reference V.5

1. R. D. Andrews, A. V. Tobolsky and E. E. Hanson, *J. Appl. Phys.*, **17**, 352 (1946).

6. CHEMICAL CREEP UNDER CONSTANT LOAD [1]

If a vulcanized rubber sample is subjected to a constant load in the temperature range of chemorheological behavior, it will first exhibit an immediate elastic response and then will continue to elongate indefinitely because of the scission of the network. This phenomenon may be termed chemical creep.

The simplest case to treat is that *where scission occurs exclusively*. It is convenient to start with the equation for rubber elasticity expressed in the form

$$6.1 \qquad F = n(0)\mathbf{R}T \left\{ \frac{L(0)}{L_u} - \left[\frac{L_u}{L(0)} \right]^2 \right\}$$

In this equation F represents the stress per *original* cross-sectional area, which under the conditions of the experiment remains constant with time. $n(0)$ is the moles of network chains per cubic centimeter at zero time. L_u is the unstretched length and $L(0)$ the length attained immediately after the application of stress F.

At time t the equation may be written as follows,

$$6.2 \qquad F = n(t)\mathbf{R}T \left\{ \frac{L(t)}{L_u} - \left[\frac{L_u}{L(t)} \right]^2 \right\}$$

where $L(t)$ is the length which the sample has attained at time t and $N(t)$ is the number of network chains per cubic centimeter still uncut at time t.

Eliminating between equations 6.1 and 6.2 one obtains

6.3
$$\frac{n(t)}{n(0)} = \frac{L(0)/L_u - [L_u/L(0)]^2}{L(t)/L_u - [L_u/L(t)]^2}$$

Equation 6.3 has been derived on the basis that scission occurs to the complete exclusion of cross linking, a situation which occurs only rarely. We may, however, define the experimentally measurable function on the right-hand side of equation 6.3 as the chemical creep function CCF:

6.4
$$CCF = \frac{L(0)/L_u - [L_u/L(0)]^2}{L(t)/L_u - [L_u/L(t)]^2}$$

In the absence of cross linking a comparison of equations 6.3 and 3.2 shows that the chemical creep function CCF and the chemical stress-relaxation function $f(t)/f(0)$ should be identical. We might expect this

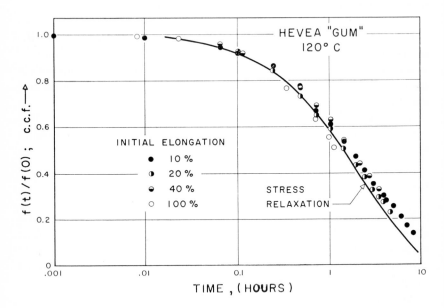

Figure V.16. Chemical creep function at 120°C for a sulfur-cured natural rubber compared with the stress-decay curve at 120°C. [After A. V. Tobolsky and R. D. Andrews, *J. Chem. Phys.*, **11**, 125 (1945).]

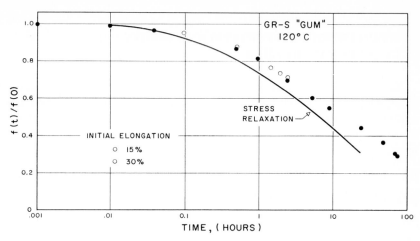

Figure V.17. Chemical creep function at 120°C for a sulfur-cured GR-S compared with the stress-decay curve at 120°C. [After A. V. Tobolsky and R. D. Andrews, *J. Chem. Phys.*, **11**, 125 (1945).]

to be so even where cross linking occurs, if the scission reaction predominates, as is shown in Figure V.16. If cross linking predominates, the CCF decays much more slowly than the stress-relaxation function, as shown in Figure V.17.

We may, of course, regard chemically interchanging networks as a special case of the picture we have developed of concurrent scission and cross linking. In this special case the rates of scission and cross linking are *exactly equal*.

We have already treated creep under constant load for interchanging networks (or for equal rates of scission and cross linking) in Chapter IV, section 14.

Reference V.6

1. A. V. Tobolsky and R. D. Andrews, *J. Chem. Phys.*, **13**, 125 (1945).

7. MECHANISM OF OXIDATIVE SCISSION IN NATURAL RUBBER

Natural-rubber oxidation by molecular oxygen involves a radical chain reaction [1] identical with the mechanism proposed to explain the oxidation of most hydrocarbons.[2] In the case where an external initiator (a free-radical source) is used, the following mechanism applies at intermediate or high oxygen pressure.

(a)   Initiator $\to$ 2R'· $\Big\}$

(a') R'· + RH $\to$ R· + R'H $\Big\}$ initiation

(b)   R· + O$_2$ $\to$ RO$_2$· $\Big\}$

(c)   RO$_2$· + RH $\to$ ROOH + R· $\Big\}$ propagation

(d)   RO$_2$· + RO$_2$· $\to$ termination products   termination

In the above equations RH represents natural rubber ($-CH_2-CH= C(CH_3)CH_2-)_n$. Radicals originating from the external initiator interact with the rubber in step a' to form R· either by the abstraction of an α-methylenic hydrogen atom or by attack at the double bond. A side reaction occurring in propagation is the intramolecular reaction of RO$_2$· as follows.[3]

$$OO·$$
$$|$$
$$-CH_2-C(CH_3)=CH-CH-CH_2-C(CH_3)=CH_2-$$

$$\overbrace{\qquad O-O \qquad}$$
$$-CH_2-C(CH_3)=CH-CH-CH_2-C(CH_3)-CH-CH_2- \xrightarrow{O_2}$$

$$\overbrace{\qquad O-O \qquad}$$
$$-CH_2-C(CH_3)=CH-CH-CH_2-C(CH_3)-CH-CH_2-$$
$$|$$
$$O$$
$$|$$
$$O·$$

A very noticeable consequence of the oxidation is scission of polyisoprene chains which we have emphasized in the preceding sections. This scission reaction has very recently been associated with a definite step in the kinetic sequence outlined above.[4]

This was accomplished by a kinetic study of scission of unvulcanized natural rubber in the form of dilute solutions of rubber in benzene which were exposed to a continuous supply of molecular oxygen at 1 atm pressure. The studies were made in the temperature range of 60 to 80°, and the oxidation chains were initiated by the well-studied catalysts benzoyl peroxide (Bz_2O_2), ditertiary butyl peroxide (DTBP), and 2-azobisisobutyronitrile (Azo-I). The rates at which these catalysts produce radicals are fairly accurately known from other studies.

The oxidation of natural rubber (and the accompanying scission) which occurs in the absence of external initiators is largely initiated by the hydroperoxides formed along the rubber chain. This is clearly an autocatalytic reaction, and for this reason the oxidation in the absence of external initiators is called autoxidation. Under the conditions of the kinetic studies reported here, autoxidation and autoxidative scission were negligible compared with the oxidation and accompanying scission produced by the external initiators.

Scission was measured by following the number-average molecular weight of the rubber as a function of time. The total moles of cuts per cubic centimeter of rubber which have occurred up to time t is denoted by $Q(t)$ and can be obtained from

7.1
$$Q(t) = d \left[\frac{1}{\overline{M}_n(t)} - \frac{1}{\overline{M}_n(0)} \right]$$

where $\overline{M}_n(t)$ is the number-average molecular weight at time t, $\overline{M}_n(0)$ is the initial number-average molecular weight and d is the density.

The rate R_i (in moles per cubic centimeter per second) at which the initiators used produce radicals is given by

7.2
$$R_i = 2k_d[\text{Init}]$$

$$-d[\text{Init}]/dt = k_d[\text{Init}]$$

where k_d is the rate constant for spontaneous first-order homolytic cleavage of the individual initiators. It is assumed that induced decomposition of these initiators is slight under these conditions.

Integration of equation 7.2 gives

7.3
$$\{R\cdot\}_t = 2[\text{Init}]_0[1 - \exp(-k_dt)]$$

where $\{R\cdot\}_t$ is the total moles of radicals per cubic centimeter which have been produced to time t. The values of k_d are well known for these initiators at the temperatures used; hence $\{R\cdot\}_t$ can be computed.

Table V.3

EXPERIMENTAL CONDITIONS FOR SCISSION STUDY

Initiator	$[\text{Init}]_0 \times 10^4$, moles/cm^3 of Rubber	RH Concentration, cm^3/liter	Temperature, °C	k_d sec^{-1}
Azo-I	1.76	1.16	70	3.80×10^{-5}
DTBP	19.5	1.39	70	1.44×10^{-8}
Bz$_2$O$_2$	1.01	1.02	60	3.34×10^{-6}
Bz$_2$O$_2$(1)	0.89	0.944	80	4.3×10^{-5}
Bz$_2$O$_2$(2)	3.02	1.00	80	4.3×10^{-5}

Table V.3 shows the experimental conditions of initiator concentration, temperature and rubber concentration in benzene at which the scission studies were made.

In Table V.4 are tabulated the data obtained for $\{R\cdot\}_t$ from equation 7.3 and $Q(t)$ from equation 7.1 under the experimental conditions used. It is seen that, for all three initiators, $Q(t)/\{R\cdot\}_t$ was of the order of magnitude of unity. Clearly one scission must occur for every oxidation chain, and $Q(t)/\{R\cdot\}_t$ must be a measure of initiator efficiency.

Since widely different initiation rates were used, scission could occur in the propagation step of the chain reaction only if under all our initiating conditions the kinetic chain length was unity. But this would mean one scission per oxygen molecule absorbed under all initiating conditions. However, it was shown that at these temperatures under purely thermal initiation there were approximately 30 molecules of oxygen absorbed per cut. These facts rule out the possibility of scission in the propagation steps.

The radicals $R'\cdot$ from the initiator can either react with rubber hydrocarbon RH to start an oxidation chain or they might add oxygen to form $R'O_2\cdot$. The direct attack of $R'\cdot$ on RH cannot cause scission, since it was shown that scission was negligible in the absence of oxygen. It is likewise very difficult to envisage that $R'O_2\cdot$ reacting with RH to start an oxidation chain will produce cleavage of RH. If this were so, there would be also cleavage in the propagation step $RO_2\cdot + RH \rightarrow ROOH + R\cdot$ since it is difficult to conceive that $R'O_2\cdot$ from *all* the initiators used should be uniquely different from $RO_2\cdot$.

It was therefore concluded that scission occurs in the termination step of the reaction where the collision of two peroxy radicals results in two cleavages.

Table V.4

RADICALS PRODUCED VERSUS CHAIN CLEAVAGES MEASURED DURING
OXIDATION OF NATURAL RUBBER [a]

Time, hours	$Q(t) \times 10^4$	$\{R\cdot\}_t \times 10^4$	$Q(t)/\{R\cdot\}_t$
Azo-I, 70°C			
2.08	0.601	0.99	0.61
3.93	1.38	1.47	0.94
5.35	1.86	1.82	1.02
7.73	2.48	2.22	1.12
15.60	3.14	3.10	1.01
29.93	3.72	3.45	1.08
DTBP, 70°C			
2.05	0.38	0.41	1.08
3.37	0.75	0.68	1.10
4.68	0.93	0.95	0.98
6.17	1.20	1.25	0.96
8.42	1.59	1.70	0.94
10.45	1.90	2.12	0.90
12.63	2.35	2.56	0.90
22.75	4.50	4.60	0.98
25.45	5.20	4.90	1.06
28.70	6.05	5.80	1.04
32.78	6.99	6.61	1.06
36.00	7.56	7.29	1.04
Bz$_2$O$_2$, 60°C			
2.18	0.184	0.54	0.34
4.13	0.382	1.00	0.38
6.70	0.631	1.57	0.40
9.25	0.920	2.12	0.43
13.30	1.20	2.97	0.40
24.60	2.28	5.15	0.44
Bz$_2$O$_2$(1), 80°C			
1.95	2.40	4.65	0.52
2.87	3.37	6.36	0.53
4.27	4.50	8.63	0.52
5.87	5.55	10.52	0.53
7.17	6.39	11.99	0.53
10.97	7.35	14.50	0.51
14.52	7.95	15.94	0.50
22.92	8.66	17.31	0.50
Bz$_2$O$_2$(2), 80°C			
1.80	0.481	1.48	0.33
3.87	1.15	2.72	0.42
6.76	1.71	3.93	0.44
9.65	2.12	4.70	0.45

[a] A. V. Tobolsky and A. Mercurio, *J. Am. Chem. Soc.*, **81**, 5535 (1959).

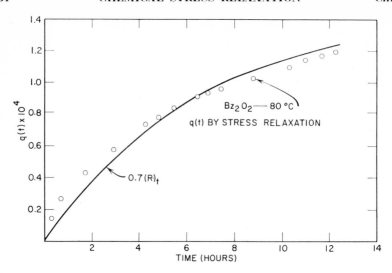

Figure V.18. $q(t)$ vs. t and $0.7\{R\cdot\}_t$ vs. t for the catalyzed oxidative degradation of a radiation-cured natural-rubber network. $q(t)$ is measured by stress relaxation. [After A. V. Tobolsky and A. Mercurio, *J. Am. Chem. Soc.*, **81**, 5539 (1959).]

A study of scission was also carried out in radiation-cured natural-rubber networks, into which a known amount of benzoyl peroxide was incorporated.[5] The moles of cuts per cubic centimeter of rubber $q(t)$ were determined by the technique of stress relaxation using equation 3.5. This was compared with the computed value of $\{R\cdot\}_t$ for benzoyl peroxide, using the known value of k_d for benzoyl peroxide at 80°C. This comparison is shown in Figure V.18, where the experimental points for $q(t)$ are shown to coincide rather closely with $0.7\{R\cdot\}_t$. Here again the number of cuts divided by the total number of radicals produced by the initiator is of the order of magnitude of unity. The quantity 0.7 probably represents the initiator efficiency under these conditions.

In the absence of a more effective source of radicals, the rubber hydroperoxide ROOH will act as the source of initiating radicals for oxidation and hence for scission. This source of initiation is unavoidably important at high temperatures, and in fact is the method by which oxidation was undoubtedly initiated in the stress-relaxation studies shown in Figures V.8 and V.9. The kinetics of the autoxidation reaction has some very interesting features, in particular the existence of steady-state concentrations of hydroperoxide.[6]

References V.7

1. Reviewed in N. Grassie, *The Chemistry of High Polymer Degradation Processes*, Chapter 4, Interscience Publishers, New York, 1956.
2. J. Bolland and G. Gee, *Trans. Faraday Soc.*, **42**, 236 (1946).
3. J. Bolland and H. Hughes, *J. Chem. Soc.* (**1949**), 492.
4. A. V. Tobolsky and A. Mercurio, *J. Am. Chem. Soc.*, **81**, 5535 (1959).
5. A. V. Tobolsky and A. Mercurio, *J. Am. Chem. Soc.*, **81**, 5539 (1959).
6. A. V. Tobolsky, D. Metz and R. B. Mesrobian, *J. Am. Chem. Soc.*, **72**, 1942 (1950).

8. POLYSULFIDE RUBBERS

The basic facts regarding chemical stress relaxation of polysulfide rubbers have already been discussed in Chapter IV, section 12. Stress relaxation in these rubber networks occurs through interchange of di-, tri- or tetrasulfide linkages with each other or with mercaptan and mercaptide linkages.

The existence of disulfide-disulfide and disulfide-mercaptan interchanges was in fact simultaneously discovered by stress-relaxation studies [1,2] and by the observation that mixed latexes of polysulfide rubbers formed copolymers.[3] These findings were first extended to small molecules in the case of the interchange of propyl disulfide and decyl mercaptan: [4]

$$CH_3CH_2CH_2SSCH_2CH_2CH_3 + CH_3(CH_2)_8CH_2SH \rightarrow$$

$$CH_3CH_2CH_2SSCH_2(CH_2)_8CH_3 + CH_3CH_2CH_2SH$$

It was found that this interchange requires several hours at 130°C if the ingredients are very pure but proceeds rapidly at room temperature with ionic catalysts. Similarly, in the polymerization of ring disulfides to linear polymers, it was found that polymerization was slow, even in the presence of a trace of water or of mercaptan. However, in the presence of an ionic reagent (bases such as sodium butyl mercaptide or Lewis acids such as $FeCl_3$ plus a trace of water), the polymerization is rapid.[5]

The findings concerning disulfide-disulfide interchanges have been extensive since these pioneering studies, and the subject has been recently reviewed.[6]

In the terminology of this chapter, the intermittent stress measurements on polysulfide rubbers show no change with time; i.e., the net effect of bond breaking and re-forming on the physical properties of an unstretched rubber network is zero. The stress decay at constant extension closely approximates Maxwellian decay and is unaffected by per cent extension or by the presence or absence of oxygen. The chemical relaxation times τ_{ch} at different temperatures obey the Arhennius law (see Figure V.19). The activation energy obtained by plotting $\log \tau_{ch}$ vs. $1/T$ for most polysulfide polymers is approximately 24 kcal/mole.

8.1 $$\tau_{ch} = A^{-1} \exp (E_{act}/RT)$$

Because of the "flat" intermittent curve, the permanent-set curve is the mirror image of the stress-decay curve, as shown in Figure V.20.

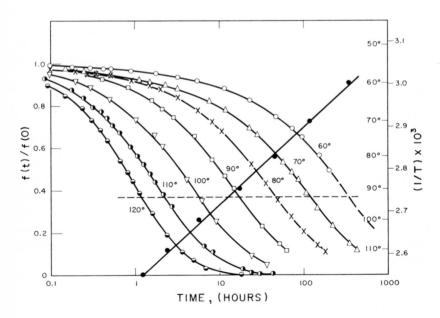

Figure V.19. Stress-decay curves for polysulfide rubber H-10 (Thiokol ST) at different temperatures. [After M. D. Stern and A. V. Tobolsky, *J. Chem. Phys.*, **14**, 93 (1946).]

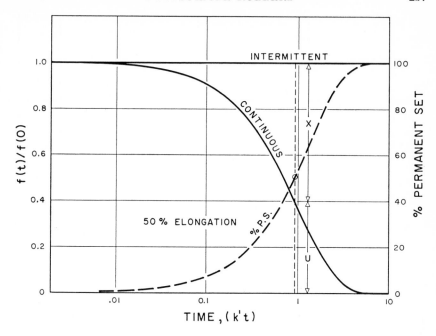

Figure V.20. Stress decay, intermittent stress measurements and permanent set in polysulfide rubbers.

The theory of creep under constant load which would apply for these substances is discussed in Chapter IV, section 14.

It is noteworthy that the chemical stress relaxation is very markedly affected by *traces* of mercaptan, by elemental sulfur which is allowed to diffuse into the rubber, by ionic reagents of all sorts, and by ultraviolet light.[2] In the last case, exchange *may* proceed via a radical mechanism.

A significant observation is the extremely large difference in chemical relaxation times observable in these rubbers, as illustrated in Figure V.21. Part of these very large variations may be due to the differences in basic chain structure of the polymers, i.e., the relative amount of disulfide, trisulfide and tetrasulfide linkages. But much of the variation in chemical relaxation time is due to adventitious traces of ionic catalysts introduced during cure.

In principle, therefore, a polysulfide rubber network free from any ionic impurities and as free as possible from mercaptan and especially mercaptide groups should be quite stable toward chemical stress relaxation.

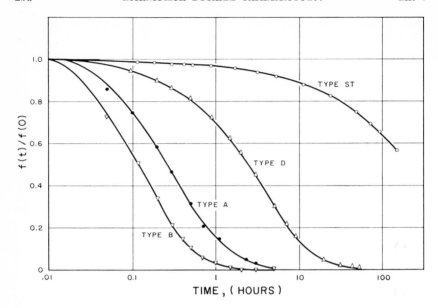

Figure V.21. Chemical stress decay for various polysulfide rubbers at 60°C. Type A: polyethylene tetrasulfide cured with ZnO. Type B: polydiethylether tetrasulfide cured with ZnO. Type D: polydiethylether disulfide cured with ZnO. Type ST: polydiethylformal disulfide cured with benzothiazyl disulfide. [After M. D. Stern and A. V. Tobolsky, *J. Chem. Phys.*, **14**, 93 (1946).]

In order to test this hypothesis, a low-molecular-weight polysulfide polymer of the following type of structure was prepared.[7, 8]

$$\text{HS} \text{—} \cdots \text{—SS} \text{—} \cdots \text{—SS} \text{—} \cdots \text{—SS} \text{—} \cdots \underset{|}{\text{—}} \text{—SS} \text{—} \cdots \text{—SS} \text{—} \cdots \text{—SS} \text{—} \cdots \text{—SH}$$

$$\text{SS} \text{—} \text{—SS} \text{—} \cdots \text{—SH}$$

The chain segments between disulfide linkages were diethylformal segments $-CH_2CH_2OCH_2OCH_2CH_2-$. The number-average degree of polymerization was 11, and the mole per cent of trifunctional branch points in the molecules was 2%. This substance is a viscous liquid, with a viscosity of 560 poises at 30°C.

This liquid polymer can be cured to a three-dimensional network by reactions which join together the —SH terminals.

(A) $-\!\!\!\wedge\!\!\!- SH + PbO_2 + HS -\!\!\!\wedge\!\!\!- \longrightarrow -\!\!\!\wedge\!\!\!- SPbS -\!\!\!\wedge\!\!\!- + H_2O$

(B) $-\!\!\!\wedge\!\!\!- SH + PbO_2 + HS -\!\!\!\wedge\!\!\!- \xrightarrow[\text{heat}]{\text{prolonged}} -\!\!\!\wedge\!\!\!- S -\!\!\!\wedge\!\!\!- + PbS + H_2O$

(C) $\sim$ SH + MnO$_2$ + HS $\sim$ ⟶ $\sim$ S—S $\sim$ + MnO + H$_2$O

(D) $\sim$ SH + $\frac{1}{3}$NOH $=\!\!\!\!\big\langle\bigcirc\big\rangle\!\!\!\!=$ NOH + HS $\sim$ ⟶

     $\sim$ S—S $\sim$ + $\frac{1}{3}$H$_2$N $-\!\!\!\!\big\langle\bigcirc\big\rangle\!\!\!\!-$ NH$_2$ + $\frac{2}{3}$ H$_2$O

(E) $\sim$ SH + O$=$C$=$N—R—N$=$C$=$O + HS $\sim$ ⟶

     $\sim$ S—CO—NH—R—NH—CO—S $\sim$

The results of curing the liquid polysulfide by methods A through E and then studying the chemical relaxation times at 80°C of the networks thus formed is shown in Table V.5.[8] It is apparent that a tremendous variation in τ_{ch} is observed. Cure A which results in highly ionized lead mercaptide linkages shows the fastest relaxation time. Cures B, C and D have intermediate values of τ_{ch}. Cure E which produces no ionic substances has by far the largest value of τ_{ch}. It is perhaps significant that the activation energy for τ_{ch} of cure E is 36.6 kcal, which differs from the commonly observed value of 24 kcal. Chemical stress relaxation in this network may occur via cleavage of the isothiourethane linkage —S—CO—NH—R—NH—CO—S— rather than at the disulfide linkage.

Table V.5

CHEMICAL RELAXATION TIME τ_{ch} AT 80°C FOR POLYSULFIDE RUBBER CURED WITH DIFFERENT CHEMICAL AGENTS[a]

Curing Agent	Weight of Curing Agent per 100 parts of Polymer	τ_{ch}, hours
A. Lead peroxide	7.3	0.68
B. Lead peroxide plus 5 days of heating at 80°C	7.3	15
C. Manganese dioxide plus morpholine	18.9 ± 2.0	32
D. p-Quinone dioxime	2.5	15
E. 2,4-Toluene diisocyanate plus N-methyl-2-pyrollidone	7.0 ± 0.5	200

[a] A. V. Tobolsky and P. C. Colodny, *J. Appl. Polymer Sci.*, **2**, 39 (1959).

References V.8

1. M. D. Stern and A. V. Tobolsky, *J. Chem. Phys.*, **14**, 93 (1946).
2. M. Mochulsky and A. V. Tobolsky, *Ind. Eng. Chem.*, **40**, 2155 (1948).
3. E. M. Fettes and F. O. Davis, private communication to the author in 1946.
   E. M. Fettes and J. S. Jorczak, *Ind. Eng. Chem.*, **42**, 2217 (1950).
4. G. Gorin, A. V. Tobolsky and G. Dougherty, *J. Am. Chem. Soc.*, **71**, 3155 (1949);
   G. Gorin, Ph.D. thesis, Princeton University, 1949.
5. A. V. Tobolsky, F. Leonard and G. P. Roeser, *J. Polymer Sci.*, **3**, 604 (1948).
6. E. M. Fettes, F. O. Davis and E. Bertozzi, *J. Polymer Sci.*, **19**, 17 (1956).
7. J. S. Jorczak and E. M. Fettes, *Ind. Eng. Chem.*, **43**, 324 (1951).
8. P. C. Colodny and A. V. Tobolsky, *J. Appl. Polymer Sci.*, **2**, 39 (1959).

9. SILICONE RUBBERS

Ring siloxanes such as octamethylcyclotetrasiloxane may be catalytically transformed into long chains by shaking with a small quantity of sulfuric acid.[1,2]

$$
\begin{array}{cc}
(CH_3)_2Si\!-\!O\!-\!Si(CH_3)_2 & \\
\quad| \qquad\quad | & \xrightarrow{(H_2SO_4)} \\
\quad O \qquad\quad O & \\
\quad| \qquad\quad | & \\
(CH_3)_2Si\!-\!O\!-\!Si(CH_3)_2 &
\end{array}
\left[
\begin{array}{cc}
CH_3 & CH_3 \\
| & | \\
-Si\!-\!O\!-\!Si\!-\!O \\
| & | \\
CH_3 & CH_3
\end{array}
\right]_n
$$

Films of lightly cross-linked silicone rubbers were prepared directly from octamethylcyclotetrasiloxane (100 parts by weight), cross-linking agent (3.0 parts by weight) and fuming sulfuric acid (0.1 part by weight).[3] The cross-linking agent was the hydrolysis product of an equimolar mixture of $(CH_3)_2SiCl_2$ and $(CH_3)SiCl_3$ with a number-average molecular weight of 1,320.

The rubber films prepared in this manner were found to be highly labile at low relative humidities because the presence of catalyst in the films caused continual interchange of the SiO bonds. This very rapid interchange is shown in stress-relaxation experiments. In Figure V.22 are shown the results of such studies on these silicone rubber films at 60°C and at various relative humidities. It is clear that water vapor in the atmosphere above these films acts to stabilize the catalyst and thus slow down the bond interchange. The effect of water vapor, however, is perfectly reversible; films subject to high relative humidities and therefore stabilized become labile again when the relative humidity is lowered. A permanent stabilization of these films can be achieved by soaking them in pyridine.

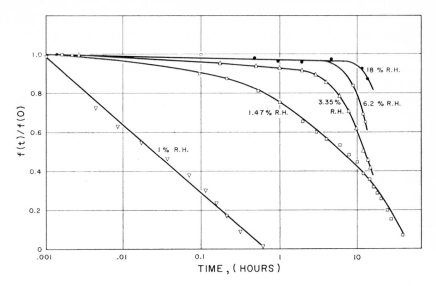

Figure V.22. Chemical stress decay at 60°C of a specially prepared silicone rubber under various relative humidities. [After D. H. Johnson, J. R. McLoughlin and A. V. Tobolsky, *J. Phys. Chem.*, **58**, 1073 (1954).]

Commercial silicone rubbers are made by cross-linking linear poly-dimethylsiloxane with benzoyl peroxide. Various mineral fillers are used to increase the modulus and to strengthen the rubbers. The fillers used include finely dispersed silica, titanium dioxide, iron oxide, etc. It was found that the chemical relaxation times of various specially pre-pared silicone rubbers varied very widely depending on the filler and on the exact method of preparation of the sample.[4] It was deduced that in these samples chemical stress relaxation was due to a catalyzed inter-change of SiO linkages, the catalyst being some unknown ionizable sub-stance.[4]

The most important catalyst for these interchanges in commercial rubbers was shown to be benzoic acid.[5] The benzoyl peroxide used for cross linking acts on the methyl groups of two adjacent siloxane chains to produce a cross link in the following manner:

The benzoic acid produced as a side product acts to catalyze the SiO interchanges and is responsible for chemical stress relaxation at high temperatures and for the formation of volatile ring siloxanes.

By curing linear siloxane chains with high-energy radiation it is possible to produce a cross-linked rubber network without acidic or basic byproducts. These radiation-cured rubbers have been shown to be very much more resistant to chemical stress relaxation than the benzoyl peroxide cures.[5]

References V.9

1. W. Patnode and D. F. Wilcock, *J. Am. Chem. Soc.*, **68**, 358 (1946).
2. A. V. Tobolsky, F. Leonard and G. P. Roeser, *J. Polymer Sci.*, **3**, 604 (1948).
3. D. H. Johnson, J. R. McLoughlin and A. V. Tobolsky, *J. Phys. Chem.*, **58**, 1073 (1954). J. R. McLoughlin, Ph.D. thesis, Princeton University, 1951.
4. A. V. Tobolsky and G. M. Brown, reported in Ph.D. thesis by G. M. Brown, Princeton University, 1948.
5. R. C. Osthoff, A. M. Bueche and W. I. Grubb, *J. Am. Chem. Soc.*, **76**, 4659 (1954).

10. POLYURETHANE RUBBERS

The polyurethane rubbers are an important new class of elastomers obtained from low-molecular-weight polyesters and diisocyanates or from low-molecular-weight polyethers and diisocyanates.[1] In addition to the ester and ether linkages these rubber networks contain the following linkages:

Chemical stress-relaxation studies were carried out on a commercial polyurethane rubber based on a polyether (1), a commercial polyurethane based on a polyester (2) and on a polyester rubber without any urethane linkages (3).[2] The polyester polymer (3) was a high-molecular-weight polymer prepared from ethylene glycol, propylene glycol, adipic acid and a few mole per cent of maleic acid. The last was introduced as active sites for cross linkage, and the chemical curing agent was benzoyl peroxide.

The chemical relaxation times at 120°C for rubbers 1, 2 and 3 were respectively 2.1, 3.0 and over 500 hr. Clearly the weak linkages in rubbers 1 and 2 responsible for stress decay were linkages common to these rubbers which do not occur in rubber 3. These can only be the urethane, disubstituted urea or biuret linkages pictured above.

To find which of these three linkages was the weak linkage responsible for stress decay at 120°C, a series of rubbers 4, 5 and 6 were prepared.[3]

First a typical polyester used in the preparation of polyurethane rubbers was synthesized from adipic acid and a mixture of ethylene and propylene glycols, these glycols being in the mole ratio 4:1. A slight excess of glycol to acid was used in making the polyester so that a hydroxyl-terminated polymer of number-average molecular weight 1,580 was produced. This polyester will be designated as P.

A typical diisocyanate used in the further polymerization reactions is 2,4-toluene diisocyanate.

$$CH_3$$

(structure of 2,4-toluene diisocyanate: benzene ring with CH₃, and two $N{=}C{=}O$ groups)

We shall now write the basic reactions involved in isocyanate polymerizations:

(A) $\sim\!\!N{=}C{=}O\ +\ HO\!\sim\ \longrightarrow\ \sim\!\!NH{-}CO{-}O\!\sim$
urethane linkage

(B) $\sim\!\!N{=}C{=}O\ +\ HOH\ +\ O{=}C{=}N\!\sim\ \longrightarrow\ \sim\!\!NH{-}CO{-}NH\!\sim\ +\ CO_2$
disubstituted urea linkage

(C) $\sim\!\!N{=}C{=}O\ +\ \sim\!\!NH{-}CO{-}NH\!\sim\ \longrightarrow\ \sim\!\!NH{-}CO{-}N{-}CO{-}NH\!\sim$
biuret linkage

By reacting polyester P with an excess of 2,4-toluene diisocyanate, an isocyanate-terminated polyester was prepared which we shall designate as "prepolymer" A. The molecules of A have a urethane linkage adjacent to each of their isocyanate terminals.

Both polyester P and prepolymer A are viscous liquids. They were cured to cross-linked rubbers designated as 4, 5 and 6 in the following ways:

$$P + \text{methyl triphenyl triisocyanate} \qquad (4)$$

$$A + 1,2,6\text{-hexanetriol} \qquad (5)$$

$$A + \text{water} \qquad (6)$$

Rubber 4 obviously contained only ester and urethane linkages. The same is true of rubber 5. Rubber 6, on the other hand, contained urethane, disubstituted urea and biuret linkages. The total number of urethane linkages in a given mass of rubber 6 is equal to the sum of the number of disubstituted urea linkages plus the number of biuret linkages.

Chemical stress-relaxation studies were carried out on samples 4, 5 and 6 at 120°C. The result of these studies compared with samples 1, 2 and 3 is shown in Figure V.23.

It is clear that the weakest linkage in the polyurethane rubbers must be the disubstituted urea or the biuret linkages. An increase of the

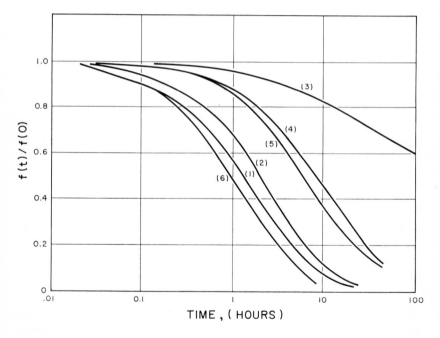

Figure V.23. Chemical stress decay at 120°C of several polyurethane rubbers and a benzoyl peroxide-cured polyester rubber. See section 10 and Table V.6 for structures of rubbers 1 through 6. [After J. A. Offenbach and A. V. Tobolsky, *J. Colloid Sci.*, **29**, 39 (1956); P. C. Colodny and A. V. Tobolsky, *J. Am. Chem. Soc.*, **79**, 4320 (1957).]

chemical relaxation time at 120°C by a factor of 10 can be achieved by eliminating these linkages.

By examination of the stress-decay curves of the two commercial rubbers 1 and 2 (Adiprene B and Vulcollan A) as compared with the specially prepared samples 4, 5 and 6, it is clear that the commercial rubbers available at the time of this study did have some disubstituted urea and biuret linkages.

In Table V.6 are given the chemical relaxation times τ_{ch} at 120°C of the rubbers 1 through 6.

Table V.6

CHEMICAL RELAXATION TIMES τ_{ch} AT 120°C OF POLYURETHANE RUBBERS AND A POLYESTER RUBBER

Rubber	Linkages	τ_{ch}, hours
1.	Ether, urethane, disubstituted urea, biuret	2.1
2.	Ester, urethane, disubstituted urea, biuret	3.0
3.	Ester	500
4.	Ester, urethane	14.0
5.	Ester, urethane	9.7
6.	Ester, urethane, disubstituted urea, biuret	1.6

References V.10

1. E. Muller, O. Bayer et al., *Rubber Chem. Tech.*, **26**, 493 (1953).
2. J. A. Offenbach and A. V. Tobolsky, *J. Colloid Sci.*, **11**, 39 (1956).
3. P. C. Colodny and A. V. Tobolsky, *J. Am. Chem. Soc.*, **79**, 4320 (1957).

CHAPTER VI

Polymerization Equilibria

1. Equilibrium Polymerization
2. Copolymerization Equilibrium

1. EQUILIBRIUM POLYMERIZATION

In the previous chapter we have considered chemical stress relaxation as a means of measuring the chemical changes which occur in a polymer network at elevated temperatures.

Some of these changes are irreversible, such as the scission and cross linking initiated by oxygen. On the other hand, the interchange reactions such as occur in the polysulfide rubber networks or the silicone rubber networks are manifestations of a dynamic state of equilibrium.

It is of interest to consider equilibrium between monomer and polymer of all sizes from a purely thermodynamic point of view.[1-5]

Three general cases of equilibrium may be distinguished: We shall classify these as case I, case II and case III. We shall designate monomer as M, polymerization initiator (where present) as XY, concentrations (generally in moles per kilogram) will be designated as $\underline{M}$, $\underline{XY}$, etc.

Case I
$$XY + M \overset{K_a}{\rightleftharpoons} XMY$$

$$XMY + M \overset{K_b}{\rightleftharpoons} XM_2Y$$

$$\cdot \ \cdot \ \cdot \ \cdot \ \cdot \ \cdot \ \cdot \ \cdot \ \cdot \ \cdot \ \cdot$$

$$XM_{n-1}Y + M \overset{K_n}{\rightleftharpoons} XM_nY$$

266

Case II
$$M \xrightleftharpoons{K_a} M^*$$

$$M^* + M \xrightleftharpoons{K_b} M_2^*$$

$$\cdots \cdots \cdots \cdots \cdots$$

$$M^*_{n-1} + M \xrightleftharpoons{K_n} M_n^*$$

$$\cdots \cdots \cdots \cdots \cdots$$

(The star represents an activated state such as a diradical or a zwitterion.)

Case III
$$M + M \xrightleftharpoons{K_a} M_2$$

$$M_2 + M \xrightleftharpoons{K_b} M_3$$

$$\cdots \cdots \cdots \cdots \cdots$$

$$M_n + M \xrightleftharpoons{K_n} M_n$$

$$\cdots \cdots \cdots \cdots \cdots$$

Examples of case I are the polymerization of ϵ-caprolactam initiated by water or by an amine.

Example case Ia

$$\overset{\displaystyle CO\text{——————}NH}{\underset{\displaystyle n CH_2\text{—}(CH_2)_3\text{—}CH_2}{|\qquad\qquad\qquad|}} + H_2O \rightleftharpoons polycaprolactam$$

Example case Ib

$$\overset{\displaystyle CO\text{————}NH}{\underset{\displaystyle n CH_2\text{—}(CH_2)_3\text{—}CH_2}{|\qquad\qquad|}} + RNH_2 \rightleftharpoons polycaprolactam$$

An example of case II is the polymerization of ring sulfur to polymeric diradicals.

Example case IIa

$$nS_8 \rightleftharpoons \cdot[SSSSSSSS]_n \cdot$$

Examples of case III are equilibrium vinyl polymerization in the absence of initiators, and equilibrium polymerization of ϵ-caprolactam to larger-sized rings.

Example case IIIa

$$n\mathrm{CH_2}{=}\mathrm{CHZ} \;\rightleftharpoons\; \mathrm{CH_2}{=}\mathrm{CHZ}{-}[\mathrm{CH_2}{-}\mathrm{CHZ}]_{n-2}{-}\mathrm{CH_2}{-}\mathrm{CH_2Z}$$

Example case IIIb

$$\begin{array}{cc}\mathrm{CO}\!\!-\!\!-\!\!-\!\!-\!\!-\!\!-\!\!-\mathrm{NH} \\ \mid \qquad\qquad\quad \mid \\ n\mathrm{CH_2}{-}(\mathrm{CH_2})_3{-}\mathrm{CH_2}\end{array} \;\rightleftharpoons\; \textit{ring n-mer}$$

From the experimental point of view three measurable quantities are of the utmost importance in specifying the equilibrium; (1) the equilibrium concentration of monomer $\underline{M}$; (2) the equilibrium number-average degree of polymerization P; (3) where initiator is present, the equilibrium concentration of initiator $\underline{XY}$.

In order to obtain useful relations among $\underline{M}$, $\underline{P}$, $\underline{XY}$ and the equilibrium constants K_a, K_b, K_c, $\ldots$, K_n, $\ldots$, we introduce two physically reasonable approximations

(a) $\qquad\qquad K_a = K$

$$K_b = K_c = K_d = \cdots = K_n = \cdots = K_3$$

(b) $\qquad\qquad K_a = K_b = K_c = \cdots = K_n = \cdots = K_3$

Whether a given equilibrium falls under approximation a or b can sometimes be determined from chemical intuition. Example case Ia, the polymerization of ϵ-caprolactam by water clearly falls under approximation a and is thus classed as case Ia. Example case Ib, the polymerization of ϵ-caprolactam by an amine probably falls under approximation b and was thus classified as case Ib. The polymerization of sulfur very definitely falls under approximation a and is therefore classified as case IIa. The polymerization of ϵ-caprolactam to larger rings probably falls under approximation b and is thus classified as case IIIb. Vinyl polymerization in the absence of initiator has been tentatively classified as case IIIa.[5]

The mathematical problem that must be solved is to relate P and $\underline{M}$ to K, K_3 and $\underline{M}_0$ where $\underline{M}_0$ is the initial concentration of monomer. In case I we have to relate P, $\underline{M}$, $\underline{XY}$ to K, K_3, $\underline{M}_0$ and $\underline{X}_0$ (short for $\underline{XY}_0$) where $\underline{X}_0$ is the initial concentration of initiator.

The detailed mathematical steps in the treatment of case IIIa are as follows:

1.1 $M + M \xrightarrow{K} M_2$ $K = \dfrac{M_2}{\underline{M} \cdot \underline{M}}$

$$\underline{M}_2 = K \underline{M}^2$$

1.2 $M_2 + M \xrightarrow{K_3} M_3$ $K_3 = \dfrac{M_3}{\underline{M}_2 \cdot \underline{M}}$

$$\underline{M}_3 = K_3 \underline{M}_2 \underline{M} = K K_3 \underline{M}^3$$

1.3 $M_3 + M \xrightarrow{K_3} M_4$ $K_3 = \dfrac{M_4}{\underline{M}_3 \cdot \underline{M}}$

$$\underline{M}_4 = K_3 \underline{M}_3 \underline{M} = K K_3{}^2 \underline{M}^4$$

1.4 $M_n + M \xrightarrow{K_3} M_{n+1}$ $\underline{M}_{n+1} = K K_3{}^{n-2} \underline{M}^n$ for $n > 2$

Let N = total equilibrium concentration of polymer molecules:

$$N = \sum_{n=2}^{\infty} K K_3{}^{n-2} \underline{M}^n$$

$$= K \underline{M}^2 + K K_3 \underline{M}^3 + K K_3{}^2 \underline{M}^4 + \cdots$$

$$= K \underline{M}^2 [1 + K_3 \underline{M} + K_3{}^2 \underline{M}^2 + K_3{}^3 \underline{M}^3 + \cdots]$$

1.5 $= \dfrac{K \underline{M}^2}{1 - K_3 \underline{M}}$

Let $\underline{W}$ = total equilibrium concentration of monomer segments incorporated in polymer:

$$\underline{W} = \sum_{n=2}^{\infty} n K K_3{}^{n-2} \underline{M}^n$$

$$= K \underline{M}^2 [1 + 2 K_3 \underline{M} + 3 K_3{}^2 \underline{M}^2 + \cdots]$$

1.6 $= \dfrac{K \underline{M}^2}{(1 - K_3 \underline{M})^2}$

It is obvious that $P = W/N$ (where P is the number average degree of polymerization).

1.7 $P = \dfrac{W}{N} = \dfrac{1}{1 - K_3 \underline{M}}$

It is easy to see that

1.8
$$\underline{M}_0 = \underline{M} + \underline{W} = \underline{M} + \frac{K\underline{M}^2}{(1 - K_3\underline{M})^2}$$

where $\underline{M}_0$ is the initial monomer concentration.

Combining equations 1.7 and 1.8 and setting $P - 1/P = 1$ (valid for $P \gg 1$), we get

1.9
$$P = \left(\frac{\underline{M}_0 K_3{}^2}{K} - \frac{K_3}{K}\right)^{1/2}$$

We note from equation 1.7 that, if $P \gg 1$, then $K_3 \simeq 1/\underline{M}$.

The above results are equally applicable to case IIIb, with the simplification that $K = K_3$, since all constants are identical by assumption b. Equation 1.9 becomes

1.9b
$$P \simeq (\underline{M}_0 K_3)^{1/2} \simeq (\underline{M}_0/\underline{M})^{1/2}$$

The necessary relations for the other cases have been presented elsewhere.[1-4] The results are summarized in Table VI.1.[5]

Application of case Ia to the equilibrium polymerization of ε-caprolactam initiated by water. The over-all reaction can be written as follows:

$$\begin{array}{ccc}
\text{CO} & \!\text{NH} & \\
| & | & \\
n\text{CH}_2\text{---}(\text{CH}_2)_3\text{---}\text{CH}_2 & + \text{H}_2\text{O} & \rightleftharpoons \ polycaprolactam
\end{array}$$

Table VI.1 *

Eq. no.	Case	P	$\underline{M}_0$	$\underline{X}_0$	P
1.10	Ia	$1/(1 - K_3\underline{M})$	$\underline{M}(1 + KX P^2)$	$\underline{X}(1 + K\underline{M}P)$	$(\underline{M}_0 - \underline{M})/(\underline{X}_0 - \underline{X})$
1.11	Ib	$1/(1 - K_3\underline{M})$	$\underline{M}(1 + K_3 X P^2)$	$\underline{X}(1 + K_3\underline{M}P)$	$\approx (\underline{M}_0 - \underline{M})/\underline{X}_0$
1.12	IIa	$1/(1 - K_3\underline{M})$	$\underline{M}(1 + K P^2)$		$\approx [(\underline{M}_0 K_3 - 1)/K]^{1/2}$
1.13	IIIa	$1/(1 - K_3\underline{M})$	$\underline{M}(1 + K\underline{M}P^2)$		$\approx [(\underline{M}_0 K_3{}^2 - K_3)/K]^{1/2}$
1.14	IIIb	$1/(1 - K_3\underline{M})$	$\underline{M}(1 + K_3\underline{M}P^2)$		$\approx (\underline{M}_0/\underline{M})^{1/2}$

* The equation for P given in the last column is not an independent relation, but can be derived for the sake of convenience from the preceding equations. In the last four cases the equations for P are valid only for values of $P \gg 1$.

The sequence of equilibria that we use to describe the reaction is

$$\begin{array}{c} \text{CO}\underline{\hspace{2cm}}\text{NH} \\ | \qquad\qquad | \\ \text{CH}_2\text{—(CH}_2)_3\text{—CH}_2 \end{array} + \text{H}_2\text{O} \overset{K}{\rightleftharpoons} \text{HOOC(CH}_2)_5\text{NH}_2$$

$$\text{HOOC(CH}_2)_5\text{NH[—CO(CH}_2)_5\text{NH]}_{n-1}\text{—CO(CH}_2)_5\text{NH}_2$$

$$+ \begin{array}{c} \text{CO}\underline{\hspace{2cm}}\text{NH} \\ | \qquad\qquad | \\ \text{CH}_2\text{—(CH}_2)_3\text{—CH}_2 \end{array} \overset{K_3}{\rightleftharpoons}$$

$$\text{HOOC(CH}_2)_5\text{NH[—CO(CH}_2)_5\text{NH]}_n\text{—CO(CH}_2)_5\text{NH}_2$$

$$n = 0, 1, 2, 3, 4 \ldots$$

At a given temperature, for a given value of $\underline{M}_0$ and $\underline{X}_0$, P and $\underline{M}$ were available from data in the literature.[6] Referring to equation 1.10, Table VI.I, K_3 was immediately obtained from $P = 1/(1 - K_3\underline{M})$. $\underline{X}$ was then obtained from $P = (\underline{M}_0 - \underline{M})/(\underline{X}_0 - \underline{X})$. Finally, K was obtained

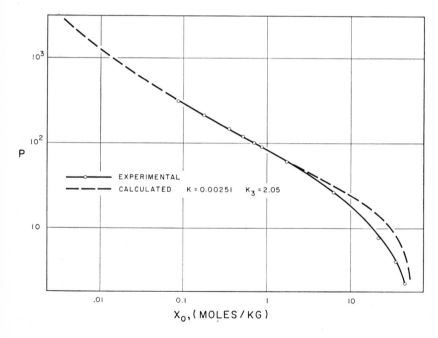

Figure VI.1. Degree of polymerization versus water concentration for the equilibrium polymerization of caprolactam at 220°C. Calculated and experimental curves are shown. [After A. V. Tobolsky and A. Eisenberg, *J. Am. Chem. Soc.*, **81**, 2302 (1959).]

from $\underline{X}_0 = \underline{X}(1 + K\underline{M}P)$. The consistency of the equilibrium treatment was then conveniently checked by predicting the value of $\underline{X}_0$ corresponding to a selected value of P, using the values of K and K_3 determined above. Very satisfactory results were obtained,[4] as shown in Figure VI.1.

This procedure was carried out at two temperatures. Application of the van't Hoff equation to the values of K and K_3 gave

1.15 $$K = \exp \frac{\Delta S°}{R} \exp \left(- \frac{\Delta H°}{RT} \right)$$

$$K_3 = \exp \frac{\Delta S°_3}{R} \exp \left(- \frac{\Delta H°_3}{RT} \right)$$

$$\Delta S° = -6.8 \text{ eu} \qquad \Delta S_3° = -7.0 \text{ eu}$$

$$\Delta H° = +2240 \text{ cal/mol} \qquad \Delta H_3° = -4030 \text{ cal/mol}$$

corresponding to the initiation and propagation reactions, respectively. The standard state chosen was 1 mole/kg, and all concentrations discussed in this paper are based on the units moles per kilogram.

Since $P = 1/(1 - K_3\underline{M})$ it may be pointed out that, for large values of P,

1.16 $$\underline{M} \simeq 1/K_3$$

hence in the range of high degrees of polymerization, $\underline{M}$ is independent of the initiator concentration.

Application of case Ib to the equilibrium polymerization of ε-caprolactam initiated by an alkylamine. The over-all reaction can be written as follows:

$$\begin{array}{c} \text{CO} \underline{\hspace{2cm}} \text{NH} \\ | \qquad\qquad | \\ n\text{CH}_2\text{—(CH}_2)_3\text{—CH}_2 + \text{RNH}_2 \rightleftharpoons \textit{polycaprolactam} \end{array}$$

The sequence of equilibria that we use to describe the reaction is

$$\text{RNH}_2 + \text{CL} \overset{K_3}{\rightleftharpoons} \text{R(CL)NH}_2$$

$$\text{R(CL)}_n\text{NH}_2 + \text{CL} \overset{K_3}{\rightleftharpoons} \text{R(CL)}_{n+1}\text{NH}_2$$

$$n = 1, 2, 3, 4 \ldots$$

In the above equations CL represents caprolactam and (CL) represents

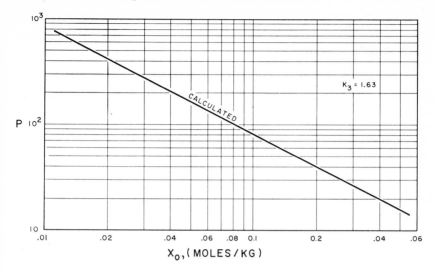

Figure VI.2. Degree of polymerization versus initiator concentration for the equilibrium polymerization of caprolactam at 240°C. An initiator is presupposed for which $K_1 = K_3$. (After A. V. Tobolsky and A. Eisenberg, unpublished.)

—$NHCO(CH_2)_5$—. In this case we take $K = K_3$ as a good approximation since the same functional groups are involved in the equilibria.

No satisfactory equilibrium data exist in the literature for this case. We venture to predict that this equilibrium can be described by using the results of case Ia above merely by replacing K by K_3.

The first important prediction is obtained from equation 1.16, namely, $\underline{M} \simeq 1/K_3$. This shows immediately that the equilibrium concentration of monomer is a function of temperature only, and is independent of the nature of the initiator. That is, we can expect the same $\underline{M}$ whether water or amine is used as the initiator.

The second important consequence is given by the equation below, which can be derived [5] from equation 1.11.

1.17
$$P \simeq \frac{\underline{M}_0 - \underline{M}}{\underline{X}_0} \simeq \frac{\underline{M}_0 - 1/K_3}{\underline{X}_0}$$

Figure VI.2 shows a plot of equation 1.17 applicable at 240°C.

Expressing K_3 as a function of temperature from equation 11.15, one obtains

1.18
$$P \simeq \frac{\underline{M}_0 - \exp(-4030/\mathbf{R}T) \exp(7.0/\mathbf{R})}{\underline{X}_0}$$

Equations 1.16 and 1.17 should also apply for other initiators, such as organic acids or amino acids. For alkylamine initiation a catalyst such as HCl is required.

Application of case IIa to the thermal polymerization of sulfur. The over-all reaction can be written as follows:

$$nS_8 \rightleftharpoons S_{8n}*$$

the star denoting a diradical. The sequence of steps that we use to describe the final equilibrium is:

$$S_8 \overset{K}{\underset{\longleftarrow}{\longrightarrow}} S_8*$$

$$S_{8n}* + S_8 \overset{K_3}{\underset{\longleftarrow}{\longrightarrow}} S_{8(n+1)}*$$

Approximate data are available in the literature giving P and $\underline{M}$ as a function of temperature.[7,8] Referring to equation 1.12 and Table VI.1, K_3 may be calculated at any temperature from a knowledge of P and $\underline{M}$ by use of the relationship $P = 1/(1 - K_3\underline{M})$. K may then be calculated from $\underline{M}_0 = \underline{M}(1 + KP^2)$, recalling that $\underline{M}_0$ is a constant equal to 3.90 moles/kg over the entire temperature range. If this procedure is repeated for another temperature, plots of $\ln K$ vs. $1/T$ and $\ln K_3$ vs. $1/T$ may be constructed, and $\Delta H°$, $\Delta S°$, $\Delta H_3°$, and $\Delta S_3°$ obtained. The results are [3]

1.19
$$\ln K = \frac{\Delta S°}{R} - \frac{\Delta H°}{RT}$$

$$\ln K_3 = \frac{\Delta S_3°}{R} - \frac{\Delta H_3°}{RT}$$

1.20 $\Delta H° = 32,800$ cal/mole $\Delta S° = 23.0$ cal/deg mole

$\Delta H_3° = 3,170$ cal/mole $\Delta S_3° = 4.63$ cal/deg mole

The linearity of the plots of $\ln K$ vs. $1/T$ and $\ln K_3$ vs. $1/T$ is striking evidence for the validity of the theory. Inasmuch as $\Delta H°$, $\Delta H_3°$, $\Delta S°$ and $\Delta S_3°$ are all independent of temperature, accurate expressions for K and K_3 can in principle be obtained from measurements of P and $\underline{M}$ at only two temperatures, both of which may lie above the "transition temperature" of sulfur. Equation 1.12 taken in conjunction with equations 1.19 and 1.20 can then be used to predict the values of $\underline{M}$ and P at all temperatures, as shown in Figures VI.3 and VI.4. Excellent agreement is obtained when these computed curves are compared with the "experimental" data of references 7 and 8.

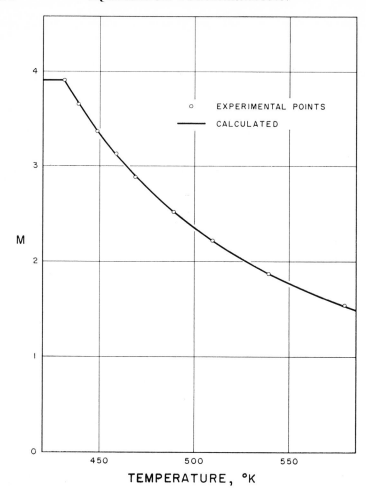

Figure VI.3. Equilibrium monomer concentration (moles per kilogram) versus temperature for the equilibrium polymerization of elemental sulfur. [After A. V. Tobolsky and A. Eisenberg, *J. Am. Chem. Soc.*, **81**, 780 (1959).]

It is interesting to note that an explicit relation among P, K and K_3 can be written by eliminating M between two of the relations shown in equation 1.12.

$$1.21 \qquad\qquad M_0 = \frac{P - 1}{PK_3} + \frac{K}{K_3} P(P - 1)$$

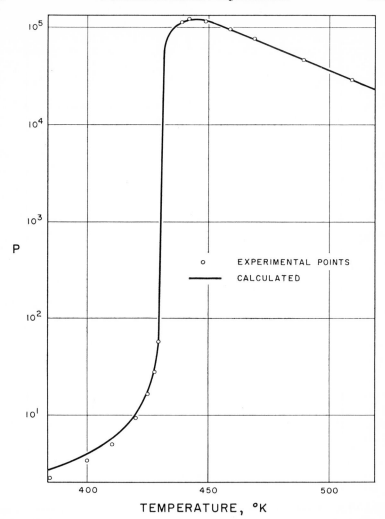

Figure VI.4. Degree of polymerization versus temperature for the equilibrium polymerization of sulfur. [After A. V. Tobolsky and A. Eisenberg, *J. Am. Chem. Soc.*, **81**, 780 (1959).]

which for values of $P \gg 1$ becomes

1.22 $$P = [(M_0 K_3 - 1)/K_3]^{\frac{1}{2}}$$

Application of case IIIa to the equilibrium polymerization of vinyl monomers. Consider this equilibrium to take place according to the following steps:

$$CH_2\!\!=\!\!CHX + CH_2\!\!=\!\!CHX \overset{K}{\rightleftharpoons} dimer$$

$$CH_2\!\!=\!\!CX(CH_2CHX)_n\!\cdot\!CH_2CH_2X + CH_2\!\!=\!\!CHX \overset{K_3}{\rightleftharpoons}$$

$$CH_2\!\!=\!\!CX(CH_2CHX)_{n+1}CH_2CH_2X$$

$$n = 0, 1, 2, 3 \ldots$$

One must emphasize that the particular manner in which the equilibrium is written need bear no relation whatever to the mechanism. Equilibrium depends only on initial and final states.

From an a priori point of view, K might well be equal to K_3, and therefore case IIIb might equally be applicable. A decision as to which approximation is correct can be based only on experimental findings.

In treating equilibrium polymerization of vinyl monomers, particularly methyl methacrylate, Dainton and Ivin and Bywater [9, 10] implicitly treat the problem as a one-constant case, and derive by other methods the relation which in our notation is (see equation 1.16)

$$K_3 \simeq 1/\underline{M}$$

Bywater also carried out measurements of $\underline{M}$ and hence K_3 at several temperatures.[10]

From Table VI.1, it is clear that this relation is valid for either the one-constant case IIIb, *or* the two-constant case IIIa.

If a one-constant treatment is indeed applicable, then the degree of polymerization should be related to the equilibrium monomer concentration $\underline{M}$ as follows (see Table VI.1):

$$P = (\underline{M}_0/\underline{M})^{\frac{1}{2}}$$

For the experimental results of Bywater this would lead to a maximum value of P of 5 at 130°C. No values for P were given in this paper.

We have repeated the experiments of Bywater and do indeed verify fairly closely his results for "equilibrium" monomer concentration, with a reservation discussed later.

However, we have determined P in this system and find a value of 500 to 650, in definite contradiction to a one-constant theory.[5]

Such a result is not at all inconsistent with a two-constant theory where

$$P = [(\underline{M}_0 K_3{}^2 - K_3)/K]^{\frac{1}{2}}$$

In fact, from the measured value of P, a value of K can be determined which is about 3×10^{-5} (cf. $K_3 \simeq 3$).

The reservation stated above concerning experimental findings is that in our results we find the "equilibrium" monomer concentration obtained in the experimental method of Bywater to depend on the light intensity. The results of Bywater may perhaps be more aptly described as photostationary states than as equilibrium states.[5]

Application of case IIIb to the polymerization of ε-caprolactam to larger rings. The formation of larger ring systems in the course of the polymerization of ε-caprolactam is a well-known phenomenon. We consider this equilibrium to be subject to case IIIb, since essentially only one type of reaction is involved in the formation of large rings, which we believe to occur by bond interchange:

$$2\overline{\mathrm{NH(CH_2)_5CO}} \underset{\rightleftharpoons}{\overset{K_3}{\rightleftharpoons}} \overline{\mathrm{NH(CH_2)_5CONH(CH_2)_5CO}}$$

$$\underline{\mathrm{(NH(CH_2)_5CO)}_x} + \overline{\mathrm{NH(CH_2)_5CO}} \overset{K_3}{\rightleftharpoons} \underline{\mathrm{(NH(CH_2)_5CO)}_{x+1}}$$

$$x = 2, 3, 4, 5, 6 \ldots$$

Ideally, this equilibrium could be studied with completely dry ε-caprolactam at appropriate temperatures, thus eliminating the mechanism of ring-chain equilibrium. Under normal circumstances (i.e., water initiation), two simultaneous equilibria have to be accounted for, i.e., the ring-chain equilibrium, and the ring–large-ring equilibrium. Since large rings are present only in relatively small concentrations, these may be neglected in studying the ring-chain system, and this was actually done (see Application Ia). Once $\underline{M}$ is known for this simplified system, it could be regarded as $\underline{M}_0$ for the ring–large-ring equilibrium.

Some recent developments

It has been shown that α-methyl styrene in tetrahydrofuran reaches equilibrium with its polymer in the presence of sodium naphthalene used as initiator.[11] Very good agreement with these results have been obtained in this laboratory, and the experiments have been extended to include a very wide range of initial monomer concentrations and initiator concentrations.[12] Measurements of equilibrium $\underline{M}$ and P give excellent agreement with case Ia with the simplification that K is very large. It happens that two molecules of sodium naphthalene react quantitatively with the monomer in the initiation steps. For this case $P \approx 2(\underline{M}_0 - \underline{M})/\underline{X}_0$.

When sodium diphenylacetylene is used as the initiator, case Ia was found to apply without the previous simplification.[12] $\underline{M}$ was found to be the same as obtained with sodium naphthalene. However, for a given X_0, P was higher than with the same amount of sodium naphthalene, since $P = 2(M_0 - M)/(X_0 - X)$ and X is not negligible in this case. X can in fact be computed from P and then K computed from the relation $X_0 = X (1 + 2KXM^2P)$.

Case IIa has been applied to the polymerization of selenium to polymeric diradicals.[13] The rather limited experimental data can be very well explained by exactly the same mathematical approach as is used for sulfur. For selenium we find:

$$\Delta H° = 25{,}000 \text{ cal/mole} \qquad \Delta S° = 23.0 \text{ cal/deg mole}$$

$$\Delta H_3° = 2270 \text{ cal/mole} \qquad \Delta S_3° = 5.47 \text{ cal/deg mole}$$

A tabulation of some heats and entropies of polymerization has been presented in the literature.[14] The theoretical formulation on which this is based does not take into account the initiation equilibria. In terms of the theory presented here these tabulated values may generally be accurately identified as ΔH_3 and ΔS_3.

The use of weight fractions or volume fractions for activities in the law of mass action is of course an approximation which is justifiable by the constancy of the calculated equilibrium constants. It is also in part justifiable by the fundamental theory of polymer solutions.[15, 16]

References VI.1

1. A. V. Tobolsky, *J. Polymer Sci.*, **25**, 220 (1957).
2. A. V. Tobolsky, *J. Polymer Sci.*, **31**, 126 (1958).
3. A. V. Tobolsky and A. Eisenberg, *J. Am. Chem. Soc.*, **81**, 780 (1959).
4. A. V. Tobolsky and A. Eisenberg, *J. Am. Chem. Soc.*, **81**, 2302 (1959).
5. A. V. Tobolsky and A. Eisenberg, *J. Am. Chem. Soc.*, **82**, 289 (1960).
6. F. Wiloth, *Z. physik. Chem.*, **4**, 66 (1955); P. H. Hermans, A. J. Staverman et al., *Recueil*, **74**, 1376 (1956).
7. G. Gee, *Trans. Faraday Soc.*, **48**, 515 (1952).
8. F. Fairbrother, G. Gee and G. T. Merrill, *J. Polymer Sci.*, **16**, 459 (1955).
9. F. S. Dainton and K. J. Ivin, *Nature*, **162**, 705 (1948).
10. S. Bywater, *Trans. Faraday Soc.*, **51**, 1267 (1955).
11. D. T. Worsfold and S. Bywater, *J. Polymer Sci.*, **26**, 299 (1957); H. W. McCormick, *ibid.*, **25**, 488 (1957).
12. A. V. Tobolsky, A. Rembaum and A. Eisenberg, manuscript in preparation.
13. A. Eisenberg and A. V. Tobolsky, manuscript in preparation.
14. F. S. Dainton and K. J. Ivin, *Quart. Rev.*, **12**, 67 (1958).
15. A. V. Tobolsky, *J. Chem. Phys.*, **12**, 402 (1944).
16. P. J. Flory, *J. Chem. Phys.*, **12**, 425 (1944).

2. COPOLYMERIZATION EQUILIBRIUM [1]

Stress-relaxation studies show the existence of interchange reactions in cross-linked polymer networks. Interchange reactions occurring in copolymer chains or in networks composed of copolymer chains will ultimately lead to copolymer equilibrium, that is, an equilibrium distribution of compositional sequence lengths along the chains. It is of interest to consider this relatively little discussed topic from a quite general point of view, including the experimental conditions under which equilibrium copolymerization might be achieved.

In the usual method of preparing vinyl copolymers the composition and structure of the products are determined by the relative rates of reaction of the two monomers with the two types of active (radical) growing chain ends. Various monomers differ widely in reactivity so that, in general, it is extremely difficult to prepare copolymers of desired composition and structure by this method.

On the other hand, it is known that at sufficiently high temperatures certain vinyl polymers tend to undergo depolymerization reactions which involve radical chain mechanisms of a sort inverse to those occurring in polymerization. With some polymers, for example, methyl methacrylate, it is possible to recover most of the monomer by heating polymer under vacuum. It has further been suggested that in polymers of this type equilibrium polymerization-depolymerization may govern the molecular weight distribution at quite elevated temperatures. By the same token it is expected that, if a copolymer were treated in this manner, depolymerization-polymerization would determine both the molecular weight distribution and the structural sequence distribution of the copolymer. Undoubtedly, in many cases, subsidiary reactions leading to branching, such as chain transfer, can and do occur at these temperatures, but these secondary reactions are ignored here. We expect that, in cases involving monomers such as methyl methacrylate, these side reactions can be minimized and we can assume that equilibrium polymerization-depolymerization will be achieved at sufficiently high temperatures and will determine the copolymer structure and composition as well as the molecular weight-distribution curve.

It should be possible to produce equilibrium copolymers by heating at sufficiently high temperatures: (1) a mixture of the two monomers, (2) a mechanical mixture of the two polymers, (3) a mixture of one monomer and another polymer or (4) a copolymer of the two monomers. It should be pointed out that, in order for this equilibrium to be achieved at an appreciable rate, it is likely that in many cases the temperatures required would lead to the formation of rather low-molecular-weight materials. It should be pointed out that mutual solubility and diffusion of one material into the other are also difficulties to be overcome.

The use of powerful ionic catalysts for polymerization, which has come to the fore in recent years, suggests another possibility. Since these catalysts may be powerful catalysts for depolymerization as well as for polymerization, it is possible that with the use of such catalysts equilibrium copolymerization may be achieved from a mixture of two monomers even at relatively low temperatures.

The considerations presented here apply also to the copolymerization of ring compounds, condensation copolymerization, etc., as well as to vinyl copolymerization.

We first treat the case of an infinite copolymer molecule mathematically to determine the sequence distribution along the chain. This has been accomplished by two independent methods, each of which leads to the same end result, namely,[1]

$$2.1 \quad \frac{(N_A - M_{AB})(N_B - M_{AB})}{M_{AB}^2} = K = (f_{AA}f_{BB}/f_{AB}^2) \exp \frac{\Delta E_{AB}}{RT}$$

where N_A is the number of monomeric units of type A, N_B is the number of monomeric units of type B, M_{AB} is the number of AB neighbor pairs along the chain, K is an equilibrium constant which is expressible in terms of vibrational partition functions f_{AA}, f_{BB} and f_{AB} and the energy change ΔE_{AB}. The partition functions f_{AA} and f_{BB} may include a symmetry factor of 2. The quantity ΔE_{AB} is defined as $2E_{AB} - E_{AA} - E_{BB}$, where E_{AA} is the energy per mole of an A—A bond, E_{BB} is the energy per mole of a B—B bond, and E_{AB} is the energy per mole of an A—B bond. The energy E_{AA} is approximately the heat of polymerization per mole of monomer A and similarly for E_{BB} and E_{AB}.

The distribution in sequence lengths is given by the formula

$$2.2 \quad n_x^A = N_A p_{AA}^{x-1}(1 - p_{AA})^2$$

$$n_x^B = N_B p_{BB}^{x-1}(1 - p_{BB})^2$$

where n_x^A is the number of A sequences of length x in the copolymer chain, n_x^B is the number of B sequences of length x in the copolymer chain and p_{AA} and p_{BB} are defined by the equation

$$2.3 \quad p_{AA} = \frac{N_A - M_{AB}}{N_A} \qquad p_{BB} = \frac{N_B - M_{AB}}{N_B}$$

The problem of equilibrium copolymerization is, in fact, mathematically identical with the Ising problem [2] (in ferromagnetism) and of course leads to the same solution.

References VI.2

1. T. Alfrey and A. V. Tobolsky, *J. Polymer Sci.*, **38**, 269 (1959).
2. E. Ising, *Z. Physik*, **31**, 253 (1925).

The Partition Function

The partition function of an assembly of N molecules is defined by

A.1 $$Q = \sum_i \exp\left(-\frac{E_i}{kT}\right)$$

where E_i is the energy of the ith state *of the entire assembly*.

For a gaseous assembly of N monatomic molecules occupying the volume V at temperature T one can show that [1]

A.2 $$Q_{gas} = g_0^N (2\pi m kT)^{3N/2} V^N / N! h^{3N}$$

where m is the molecular mass, and g_0 the electronic degeneracy of the ground state. Equation A.2 holds if the average number of molecules occupying each molecular quantum state is small. This obtains for all chemical gases (but not for an electron gas) at temperatures above 5°K.

To obtain the equation of state one uses the fundamental formulas

A.3 $$A = -kT \ln Q$$

A.4 $$p = -(\partial A / \partial V)_T$$

from which is readily derived the ideal gas law $pV = NkT$.

For an Einstein crystal of **N** atoms it can be shown that [2]

A.5 $$Q_{crystal} = \exp\left(-\frac{U_L(V)}{kT}\right) \exp\left(\frac{3Nh\nu}{2kT}\right) [1 - \exp(-h\nu/kT)]^{-3N}$$

where $U_L(V)$ denotes the lattice energy per mole with each atom in its equilibrium position, and ν is the Einstein frequency which is also a function of the volume.[3]

Using equations A.3, A.4 and A.5 one obtains

A.6 $A = U_L(V) + \frac{3}{2}\mathbf{N}\mathbf{h}\nu + 3\mathbf{N}\mathbf{k}T \ln\left[1 - \exp\left(-\mathbf{h}\nu/\mathbf{k}T\right)\right]$

A.7 $p = -\left(\dfrac{\partial U_L}{\partial V}\right)_T - \frac{3}{2}\mathbf{N}\mathbf{h}\left(\dfrac{\partial \nu}{\partial V}\right)_T$

$$-3\mathbf{N}\mathbf{h}\left(\dfrac{\partial \nu}{\partial V}\right)_T\left(\exp\dfrac{\mathbf{h}\nu}{\mathbf{k}T} - 1\right)^{-1}$$

The second two terms on the right-hand side of equation A.6 represent A_E, the contribution of the lattice vibrations to the free energy, in the Einstein approximation. Equation A.6 can be written as

A.8 $A = U_L(V) + A_E(T, V)$

In the Debye treatment of the crystal it is assumed that instead of $3\mathbf{N}$ identical frequencies one has a distribution of frequencies $N(\nu)\, d\nu$ defined by the following equation:

A.9 $N(\nu)\, d\nu = (9N/\nu_m{}^3)\nu^2\, d\nu$ $0 < \nu < \nu_m$

               $N(\nu)\, d\nu = 0$ $\nu > \nu_m$

$$\int_0^{\nu_m} N(\nu)\, d\nu = 3\mathbf{N}$$

All the previous equations for the Einstein crystal can be applied to a Debye crystal by using the following operation:

A.10 $3\mathbf{N}\, f(\nu) \rightarrow \int_0^{\nu_m} N(\nu)\, f(\nu)\, d\nu$

where $f(\nu)$ is any function of the frequency.

The Debye temperature θ_D is defined as

A.11 $\theta_D = \mathbf{h}\nu_m/\mathbf{k}$

References for Appendix A

1. K. G. Denbigh, *The Principles of Chemical Equilibrium*, Chapter 12, Cambridge University Press, New York, 1955.
2. E. A. Guggenheim, *Boltzmann's Distribution Law*, Chapter 8, Interscience Publishers, New York, 1955.
3. J. E. Mayer and M. G. Mayer, *Statistical Mechanics*, Chapter II, John Wiley & Sons, New York, 1940; R. Fowler and E. A. Guggenheim, *Statistical Thermodynamics*, Chapter IV, Cambridge University Press, Cambridge, England, reprinted 1956.

Configurational Entropy of a Gas

Consider two vessels of volumes V_1 and V' surrounded by a heat-impervious envelope and connected by a tube. Place in this system N molecules of an ideal gas. Let us now ask what is the probability of finding the N molecules in the volume V_1, which we shall call state 1, as compared to the probability of finding the N molecules distributed throughout the volume $V_1 + V' = V_2$ which we shall call state 2. The probability of finding any one molecule in volume V_1 is given by the expression V_1/V_2. The probability P of having N noninteracting molecules all present in volume V_1 is given by

B.1
$$P = (V_1/V_2)^N$$

The probability P may also be regarded as the ratio of the number of configurations Ω_1 available to the molecules in state 1 as compared to the number of configurations Ω_2 available to the molecules in state 2. The assumption is clearly made that all configurations (or microstates or complexions) are equally probable.

B.2
$$P = \frac{\Omega_1}{\Omega_2} = \left(\frac{V_1}{V_2}\right)^N$$

From Boltzmann's equation the entropy difference between these states is

B.3
$$S_1 - S_2 = \mathbf{k} \ln \frac{\Omega_1}{\Omega_2} = N\mathbf{k} \ln \frac{V_1}{V_2}$$

From this result the equation of state can be immediately derived.

An exact derivation of Ω for a "classical" monatomic gas as a function of U and V gives [1]

B.4
$$\Omega = g_0{}^N \left(\frac{V}{N}\right)^N \left(4\pi e^{5/3}\,\frac{mU}{3\mathbf{h}^2 N}\right)^{3N/2}$$

where m is the molecular mass, g_0 is the ground-state degeneracy, e is the base of the natural logarithmic scale and U, the internal energy, is a function of T only.

Reference for Appendix B

1. J. E. Mayer and M. G. Mayer, *Statistical Mechanics*, p. 116, John Wiley & Sons, New York, 1940.

Equation of State
for Molecular Crystals

The Helmholtz free energy of a crystal may be written as (see equations A.8 and A.10)

C.1 $$A = U_L(V) + A_D(T, V)$$

where $A_D(T, V)$ represents the vibrational free energy in the Debye approximation.

In the Debye approximation, by inspection of equations A.6, A.8 and A.10, it is clear that $A_D(T, V)$ is equal to T times a function of θ/T. θ is the Debye temperature, defined as $h\nu_m/\mathbf{k}$. The dependence of A_D on volume may be described by specifying the dependence of θ on volume.

C.2 $$A_D = Tf(\theta/T)$$

The pressure is given by

C.3 $$p = -\frac{dU_L(V)}{dV} - \left(\frac{\partial A_D}{\partial \theta}\right)_{T,V} \left(\frac{\partial \theta}{\partial V}\right)_T$$

Utilizing equation C.2, one notes that [1]

C.4 $$\left(\frac{\partial A_D}{\partial \theta}\right)_{T,V} = \frac{d(A_D/T)}{d(\theta/T)}$$

$$= \theta^{-1}\left[\frac{(\partial A_D/T)}{\partial(1/T)}\right]_{\theta,V}$$

287

By a well-known thermodynamic formula

C.5
$$\left[\frac{\partial(A_D/T)}{\partial(1/T)} \right]_V = U_D$$

Therefore, combining equations C.3, C.4 and C.5 yields

C.6
$$p = -\frac{dU_L(V)}{dV} + \frac{\gamma U_D}{V}$$

where U_D is the internal energy due to lattice vibrations in the Debye approximation, and γ is the Gruneisen constant defined as

C.7
$$\gamma = -\left(\frac{\partial \ln \theta}{\partial \ln V} \right)_T$$

We assume that the Gruneisen constant is fairly temperature-independent. Furthermore, from the relation between the Debye temperature and the bulk modulus (Chapter I, equations 5.11 and 5.14),

C.8
$$\theta \sim V^{\frac{1}{6}} B^{\frac{1}{2}} \sim V^{\frac{1}{6}} \left[-\frac{1}{V} \left(\frac{\partial p}{\partial V} \right)_T \right]^{\frac{1}{2}}$$

from which one can readily derive by using equations C.8 and C.7 [2]

C.9
$$\gamma = -\tfrac{2}{3} - \tfrac{1}{2}V \left(\frac{\partial^2 P}{\partial V^2} \right)_T \Big/ \left(\frac{\partial P}{\partial V} \right)_T$$

We assume that the Gruneisen constant will be given with sufficient accuracy at all temperatures by evaluating $(\partial^2 P/\partial V^2)_T$ and $(\partial P/\partial V)_T$ at $T = 0°K$. This can be readily accomplished by using equation 3.8 of Chapter I. The ratio $V(d^2 P/dV^2)/(dP/dV)$ turns out to be -9. The Gruneisen constant for molecular crystals is, therefore,

C.10 $\gamma = 3.83$

Inserting this value and equation 3.8 of Chapter I into equation C.6, there results the new equation

C.11
$$p = 37.64 p^* \left[\left(\frac{V_0}{V} \right)^5 - \left(\frac{V_0}{V} \right)^3 + 3.83 \frac{U_D}{V} \right]$$

The Debye function U_D is an elementary function which is tabulated for all values of θ/T. Here θ is considered a constant, as defined at $0°K$ and zero pressure in section 5 of Chapter I. For molecular crystals the Debye temperature is given by equation 5.17 of Chapter I.

The very same treatment can be used in the Einstein approximation, in which case equation C.11 would end up as having U_D replaced by U_E. All the mathematical steps presented in this appendix apply equally to the Debye or Einstein approximation.

The curve of volume versus temperature at zero pressure can be obtained from equation C.11 by setting $p = 0$.

By differentiating equation C.6 with respect to T at constant V, one obtains

C.12
$$\left(\frac{\partial p}{\partial T}\right)_V = -\left[\left(\frac{\partial p}{\partial V}\right)_T\right]\left[\left(\frac{\partial V}{\partial T}\right)_p\right] = \frac{\gamma C_V}{V}$$

Hence

C.13
$$a = \frac{1}{V}\left(\frac{\partial V}{\partial T}\right)_V = \frac{\gamma C_V}{BV}$$

where a is the volume coefficient of expansion $(1/V)(\partial V/\partial T)_p$, B is the bulk modulus and C_V is the specific heat. Since γ and B are approximately independent of temperature, it is seen that a varies with temperature in the same manner as C_V.

If one takes $\gamma = 3.83$ and $B = B_0 = 1.07 \times 10^2(\epsilon^*/r^{*3})$, the latter from equation 3.10 of Chapter I, one obtains

C.14
$$\left(\frac{\partial V}{\partial T}\right)_p = 3.58 \times 10^{-2}\frac{r^{*3}}{\epsilon^*}C_V$$

Integrating equation C.14 at constant (zero) pressure, one obtains

C.15
$$V(T) = V_0\left(1 + 3.58 \times 10^{-2}\frac{r^{*3}}{\epsilon^*}\frac{U_D(T)}{V_0}\right)$$

Equation C.15 for the molecular crystal is completely determined in terms of ϵ^* and r^*, since, by equation 3.7 of Chapter I, V_0 is equal to $0.69Nr^{*3}$, and U_D is a universal function of T/θ with θ defined by equation 5.17 of Chapter I. We can therefore write

C.16
$$V\left(\frac{T}{\theta}\right) = V_0\left[1 + 5.55 \times 10^{-2}\frac{U_D(T/\theta)}{N\epsilon^*}\right]$$

At large values of T/θ, U_D is equal to $3NkT$. The limiting value of the coefficient of expansion at high temperatures is approximately

C.17
$$a = 0.167(k/\epsilon^*)\qquad\text{for large values of }T/\theta$$

References for Appendix C

1. C. Kittel, *Introduction to Solid State Physics*, 2d ed., pp. 153 and 154, John Wiley & Sons, New York, 1956.
2. J. C. Slater, *Introduction to Chemical Physics*, pp. 238 and 239, McGraw-Hill Book Co., New York, 1939.

The Expected Square of the Length of a Hydrocarbon-Type Chain[1]

We wish to calculate the expected square of the end-to-end length of a random hydrocarbon-type chain of $\mathfrak{N}$ links which are represented by vectors $(X^{(i)}, Y^{(i)}, Z^{(i)})$, $i = 0, 1, 2, 3, \ldots, \mathfrak{N} - 1$. Each vector is represented by one of the eight combinations $(\pm 1, \pm 1, \pm 1)$, and the successive links differ only in the change of exactly one sign.[2] The magnitude of the components is taken as unity for simplicity in calculation; at the end of the calculation we will recall that the actual lengths of the components are $l_0/3^{1/2}$, where l_0 is the bond length.

The probability that two successive changes in sign occur at the *same* coordinate so that $(X^{(i+2)}, Y^{(i+2)}, Z^{(i+2)})$, is identical with $(X^{(i)}, Y^{(i)}, Z^{(i)})$ and is taken to be a; the second change of sign occurs at one of the *other* two places with probability $(1 - a)/2$. These three situations correspond to the *trans* and the two *gauche* configurations. The expected length for a hydrocarbon-type chain of $\mathfrak{N}$ links was solved long ago by H. Eyring[3] *if* the energies, and hence the probabilities, of all three configurations are the same. This corresponds to the special case where $a = \frac{1}{3}$. We seek the general solution.[1]

We may choose the coordinate system so that $(X^{(0)}, Y^{(0)}, Z^{(0)}) = (1, 1, 1)$ and $(X^{(1)}, Y^{(1)}, Z^{(1)}) = (-1, 1, 1)$. The next link has the possible forms $(1, 1, 1)$, $(-1, -1, 1)$ and $(1, -1, -1)$ with probability a, $(1 - a)/2$, $(1 - a)/2$.

We calculate the expected square of the length denoted by $E\mathfrak{N}$.

D.1 $\quad E\mathfrak{N} = E\{(X^{(0)} + \cdots + X^{(\mathfrak{N}-1)})^2$

$$+ (Y^{(0)} + \cdots + Y^{(\mathfrak{N}-1)})^2 + (Z^{(0)} + \cdots + Z^{(\mathfrak{N}-1)})^2\}$$

$$= 3\mathfrak{N} + 2 \sum_{i=0}^{\mathfrak{N}-2} \sum_{j=i+1}^{\mathfrak{N}-1} E\{X^{(i)}X^{(j)} + Y^{(i)}Y^{(j)} + Z^{(i)}Z^{(j)}\}$$

$$= 3\mathfrak{N} + 2 \sum_{i=0}^{\mathfrak{N}-2} \sum_{k=1}^{\mathfrak{N}-1-i} E\{X^{(0)}X^{(k)} + Y^{(0)}Y^{(k)} + Z^{(0)}Z^{(k)}\}$$

Put

D.2 $\qquad L_k = E\{X^{(0)}X^{(k)} + Y^{(0)}Y^{(k)} + Z^{(0)}Z^{(k)}\}$

Clearly from the sequences discussed above

D.3 $\qquad L_0 = 3 \qquad L_1 = 1 \qquad L_2 = -1 + 4a$

Furthermore we can simplify the expression for $E\mathfrak{N}$

D.4 $\qquad E\mathfrak{N} = 3\mathfrak{N} + 2 \sum_{i=0}^{\mathfrak{N}-2} \sum_{k=1}^{\mathfrak{N}-1-i} L_k$

$$= -3\mathfrak{N} + 2 \sum_{i=0}^{\mathfrak{N}-1} \sum_{k=0}^{\mathfrak{N}-1-i} L_k$$

$$= -3\mathfrak{N} + 2 \sum_{k=0}^{\mathfrak{N}-1} (\mathfrak{N} - k)L_k$$

Now put $(X^{(0)}, Y^{(0)}, Z^{(0)}) = (1, 1, 1)$ and $U^{(i)} = X^{(i)} + Y^{(i)} + Z^{(i)}$. Then $L_i = E(U_i)$. The variable $U^{(i)}$ can assume the four values ± 3, ± 1. We consider the sequence of *pairs* $(U_0 U_1)$, $(U_1 U_2)$, $(U_2 U_3)$, $\ldots$, $(U_i U_{i+1})$, $\ldots$, $(U_{n-1} U_n)$. Each member of this sequence is a state with the possible values (3 1), (1 3), (1 -1), (-1 1), (-1 -3) and (-3 -1). The sequence of pairs is a Markoff chain with the following matrix P of transition probabilities:

D.5

		3 1	1 3	1 -1	-1 1	-1 -3	-3 -1
	3 1	0	a	$1 - a$	0	0	0
	1 3	1	0	0	0	0	0
$P =$	1 -1	0	0	0	$(1 + a)/2$	$(1 - a)/2$	0
	-1 1	0	$(1 - a)/2$	$(1 + a)/2$	0	0	0
	-1 -3	0	0	0	0	0	1
	-3 -1	0	0	0	$1 - a$	a	0

For a thorough definition of a Markoff chain see reference 4.

The matrix of transition probabilities appropriate for $0 \rightarrow i$ transition in the sequence is denoted by $P^{(i)}$. If the first row of $P^{(i)}$ has elements $p_{11}^{(i)}, \ldots, p_{16}^{(i)}$, the probability that $U^{(i)} = 3, 1, -1, -3$ equals respectively $p_{11}^{(i)}, p_{12}^{(i)} + p_{13}^{(i)}, p_{14}^{(i)} + p_{15}^{(i)}, p_{16}^{(i)}$, and hence

D.6 $\qquad L_i = 3(p_{11}^{(i)} - p_{16}^{(i)}) + (p_{12}^{(i)} + p_{13}^{(i)} - p_{14}^{(i)} - p_{15}^{(i)})$

The method of solving for the elements $p_{jk}^{(i)}$ of matrix $P^{(i)}$ in terms of the known elements p_{jk} of matrix P is presented for the general case of a Markoff chain in W. Feller's book,[4] especially the top few paragraphs on page 384 and, alternatively, the italicized paragraph on page 383. The solutions are couched in terms of the eigenvalues and eigenvectors of the matrix P. Specializing to the matrix P here under consideration (equation D.5), it has three eigenvectors of the symmetric pattern (x, y, z, z, y, x) which will not contribute to L_i, and three eigenvectors of the antisymmetric form (x, y, z, $-z$, $-y$, $-x$). This consideration considerably simplifies the calculations. The eigenvalues corresponding to the antisymmetric eigenvectors are -1, Q' and Q'', where Q', Q'' are roots of

D.7 $\qquad\qquad Q^2 - \dfrac{1-a}{2} Q + \dfrac{1-3a}{2} = 0$

$$Q' + Q'' = \dfrac{1-a}{2} \qquad Q'Q'' = \dfrac{1-3a}{2}$$

The $p_{jk}^{(i)}$ values obtained by the procedure discussed above (reference 4) are couched in terms of Q' and Q''. When these are substituted in equation D.6, one obtains

D.8 $\quad L_i = \dfrac{1}{(Q'' - Q')} \left[3(Q'')^{i+1} - 3(Q')^{i+1} - \dfrac{1-3a}{2} (Q'')^i - (Q')^i \right]$

$$= \dfrac{1}{DQ} D \left(3Q^{i+1} - \dfrac{1-3a}{2} Q^i \right)$$

The definition of the operator D is clear from the equation.

We recall that the expression for $E_{\mathfrak{N}}$ contained the term $\sum\limits_{k=0}^{\mathfrak{N}-1} (\mathfrak{N} - k)L_k$. Note that

D.9 $\qquad \sum\limits_{k=0}^{\mathfrak{N}-1} (\mathfrak{N} - k)Q^k = \dfrac{\mathfrak{N}}{1-Q} + \dfrac{Q^{\mathfrak{N}+1}}{(1-Q)^2} - \dfrac{Q}{(1-Q)^2}$

Therefore

$$\text{D.10} \quad E_{\mathfrak{N}} = -3\mathfrak{N} + \frac{2\mathfrak{N}}{DQ} D\left(\frac{3Q}{1-Q} - \frac{1-3a}{2}\frac{1}{1-Q}\right)$$

$$+ \frac{2}{DQ} D\left[\frac{3Q^{\mathfrak{N}+2}}{(1-Q)^2} - \frac{1-3a}{2}\frac{Q^{\mathfrak{N}+1}}{(1-Q)^2}\right]$$

$$- \frac{2}{DQ} D\left[\frac{3Q^2}{(1-Q)^2} - \frac{1-3a}{2}\frac{Q}{(1-Q)^2}\right]$$

To calculate the leading term note that

$$\text{D.11} \qquad D\frac{1}{1-Q} = \frac{1}{1-Q''} - \frac{1}{1-Q'} = \frac{DQ}{1-a}$$

$$\text{D.12} \qquad D\frac{Q}{1-Q} = D\left(-1 + \frac{1}{1-Q}\right) = \frac{DQ}{1-a}$$

whence

$$\text{D.13} \qquad D\left(\frac{3Q}{1-Q} - \frac{1-3a}{2}\frac{1}{1-Q}\right) = \frac{DQ}{1-a}\left(3 - \frac{1-3a}{2}\right)$$

$$= \frac{DQ(5+3a)}{2(1-a)}$$

Thus:

$$\text{D.14} \qquad E_{\mathfrak{N}} \simeq -3\mathfrak{N} + \frac{(5+3a)\mathfrak{N}}{1-a} = \frac{(2+6a)\mathfrak{N}}{1-a}$$

The exact expected length can be obtained by further reduction of equation D.10.

$$\text{D.15} \quad E_{\mathfrak{N}} = \frac{(2+6a)\mathfrak{N}}{1-a} - \frac{9a^2+30a-7}{2(1-a)^2} + \frac{2}{(1-a)^2}\frac{D}{DQ}\left[3Q^{\mathfrak{N}+2}\right.$$

$$\left. - \frac{7(1-3a)Q^{\mathfrak{N}+1}}{2} + \frac{5(1-3a)^2Q^{\mathfrak{N}}}{4} - \frac{(1-3a)^3Q^{\mathfrak{N}-1}}{8}\right]$$

We now recall that the length of each component, which for simplicity was taken as unity, is in reality $l_0/3^{1/2}$. The expression for the expected square of the end-to-end distance $\bar{r}^2$ which is very nearly exact for large values of $\mathfrak{N}$ is obtained from equation D.14:

D.16
$$\bar{r}^2 = \frac{(2 + 6a)\mathfrak{N}l_0^2}{3(1 - a)}$$

If the energy (or, more accurately, free energy) of the *trans* configuration is taken as zero, and the energies of the two *gauche* configurations are each taken as ϵ (per mole) the quantity a is given by

D.17
$$a = \frac{1}{1 + 2\exp(-\epsilon/RT)}$$

Hence

D.18
$$\bar{r}^2 = [\tfrac{2}{3} + \tfrac{4}{3}\exp(\epsilon/RT)]\mathfrak{N}l_0^2$$

If ϵ is zero, a is $\tfrac{1}{3}$, and equation D.16 reduces to the equation of Eyring.[3]

D.19
$$\bar{r}^2 = 2\mathfrak{N}l_0^2 \qquad \epsilon = 0$$

If ϵ/RT is very large and positive, i.e., the *gauche* configurations are nearly excluded, a approaches $1 - 2\exp(-\epsilon/RT)$, and we obtain the following asymptotic expression for $\bar{r}^2$:

D.20
$$\bar{r}^2 \simeq [\tfrac{4}{3}\exp(\epsilon/RT)]\mathfrak{N}l_0^2 \qquad \epsilon/RT \gg 1$$

If ϵ/RT is large and negative, i.e., the *trans* configuration nearly excluded, a approaches zero, and we obtain the following expression for $\bar{r}^2$:

D.21
$$\bar{r}^2 = \tfrac{2}{3}\mathfrak{N}l_0^2 \qquad -\epsilon/RT \gg 1$$

The problem of excluded volume is obviously not considered in this calculation.

Equation D.18 can be derived from simpler considerations developed by W. J. Taylor[5] and M. W. Wolkenstein.[6] The method presented in this Appendix, however, is a complete and rigorous solution of the problem that is also valid for short chains (equation D.15).[1]

Wolkenstein has also given very interesting formulae for $\bar{r}^2$ for isotactic and syndiotactic chains,[7] and for short chains.[6]

References for Appendix D

1. A. V. Tobolsky, *J. Chem. Phys.*, **31**, 387 (1959).
2. A. V. Tobolsky, R. E. Powell and H. Eyring, Chapter 5 in *The Chemistry of Large Molecules*, R. E. Burk and O. Grummitt (ed.), Interscience Publishers, New York, 1943.

3. H. Eyring, *Phys. Rev.*, **39**, 746 (1932).
4. W. Feller, *An Introduction to Probability Theory and Its Applications*, Vol. 1, 2d ed., pp. 338–349, 380–385, John Wiley & Sons, New York, 1957. The invaluable aid of Prof. W. Feller in all aspects of the mathematical solution presented in this appendix is gratefully acknowledged.
5. W. J. Taylor, *J. Chem. Phys.*, **16**, 257 (1948).
6. M. W. Wolkenstein, *Doklady Acad. Nauk USSR*, **78**, 879 (1951); *J. Phys. Chem. USSR*, **26**, 1072 (1952).
7. M. W. Wolkenstein, *J. Polymer Sci.*, **29**, 441 (1948).

Gaussian Distribution of End-to-End Distance for a Random Chain

Consider a freely jointed chain of $\mathfrak{N}$ links each of length l_0. What is the probability $W(x)$ that the vector connecting the ends has the component x along an arbitrary direction chosen as the x axis? The problem will be treated as a one-dimensional problem: We discuss a random walk of $\mathfrak{N}$ steps in one dimension, each step of length $\pm l_0/3^{1/2}$, the plus and minus signs having equal probability. The probability that a walk has $\mathfrak{N}_+$ positive steps and $\mathfrak{N}_-$ negative steps is

E.1 $$W(\mathfrak{N}_+, \mathfrak{N}_-) = (\tfrac{1}{2})^{\mathfrak{N}}\mathfrak{N}!/\mathfrak{N}_+!\mathfrak{N}_-!$$

with the condition

E.2 $$\mathfrak{N}_+ + \mathfrak{N}_- = \mathfrak{N}$$

For convenience we introduce the quantity m

E.3 $$m = \mathfrak{N}_+ - \mathfrak{N}_-$$

The distance x reached at the end of the walk is

E.4 $$x = (\mathfrak{N}_+ - \mathfrak{N}_-)l_0/3^{1/2} = ml_0/3^{1/2}$$

In terms of m, equation E.1 becomes

E.5 $$W(\mathfrak{N}, m) = \frac{\tfrac{1}{2}^{\mathfrak{N}}\mathfrak{N}!}{((\mathfrak{N} + m)/2)!((\mathfrak{N} - m)/2)!}$$

Stirling's approximation for large numbers in the form $\mathfrak{N}! \simeq (2\pi)^{\frac{1}{2}}$ $\mathfrak{N}^{\mathfrak{N}+\frac{1}{2}}/e^{\mathfrak{N}}$ is introduced into equation E.5, and also the restriction that $m/\mathfrak{N} \ll 1$. Equation E.5 becomes

E.6 $$W(\mathfrak{N}, m) \simeq \left(\frac{2}{\pi\mathfrak{N}}\right)^{\frac{1}{2}} \exp\left(-\frac{m^2}{2\mathfrak{N}}\right)$$

We wish to establish a correspondence between $W(m, \mathfrak{N})$ and $W(x)$, the latter being the probability that the distance reached after $\mathfrak{N}$ steps of the walk is x. We assume $W(x)$ to be a continuous function in order to correspond with the molecular problem stated in the second sentence of this appendix. By definition

E.7 $$W(x) = W(m, \mathfrak{N})/\Delta x$$

We note however that the smallest value of Δm is 2, and the value of Δx that corresponds to $\Delta m = 2$ is $\Delta x = 2l_0/3^{\frac{1}{2}}$. Inserting this value of Δx in equation E.7, and $m = 3^{\frac{1}{2}}x/l_0$ into E.6, one obtains [1,2]

E.8 $$W(x)\, dx = \left(\frac{3}{2\pi}\right)^{\frac{1}{2}} \left(\frac{1}{\mathfrak{N}^{\frac{1}{2}}l_0}\right) \exp\left(-\frac{3x^2}{2\mathfrak{N}l_0{}^2}\right) dx$$

Any actual chain with hindered rotation, bond angle restrictions, etc., can be approximated by an equivalent chain of $\mathfrak{N}_e$ freely rotating segments each of length l_e, as discussed in Chapter II, section 1. Equation E.8 can also be generalized to three dimensions, resulting in

E.9 $$W(x, y, z)\, dx\, dy\, dz = \left(\frac{b}{\pi^{\frac{1}{2}}}\right)^3 \exp\left[-b^2(x^2 + y^2 + z^2)\right] dx\, dy\, dz$$

$$b^2 = \frac{3}{2\bar{r}^2} = \frac{3}{2\mathfrak{N}_e l_e{}^2}$$

References for Appendix E

1. E. Guth and H. Mark, *Monatsh.*, **65**, 93 (1934).
2. W. Kuhn, *Kolloid Z.*, **68**, 2 (1934).

Size Distribution
in Linear Polymers

The size of a linear polymer molecule can be expressed in terms of the number of links in the chain, in terms of the number of repeating units along the chain (the degree of polymerization) or in terms of the molecular weight of the polymer molecule.

Many protein molecules, e.g., insulin, exist in nature as definite entities of a sharply defined molecular weight. An assembly of polymer molecules all of the same molecular weight is called monodisperse; an assembly of polymer molecules of a wide variety of molecular weights is called polydisperse.

All synthetically prepared polymers are polydisperse; indeed a continuous distribution of molecular weights is always produced. Sometimes this distribution of molecular weights is very narrow, and the synthetic polymer approximates monodispersity.

For definiteness we shall discuss size distribution in terms of the degree of polymerization although number of links in the chain or molecular weight could also be used. The two important functions are $X(x)$, the mole fraction of polymer with degree of polymerization x, and $W(x)$, the weight fraction of polymer with degree of polymerization x. Both these functions are normalized to unity.

Some frequently encountered distributions of molecular weight are given below:

F.1 $\qquad X(x) = p^{x-1}(1 - p)$

F.2 $\qquad W(x) = p^{x-1}(1 - p)^2$ $\qquad$ random distribution

In equations F.1 and F.2 the quantity p is a parameter which specifies the distribution and whose value lies between zero and unity. The random distribution is encountered in random degradation of high-molecular-weight polymers,[1] in random bifunctional condensation [2] and in random interchange.[2] In vinyl polymerizations, where transfer and disproportionation rather than coupling are the molecular-weight-controlling steps, the random distribution specifies the polymer that is produced in a very narrow range of conversion.[3] The quantity p may change as a function of conversion, so that the distribution of the entire polymer (cumulative distribution) formed up to a given conversion is represented by an integration of equations F.1 and F.2 over appropriate values of p.

For vinyl polymerizations where the molecular-weight controlling step is coupling (combination) of growing radicals, the following distribution specifies the polymer that is produced in a very narrow range of conversion.[4, 5]

F.3 $X(x) = xp^{x-1}(1 - p)^2$

                                   coupling distribution

F.4 $W(x) = x^2p^{x-1}(1 - p)^3/(1 + p)$

In the above equations the polymeric species $RM_{x-1}R$ is defined as an x-mer, with R being the initiating radical and M the polymerizing monomer. Here too, p may change as a function of conversion, so that the cumulative distribution may be much broader.

The Poisson distribution obtains when a polymer is produced by monomer addition to an initiating molecule which proceeds without termination.[6] It is specified as follows:

F.5 $X(x) = e^{-z}z^{x-1}/(x - 1)!$

F.6 $W(x) = \dfrac{z}{z + 1}\, xe^{-z}\, \dfrac{z^{x-2}}{(z - 1)!}$

In the above equations z is the number of monomers reacted per initiator; in defining x the initiator is counted as one unit.

The Poisson distribution obtains for the polymerization of ring compounds induced by an initiator, such as ethylene oxide initiated by ethylene glycol.[7] It also obtains for vinyl polymerizations in which the termination step is absent, i.e., the so-called "living polymer" technique in which anionic initiators are utilized.[8] Some of the derivations of these distributions are reviewed in reference 9.

The two most important averages which characterize the size distribution are the number-average degree of polymerization $\bar{P}_n$ and the weight-average degree of polymerization $\bar{P}_w$ defined as follows:

F.7 $\qquad \bar{P}_n = \Sigma x\, X(x) = \Sigma x\, X(x)/\Sigma X(x)$

F.8 $\qquad \bar{P}_w = \Sigma x\, W(x) = \Sigma x^2\, X(x)/\Sigma x\, X(x)$

Similar definitions apply for the number-average molecular weight $\bar{M}_n$, the weight-average molecular weight $\bar{M}_w$, the number-average number of links per chain $\bar{\mathfrak{N}}_n$ and the weight-average number of links per chain $\bar{\mathfrak{N}}_w$.

Frequently the following empirical relation is established between intrinsic viscosity in solution and molecular size x for a series of homologous *monodisperse* polymers.

F.9 $\qquad\qquad\qquad [\eta] = Kx^a$

where a generally ranges between 0.5 and 1.0.

If this relation is applied to polydisperse polymer, a viscosity average degree of polymerization $\bar{P}_v$ is obtained: [10]

F.10 $\qquad \bar{P}_v = [\Sigma x^{a+1}\, X(x)/\Sigma x\, X(x)]^{1/a}$

An exactly analogous definition obtains for the viscosity-average molecular weight $\bar{M}_v$. It will be observed that if $a = 1$ then $\bar{P}_v = \bar{P}_w$. In general, a is approximately 0.7, and so $\bar{P}_v$ lies between $\bar{P}_n$ and $\bar{P}_w$, closer in value to $\bar{P}_w$.

The definitions of $\bar{P}_n$ and $\bar{P}_w$ embodied in equations F.7 and F.8 can be applied to the various distributions in this section. For the random distribution:

F.11 $\qquad \bar{P}_n = 1/(1 - p)$

F.12 $\qquad \bar{P}_w = (1 + p)/(1 - p) \qquad$ random distribution

F.13 $\qquad \bar{P}_w/\bar{P}_n = 1 + p$

For the distribution embodied by equations F.3 and F.4:

F.14 $\qquad \bar{P}_n = (1 + p)/(1 - p)$

F.15 $\qquad \bar{P}_w = (1 + 4p + p^2)/(1 - p^2)$

F.16 $\qquad \bar{P}_w/\bar{P}_n = (1 + 4p + p^2)/(1 + p)^2$

For the Poisson distribution:

F.17 $\qquad\qquad \bar{P}_n = z + 1$

F.18 $\qquad\qquad \bar{P}_w = z + 1 + \dfrac{z}{1 + z}$

F.19 $\qquad\qquad \dfrac{\bar{P}_w}{\bar{P}_n} = 1 + \dfrac{z}{(1 + z)^2}$

The quantity $\bar{P}_w/\bar{P}_n$, often called the heterogeneity index, is a measure of the broadness of the distribution. For a monodisperse distribution, $\bar{P}_w/\bar{P}_n$ is obviously equal to unity; the larger $\bar{P}_w/\bar{P}_n$, the broader the distribution. The distributions discussed thus far are not exceptionally broad. The maximum value of $\bar{P}_w/\bar{P}_n$ for the random distribution is 2.0 (when $p = 1$); for the coupling distribution the maximum value of $\bar{P}_w/\bar{P}_n = 1.5$ (when $p = 1$). The Poisson distribution is a remarkably narrow size distribution: when $z = 99$, $\bar{P}_w/\bar{P}_n = 1.0099$, and, for larger values of z, $\bar{P}_w/\bar{P}_n$ is even smaller. Polymers with this distribution are sometimes termed "monodisperse."

Very broad distributions can be obtained in vinyl polymerizations in the presence of a chain-transfer agent, considering the total polymer obtained (cumulative polymer) rather than the polymer produced in a narrow range of conversion. In the following derivation we shall consider that chain transfer to a modifier S with chain-transfer constant c is the only important size-controlling step in the polymerization of a vinyl monomer M.[11] Initial concentrations are S_0 and M_0, current concentrations during the polymerization are S and M, fractional conversion y is $y = (M_0 - M)/M_0$.

The value of $\bar{P}_n{}'$ of the polymer being instantaneously produced is

F.20
$$\bar{P}_n{}' = \frac{1}{c}\left(\frac{M}{S}\right)$$

Since the polymer instantaneously produced has a random distribution, $\bar{P}_w{}'$ is very nearly equal to $2\bar{P}_n{}'$,

F.21
$$\bar{P}_w{}' = \frac{2}{c}\left(\frac{M}{S}\right)$$

The concentration S is given by [12]

F.22
$$S = S_0\left(\frac{M}{M_0}\right)^c$$

The cumulative values of $\bar{P}_n$ and $\bar{P}_w$ are given by the following equations:

F.23
$$\frac{M_0 - M}{\bar{P}_n} = \int_M^{M_0} dM/\bar{P}'_n$$

F.24
$$(M_0 - M)\bar{P}_w = \int_M^{M_0} \bar{P}'_w\, dM$$

By inserting the values of $\bar{P}_n{}'$ and $\bar{P}_w{}'$ in equations F.23 and F.24 and eliminating S through equation F.22, the following results are obtained: [11]

F.25 $$\overline{P}_n = \frac{(M_0/S_0)y}{1 - (1 - y)^c} \qquad y = \frac{M_0 - M}{M_0}$$

F.26 $$\overline{P}_w = \frac{(2M_0/cS_0)[1 - (1 - y)^{2-c}]}{y(2 - c)}$$

The heterogeneity index for this cumulative polymer is (for values of c other than 2):

F.27 $$\frac{\overline{P}_w}{\overline{P}_n} = \frac{2}{c(2 - c)} \frac{1 - (1 - y)^c - (1 - y)^{2-c} + (1 - y)^2}{y^2}$$

This particular type of distribution is especially applicable to the low-molecular-weight vinyl- and diene-type polymers obtained by polymerization in the presence of substantial quantities of active modifier. These substances are of particular importance as castable liquids which can be converted to rubbers.[13] If the modifier has a chain-transfer constant of unity, the heterogeneity index will have a value of 2, independent of the fractional conversion y. If the chain-transfer constant differs appreciably from unity, the cumulative polymer will have a heterogeneity index that starts at 2 at zero conversion and becomes higher as conversion increases to unity, indicating increasingly broader distributions.

Another example of a broad cumulative distribution arises during homogeneous polymerization of vinyl monomers because of depletion of catalyst, treated in the theory of dead-end radical polymerization.[14]

References for Appendix F

1. W. Kuhn, *Ber.*, **63**, 1503 (1930).
2. P. J. Flory, *J. Am. Chem. Soc.*, **58**, 1877 (1936); *ibid.*, **64**, 2205 (1942).
3. G. V. Schulz, *Z. physik. Chem.*, **B30**, 379 (1935).
4. G. V. Schulz, *Z. physik. Chem.*, **B43**, 25 (1939).
5. B. Baysal and A. V. Tobolsky, *J. Polymer Sci.*, **9**, 171 (1952).
6. H. Dostal and H. Mark, *Z. physik. Chem.*, **B29**, 299 (1935).
7. P. J. Flory, *J. Am. Chem. Soc.*, **62**, 1561 (1940).
8. R. Waack, A. Rembaum, J. D. Coombes and M. Szwarc, *J. Am. Chem. Soc.*, **79**, 2026 (1957).
9. P. J. Flory, *Principles of Polymer Chemistry*, Chapter VIII, Cornell University Press, Ithaca, N. Y., 1953.
10. P. J. Flory, *J. Am. Chem. Soc.*, **65**, 372 (1943).
11. A. V. Tobolsky, R. C. Fettes and D. H. Johnson, *Princeton Univ. Plastics Lab. Tech. Rept. 17A* (1950).
12. W. V. Smith, *J. Am. Chem. Soc.*, **68**, 2059 (1946).
13. V. Conwell, G. P. Roeser and A. V. Tobolsky, *J. Polymer Sci.*, **4**, 309 (1949).
14. A. V. Tobolsky, *J. Am. Chem. Soc.*, **80**, 5927 (1958).

APPENDIX G

Affine Transformation of a Sphere

Consider a spherical surface defined by the equation

G.1 $$x^2 + y^2 + z^2 = r_0{}^2$$

Further, consider that this sphere is subjected to the affine transformation

G.2 $$x' = \alpha x \qquad y' = \alpha^{-\frac{1}{2}} y \qquad z' = \alpha^{-\frac{1}{2}} z$$

The sphere now becomes an ellipse

G.3 $$\frac{x'^2}{\alpha^2} + \alpha y'^2 + \alpha z'^2 = r_0{}^2$$

We seek the average value of $r'^2 = x'^2 + y'^2 + z'^2$. To accomplish this we transform x, y, z and x' y' z' to polar coordinates:

G.4 $$x = r_0 \cos \theta$$

$$y = r_0 \sin \theta \sin \phi$$

$$z = r_0 \sin \theta \cos \phi$$

G.5 $$x' = \alpha r_0 \cos \theta$$

$$y' = \alpha^{-\frac{1}{2}} r_0 \sin \theta \sin \phi$$

$$z' = \alpha^{-\frac{1}{2}} r_0 \sin \theta \cos \phi$$

$$r'^2 = x'^2 + y'^2 + z'^2 = \alpha^2 r_0{}^2 \cos^2 \theta + \alpha^{-1} r_0{}^2 \sin^2 \theta$$

304

In order to obtain the average value of r'^2 we weight all orientations equally,

G.6 $$\bar{r}'^2 = \left(\frac{1}{4\pi}\right) \int_0^\pi (\alpha^2 r_0^2 \cos^2 \theta + \alpha^{-1} r_0^2 \sin^2 \theta) 2\pi \sin \theta \, d\theta$$

$$= \tfrac{1}{2} r_0^2 \int_0^\pi [\alpha^{-1} + (\alpha^2 - \alpha^{-1}) \cos^2 \theta] \, d\cos\theta$$

$$= \tfrac{1}{2} r_0^2 \int_{-1}^1 [\alpha^{-1} + (\alpha^2 - \alpha^{-1}) x^2] \, dx$$

or, finally,

G.7 $$\bar{r}'^2 = (r_0^2/3)[\alpha^2 + 2\alpha^{-1}]$$

Equation of State of Polymer Chains and Networks Incorporating Energy and Entropy Effects

Consider a one-dimensional chain whose segments of equal length x_0 point in either the positive or the negative direction. When successive segments are pointed in opposite directions, this is said to constitute an interaction, measured by an interaction energy ϵ' (per mole). The zero point of energy is assigned to the configuration consisting of successive segments pointed in the same direction, i.e., the straight or extended form. When ϵ' is negative, the interaction is favored, and hence the folded form of the chain is favored. When ϵ' is positive, the interaction or fold is disfavored, and hence the extended form of the chain is preferred. The statistical thermodynamic treatment of such a chain was presented simultaneously by Scott and Tobolsky [1,2] and by Guth and James.[3]

To what extent can physical reality be associated with this one-dimensional model? It was pointed out [2] that this model can be placed in correspondence with a hydrocarbon-type chain where the *trans* and *gauche* configurations have unequal energies, the energy of the *trans* configuration being taken as zero and that of the two *gauche* configurations being taken as ϵ. This type of chain was discussed in Appendix D, and it was there shown that the mean-square distance $\bar{r}^2$ is

H.1 $$\bar{r}^2 = [\tfrac{2}{3} + \tfrac{4}{3}\exp{(\epsilon/\mathbf{R}T)}]\mathfrak{N}l_0{}^2$$

For the mean-square value $\bar{x}^2$ of the projection of the hydrocarbon chain along the x axis, we have

H.2
$$\bar{x}^2 = \left(\tfrac{2}{3} + \tfrac{4}{3} \exp \frac{\epsilon}{\mathbf{R}T} \right) \mathfrak{N} \frac{l_0{}^2}{3}$$

For the one-dimensional chain introduced in this section as an analogue of the hydrocarbon chain, it can be readily shown by the methods of Appendix D that

H.3
$$\bar{x}^2 = [\exp (\epsilon'/\mathbf{R}T)]\mathfrak{N}x_0{}^2$$

The two models are therefore analogous if

H.4
$$\tfrac{2}{3} + \tfrac{4}{3} \exp \frac{\epsilon}{\mathbf{R}T} = \exp \frac{\epsilon'}{\mathbf{R}T}$$

and

H.5
$$x_0 = l_0/\sqrt{3}$$

The one-dimensional model may also be useful for molecules such as proteins which exhibit an intramolecular folding due to formation of hydrogen bonds between neighboring functional groups along the chain.

We address ourselves to the problem of obtaining an equation of state for a chain of $\mathfrak{N}$ segments, for which P segments are pointing in the positive direction and Q segments are pointing in the negative direction. For mathematical convenience we assume that the two end segments are pointing in opposite directions and that $P > Q$. The extension of the chain which defines its external condition of restraint is

H.6
$$L = (P - Q)x_0 = Rx_0$$

$$R = P - Q; \quad P = (\mathfrak{N} + R)/2, \quad Q = (\mathfrak{N} - R)/2$$

To maintain the chain at extension L (i.e., at a fixed value of P and Q), a tension X is required. The value of X can be obtained from the equation

H.7
$$X = -\mathbf{k}T \left(\frac{\partial \ln Z}{\partial L} \right)_T = - \frac{\mathbf{k}T(\partial \ln Z/\partial R)_T}{x_0}$$

where Z is the partition function of the chain.

We can classify the macrostates corresponding to a fixed value of P and Q with respect to a parameter I. This parameter is defined as the number of sequences of positive segments in a particular chain configuration. Since each sequence of positive segments is followed by a sequence of negative segments, I is also the number of sequences of negative segments. For example in the configuration written below the values of I, P and Q are 5, 18 and 12, respectively.

$$+++++-+++-----+-++++++-+-+-+----$$

The total number of interactions (changes from positive to negative sequences and changes from negative to positive sequences) is clearly $2I - 1$. In the above example the number of interactions is 9. The energy (per mole) of any given chain configuration is $\epsilon'(2I - 1)$. We shall assume P, Q and I to be very large so that unity can be neglected with respect to P, Q and I in the equations that follow.

The number of complexions $W(I)$ of a macrostate corresponding to a fixed value of I is given by

H.8
$$W(I) = \frac{(P - 1)!}{(I - 1)!(P - I)!} \frac{(Q - 1)!}{(I - 1)!(Q - I)!}$$

$$= \frac{\left(\dfrac{\mathfrak{N} + R}{2}\right)! \left(\dfrac{\mathfrak{N} - R}{2}\right)!}{\left(\dfrac{\mathfrak{N} + R}{2} - I\right)! \left(\dfrac{\mathfrak{N} - R}{2} - I\right)! \, (I!)^2}$$

Equation H.8 follows since $W(I)$ is the number of ways of arranging P segments into I groups such that each group has at least one segment in it, times the number of ways of arranging Q segments into I groups such that each group has at least one segment in it.

The partition function Z of the chain is given by a sum of terms corresponding to all possible values of I.

H.9
$$Z = \sum_{I=1}^{\mathfrak{N}/2} W(I) \exp\left(-2\epsilon'I/RT\right)$$

Only the maximum term of this summation corresponding to a value of $I = I_0$ contributes appreciably to the summation. The value of I_0 is obtained by differentiating the general term of the summation with respect to I (at constant R) and setting the result equal to zero. Stirling's theorem is used to express the factorials in equation H.8. The resulting value of I_0 is defined by the relation

H.10
$$\frac{\left(\dfrac{\mathfrak{N} + R}{2} - I_0\right)\left(\dfrac{\mathfrak{N} - R}{2} - I_0\right)}{I_0{}^2} = \exp\frac{2\epsilon'}{RT}$$

Z is therefore given by

H.11 $$Z = W(I_0) \exp(-2\epsilon' I_0/\mathbf{R}T)$$

From equations H.7, H.8, H.10 and H.11 one obtains the equation of state [1,2,3] valid for small values of t:

H.12 $$\sinh \frac{Xx_0}{\mathbf{k}T} = \frac{t}{(1 - t^2)^{1/2}} \exp\left(-\frac{\epsilon'}{\mathbf{R}T}\right) \approx t \exp(-\epsilon'/\mathbf{R}T)$$

$$t = R/\mathfrak{N} = L/\mathfrak{N}x_0$$

For most values of $\epsilon'/\mathbf{R}T$, equation H.12 can be approximated as follows:

H.13 $$X = \mathbf{k}T \exp\left(-\frac{\epsilon'}{\mathbf{R}T}\right)\left(\frac{t}{x_0}\right) = \mathbf{k}TL/\underline{\bar{x}}^2$$

In Figure H.1 is shown the stress-temperature curves at constant $t(t = 0.1)$ for $\epsilon' = 0$, $\epsilon' < 0$ and $\epsilon' > 0$, plotted in the form $\pm NXx_0/\epsilon'$ vs. $\pm \mathbf{R}T/\epsilon'$, according to equation H.12.

It is to be expected that the temperature dependence of the stress in a rubber network maintained at constant extension ratio should be es-

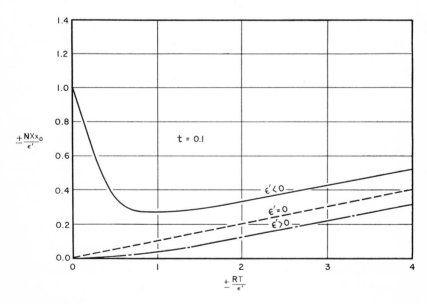

Figure H.1.   Dependence of force on temperature for $t = 0.1$ and $\epsilon' = 0$, $\epsilon' > 0$, $\epsilon' < 0$ according to equation H.12. [After K. W. Scott and A. V. Tobolsky, *J. Colloid Sci.*, **8**, 465 (1953).]

sentially the same as the force-temperature dependence of a chain maintained at constant t. With this in mind, stress-temperature measurements were made in this laboratory many years ago on cross-linked polyisobutylene (Butyl rubber) [4] and cross-linked polyethyl acrylate (Lactoprene rubber).[5] These were examined in light of equation H.12 and Figure H.1 to see whether deviations from the kinetic theory of rubber elasticity could be observed.[6] It was found that in both these rubbers stress at constant extension was strictly proportional to absolute temperature in the temperature region of rubbery behavior. This is in accord with the unmodified kinetic theory of rubber elasticity for which $\epsilon' = 0$ (see Figure H.1). It indicates an absence of energy differences between folded and extended configurations.

The configurational free energy A_c of the chain can be obtained from the expression for X given in equation H.13.

H.14
$$A_c = \int X dL = kT \left(\frac{2b^2 L^2}{3} \right)$$

$$\frac{1}{b^2} = \frac{2\bar{x}^2}{3} = \left(\frac{2}{3} \right) \mathfrak{N} x_0{}^2 \exp \left(\frac{\epsilon'}{\mathfrak{R} T} \right)$$

This can readily be generalized[7] to a three-dimensional chain as follows:

H.15
$$A_c = kT \left(\frac{2b^2 r^2}{3} \right)$$

$$\frac{1}{b^2} = \frac{2\bar{r}_0{}^2}{3} = \left(\frac{2}{3} \right) \mathfrak{N} l_0{}^2 \exp \left(\frac{\epsilon'}{R T} \right)$$

where r^2 is the square of the actual distance between chain ends and $\bar{r}_0{}^2$ is the mean square end-to-end distance in free space.

Equation H.15 can now be applied to a three-dimensional network by interpreting r^2 as the square of the distance between network junctures. The mathematical treatment of Chapter II, section 9, from equations 9.8 to 9.18 holds without change, leading to:

H.16
$$F = n R T \left[\frac{\bar{r}_i{}^2}{\mathfrak{N} l_0{}^2} \exp \left(-\frac{\epsilon'}{R T} \right) \right] \left[\alpha - \left(\frac{1}{\alpha} \right)^2 \right]$$

where $\bar{r}_i{}^2$ is the mean square distance between network junctures. From equation H.16 one obtains:

H.17
$$-\left(\frac{\partial \ln(F/T)}{\partial(1/T)} \right)_\alpha = \frac{\epsilon'}{R}$$

Recently Flory, Hoeve and Ciferri have presented a direct three-dimensional treatment for the elasticity of a rubber network in which the energy effects due to bond-angle restrictions were taken into account,[8] utilizing a mathematical procedure for the problem of chain conformation formulated by Volkenstein and Ptitsyn.[9] Their result is

H.18
$$F = nRT \left(\frac{\bar{r}_i^2}{\bar{r}_0^2}\right) \left[\alpha - \left(\frac{1}{\alpha}\right)^2 \right]$$

In equation H.18 the quantity $\bar{r}_i^2$ represents the mean-square value of the actual distance between network junctures in the isotropic state of the network and the quantity $\bar{r}_0^2$ represents the mean-square value of the end-to-end distance for the network chains considered as chains in free space at the temperature T. The identity of equation H.18 and equation H.16 with equations 9.16 and 9.18 of Chapter II is noteworthy. Since $\bar{r}_i^2$ is essentially independent of temperature, inspection of equation H.18 shows that

H.19
$$\left(\frac{\partial \ln (F/T)}{\partial T}\right)_\alpha = -\frac{d \ln \bar{r}_0^2}{dT}$$

Furthermore, for hydrocarbon chains:

H.20
$$\bar{r}_0^2 = \mathfrak{N} l_0^2 \left(\tfrac{2}{3} + \tfrac{4}{3} \exp \frac{\epsilon}{RT}\right)$$

Combining equation H.19 and H.20, one obtains

H.21
$$-\frac{\partial \ln (F/T)}{\partial (1/T)} = \frac{\epsilon}{R} \left(1 + \frac{1}{2} \exp (-\epsilon/RT)\right)^{-1}$$

$$\approx \epsilon/R$$

The result shown in equation H.21 accords well with the result obtained in H.17.

Flory, Hoeve and Ciferri applied equations H.19 and H.20 to obtain values of ϵ for cross-linked silicone rubber and cross-linked polyethylene, in the temperature range of rubbery behavior. They found that the silicone rubber obeyed the kinetic theory of rubber elasticity, i.e., $\epsilon = 0$. On the other hand, for cross-linked polyethylene they found $\epsilon = 540$ cal/mole.

This relatively large value of ϵ for cross-linked polyethylene accords quite well with the estimated energy difference for *trans* and *gauche* n-butane obtained from Raman spectra. However, it contrasts sharply

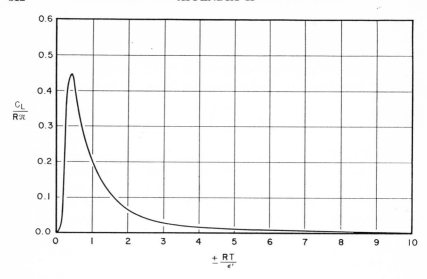

Figure H.2. Dependence of heat capacity at constant length on temperature for small extensions, according to equation H.15. [After K. W. Scott and A. V. Tobolsky, *J. Colloid Sci.*, **8**, 465 (1953).]

with the previous results obtained with Butyl and Lactoprene rubbers.[4-6] We have therefore recently checked [10] our previous results on Butyl rubber and Lactoprene rubber and find them to be experimentally valid, namely $\epsilon' \approx 0$. Many more values of ϵ' were obtained [10] on lightly cross-linked polymers by the stress-temperature method, using equation H.17. It was found that an ethylene-propylene copolymer (mole ratio 2/1) gave a value of ϵ' of 380 cal/mole. Polyethyl acrylate, polybutyl acrylate and polyoctyl acrylate gave values of $\epsilon' \approx 0$. Polybutyl methacrylate and polyoctyl methacrylate gave values of ϵ' of -500 cal/mole, indicating a preference for folded configurations. Copolymers of butyl methacrylate–ethyl acrylate (mole ratios 3/1, 1/1 and 1/3) gave $\epsilon' \approx 0$. Synthetic *cis*-1,4-polyisoprene gave $\epsilon' = 40$ cal/mole. The following polymers gave values of ϵ' that we considered zero within experimental error: *cis*-1,4-polybutadiene, vinylidene fluoride–perfluoropropylene (1/1), trifluorochloroethylene–vinylidene-fluoride (1/1) and atactic polystyrene. Amorphous isotactic polystyrene was studied, but the results were vitiated by slow crystallization.

Returning to the one-dimensional model presented earlier, the internal energy U per mole associated with chain folding is given by

H.22
$$U = 2\epsilon'I_0$$

where I_0 is defined by equation H.10.

The specific heat at constant length associated with chain folding is

H.23
$$C_L = (\partial U/\partial L)_T$$

From equations H.23, H.22 and H.10 one can show that, for $t \ll 1$ or for $t = 0$, the specific heat is [2]

H.24
$$C_L = \mathbf{R}\mathfrak{N} \left(\frac{\epsilon'}{2\mathbf{R}T}\right)^2 \operatorname{sech}^2 \frac{\epsilon'}{2\mathbf{R}T}$$

The specific heat per mole of links is of course $C_L/\mathfrak{N}$. A plot of $C_L/\mathbf{R}\mathfrak{N}$ vs. $\mathbf{R}T/\epsilon'$ is shown in Figure H.2.

A specific heat anomaly similar to that shown in Figure H.2 might also be expected in a three-dimensional network of chains whose *trans* and *gauche* configurations are of unequal energy. It would be interesting to see whether this could be observed in amorphous ethylene-propylene copolymers.

References for Appendix H

1. K. W. Scott and A. V. Tobolsky, Am. Phys. Soc. Meeting, New York, January 1948.
2. K. W. Scott and A. V. Tobolsky, *J. Colloid Sci.*, **8**, 465 (1953); K. W. Scott, Ph.D. thesis, Princeton University, 1950.
3. E. Guth and H. M. James, Am. Phys. Soc. Meeting, New York, January 1948.
4. G. M. Brown, Ph.D. thesis, Princeton University, 1948.
5. R. D. Andrews, Ph.D. thesis, Princeton University, 1948.
6. K. W. Scott, Ph.D. thesis, Princeton University, 1950.
7. H. James and E. Guth, *J. Chem. Phys.*, **11**, 455 (1943).
8. P. J. Flory, C. A. J. Hoeve and A. Ciferri, *J. Polymer Sci.*, **34**, 337 (1959).
9. M. V. Volkenstein and O. B. Ptitsyn, *Zhur. Tekh. Fiz.*, **25**, 649 (1955).
10. A. V. Tobolsky, D. Carlson and N. Indictor, manuscript in preparation.

Maximum Relaxation Times[1]

Fifteen samples of polystyrene were prepared by bulk polymerization at 60°C, using varying concentrations of 2-azobisisobutyronitrile as the initiator. The polymerizations were all carried out to low conversions (less than 10%). The polymer thus prepared is characterized by a rather narrow size distribution (see equations F.3 and F.4) with $\bar{M}_w/\bar{M}_n$ = 1.5. The viscosity-average molecular weights were obtained by

Table J.1

No.	$[\eta]$	$\bar{M}_v$	$\bar{M}_w$	τ_m(min) (at 115°C)	η_{shear} (poises) (at 115°C)
1.	1.46×10^{-1}	1.78×10^4	1.86×10^4	5.80×10^{-2}	9.84×10^6
2.	1.60×10^{-1}	2.08×10^4	2.16×10^4	1.54×10^{-1}	1.45×10^7
3.	1.87×10^{-1}	2.51×10^4	2.61×10^4	3.30×10^{-1}	2.24×10^7
4.	2.02×10^{-1}	2.82×10^4	2.94×10^4	6.07×10^{-1}	2.46×10^7
5.	2.30×10^{-1}	3.47×10^4	3.62×10^4	6.30×10^{-1}	3.16×10^7
6.	2.53×10^{-1}	4.07×10^4	4.25×10^4	1.04	3.31×10^7
7.	2.72×10^{-1}	4.47×10^4	4.67×10^4	2.05	4.77×10^7
8.	2.80×10^{-1}	4.60×10^4	4.80×10^4	4.25	1.06×10^8
9.	3.33×10^{-1}	5.76×10^4	5.90×10^4	7.69	1.17×10^8
10.	3.64×10^{-1}	6.61×10^4	6.90×10^4	1.41×10	2.36×10^8
11.	4.44×10^{-1}	8.91×10^4	9.30×10^4	1.78×10	3.33×10^8
12.	5.78×10^{-1}	1.15×10^5	1.20×10^5	7.76×10	2.46×10^9
13.	7.04×10^{-1}	1.77×10^5	1.86×10^5	4.55×10^2	1.73×10^{10}
14.	8.06×10^{-1}	2.09×10^5	2.18×10^5	8.00×10^2	1.76×10^{10}
15.	10.56×10^{-1}	3.02×10^5	3.15×10^5	1.03×10^4	1.63×10^{11}

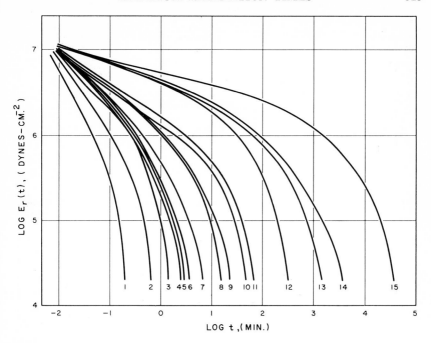

Figure J.1. Master curves $\log E_r(t)$ vs. $\log t$ at 115°C for polystyrene samples 1 through 15. (After A. V. Tobolsky and K. Murakami, Report to QMC, October 1959.)

measuring intrinsic viscosity in benzene at 25°C,[2] and the weight-average molecular weights were then calculated.[3] These quantities are all presented in Table J.1.

Stress-relaxation studies were carried out in the temperature range of rubbery flow, and the master curves $E_r(t)$, reduced to 115°C, were computed. These are shown in Figure J.1. Assuming a continuous distribution of relaxation times, the second approximation $\overline{H}_{2b}(\tau)$ was computed at 115°C and is shown in Figure J.2.

In Chapter IV, section 9, the concept of a discrete maximum relaxation time was discussed. If such a maximum relaxation time does exist, a plot of $\log E_r(t)$ versus linear time would approach a straight line at sufficiently long times, whose slope is $-1/2.303\tau_m$.

In all the samples studied here when $\log E_r(t)$ was plotted against linear time, the curves did indeed approach a straight line, as shown for four samples in Figure J.3. From the slopes of these lines values of τ_m were obtained for all samples and are presented in Table J.1.

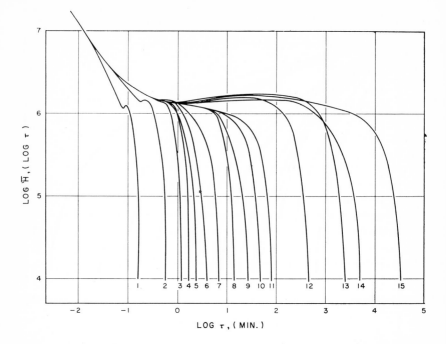

LOG τ, (MIN.)

Figure J.2. Relaxation spectra log $\overline{H}_{2b}(\tau)$ vs. log τ at 115°C for polystyrene samples 1 through 15. (After A. V. Tobolsky and K. Murakami, Report to QMC, October 1959.)

A plot of log $\overline{M}_w$ vs. log τ_m was made, as shown in Figure J.4. For values of $\overline{M}_w$ between 50,000 and 315,000, τ_m for these samples at 115°C is given by the approximate formula

J.1 $\qquad \tau_m$ (in minutes) $= 7.94 \times 10^{-16} \overline{M}_w^{3.4}$

The flow viscosity in shear was computed from $\overline{H}_{2b}$ by the following equation

J.2 $\qquad \eta = \dfrac{1}{3 \times 2.303} \int_0^\infty \overline{H}_{2b}(\tau) \, d\tau$

The integral was evaluated by graphical computation. Values thus computed are shown in the last column in Table J.1.

Values of τ_m as a function of molecular weight were also computed for polyisobutylene and polyvinyl acetate from published stress-relaxation data.[4,5] The following relation among τ_m, $\mathfrak{N}_w$, T and T_g was found for these polymers as well as for polystyrene:[6]

J.3 $\log \tau_m$ (seconds) $= \log A - 17.44 \dfrac{T - T_g}{51.6 + T - T_g} + 3.4 \log \mathfrak{N}_w$

The second term on the right-hand side is the familiar WLF equation. The quantity $\mathfrak{N}_w$ is the weight average number of chain links. The values of $\log A$ do not differ much for these three polymers. If in equation J.3 τ_m is expressed in seconds, then $\log A = -0.52$ for polyisobutylene, -0.70 for polystyrene and 0.86 for polyvinyl acetate.

If this result is borne out for other polymers equation J.3 will provide a very simple way for obtaining an approximate weight average molecular weight of a polymer by a single determination of τ_m and a measurement of T_g, provided that $\log A$ has been established for the polymer in question. The value of $\log A$ does not show a very large difference for the three polymers thus far studied.

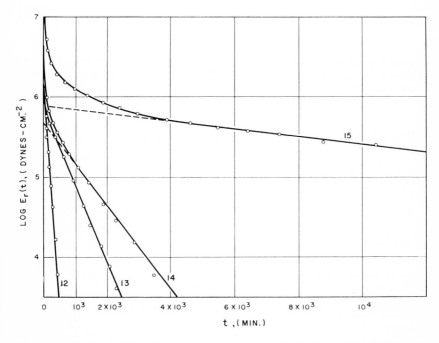

Figure J.3. Log $E_r(t)$ vs. t for polystyrene samples 12, 13, 14 and 15. (After A. V. Tobolsky and K. Murakami, Report to QMC, October 1959.)

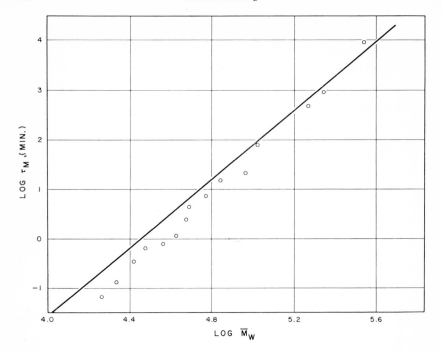

Figure J.4. Maximum relaxation time log τ_m vs. log $\overline{M}_w$ at 115°C for polystyrene samples 1 through 15. (After A. V. Tobolsky and K. Murakami, Report to QMC, October 1959.)

The following relation has been obtained among τ_m, $\bar{r}_\theta{}^2$, T and T_g.

$$J.4 \quad \log \tau_m \text{ (seconds)} = \log B - 17.44 \frac{T - T_g}{51.6 + T - T_g} + 3.4 \log (\bar{r}_\theta{}^2/l_0{}^2)$$

In equation J.4 $\bar{r}_\theta{}^2$ is the mean square end-to-end distance obtained in the polymer in a theta solvent (a solvent in which the polymer is just at the point of precipitation) and l_0 is the length of the carbon-carbon bond, equal to 1.54 Å.

In this case log B is the *same* for all three polymers, namely -2.15. If equation J.4 is borne out for other polymers, it will provide a method for obtaining $r_\theta{}^2$ directly from stress relaxation studies.

References to Appendix J

1. A. V. Tobolsky and K. Murakami, Report to QMC, Contract DA-19-129-QM-1306, October 1959.
2. B. H. Zimm, *J. Chem. Phys.*, **18**, 830 (1950).
3. B. Baysal and A. V. Tobolsky, *J. Polymer Sci.*, **9**, 171 (1952).
4. R. D. Andrews and A. V. Tobolsky, *J. Polymer Sci.*, **7**, 221 (1951).
5. K. Ninomiya, *J. Colloid Sci.*, **14**, 49 (1959).
6. A. V. Tobolsky and K. Murakami, manuscript submitted to *J. Colloid Sci.*

T_i and T_g Values for Selected Polymers

The T_i values for various amorphous polymers were determined and compared with T_g values. For convenience the T_i value was taken as the temperature at which the 10-sec modulus attained a value of 10^9 dynes/cm^2 [for most polymers $(E_1 E_2)^{1/2} \approx 10^9$ dynes/cm^2]. These values of T_i are tabulated in Table K.1 along with values of T_g obtained

TABLE K.1[a]

Polymer	T_g (°C)	$T_i{}^a$ (°C)
Natural rubber	−72	−68
Polyisobutylene	−70	−66
Ethylene-propylene copolymer (2/1)	−59[a]	−59
GR-S	−57	−53
Amorphous atactic polypropylene	−20	−18
Polybutyl methacrylate	22	25
Amorphous nylon terpolymer (nylon 6, nylon 6–6, nylon MXD-6)	...	46
Polystyrene (atactic)	100	95
Polystyrene (amorphous isotactic)	...	97
Polymethyl methacrylate	105	109

[a] A. V. Tobolsky, D. Carlson and A. Eisenberg, unpublished.

mostly from the literature. It is interesting to note that the T_i values are in general within a few degrees of the T_g values. The T_i value of an amorphous nylon terpolymer is also noteworthy.

T_g values of $-20°$ and $-125°$ C have been reported [1] from measurements of specific volume versus temperature on amorphous polypropylene and crystalline polyethylene, respectively. Our own value of T_g from vT measurements on an amorphous ethylene–propylene copolymer (mole ratio 2/1) is $-59°C$. Using this in conjunction with the value of $-20°C$ for amorphous polypropylene [1] and applying equation 5.3 of Chapter II, we obtain a value of $T_g = -81°C$ for amorphous polyethylene. This contrasts with the value of $-125°C$ reported in the literature,[1] but we believe the $-81°C$ value to be more reliable. The inflection in the vT curve obtained on crystalline polyethylene at $-125°$ may arise from some other transition than the glass transition of the amorphous regions.

Reference to Appendix K

1. M. L. Dannis, *J. Appl. Polymer Sci.*, **1**, 121 (1959).

Author Index

Subject Index

327